GREAT EXPERIMENTS IN BIOLOGY

GREAT

Edited by *Mordecai L. Gabriel*

EXPERI

and *Seymour Fogel*

IN BIO

Englewood Cliffs, N. J.

Associate Professor of Biology, Brooklyn College

MENTS

Associate Professor of Biology, Brooklyn College

LOGY

Prentice-Hall, Inc.

THE PRENTICE-HALL ANIMAL SCIENCE SERIES
H. Burr Steinbach, *Editor*

Library of Congress Cat. Card No.: 55–11373

Eleventh printing. . . . . June, 1965

PRINTED IN THE UNITED STATES OF AMERICA

36354-C

PREFACE

The emergence of scientific inquiry as a pervasive social force in our time has rekindled serious interest in the broader and more humanistic values of science. Awareness is growing that science and scientific thinking are no longer the exclusive domain of the professional scientist. Matters which a generation ago were laboratory problems for the specialist have become pressing questions of social and political policy. Responsible decisions by the citizen increasingly depend upon an understanding of what science is, how science grows and develops, and how science serves and affects society.

If science education is to convey this sense of the relevance of science to man's problems as a social being, it must not confine itself to the *results* of scientific inquiry, but must devote itself as well to the methodology and philosophic outlook that have led to these results. Successful training in science involves the development of a state of mind and a feeling of discovery, of participation in science, far more than the mere acquisition of factual knowledge.

This book is the outgrowth of a conviction that an important means of inculcating this awareness of science as a process lies in the presentation of scientific writings in the original. Many are the rewards of these firsthand contacts with the classic treasures of scientific writing. There is genuine excitement in seeing fundamental discoveries through the eyes of their discoverers; there is humanizing enrichment in becoming acquainted with the personalities of the scientific great—with meeting, say, the apologetic diffidence of Hardy in calling attention to the principle of equilibrium in populations, the naive zest of a Leeuwenhoek, or the lusty polemics and compelling lucidity of a Pasteur. Many insights into the nature of scientific discovery emerge: the "latent period" between fundamental discoveries and their application, the "happy accident," of which the penicillin story is perhaps the most often cited (and misunderstood) example, the manifold character of scientific methods, the often astonishing independence between the scientific value of an accurately reported experiment and its valid interpretation by the investigator himself. Our great unifying generalizations are revealed as organic historical accumulations in which progress in one area frequently depends on the convergence of ideas from isolated, unrelated fields.

The wealth of material available has inevitably imposed a measure of arbitrariness in selection. We have chosen less than a dozen areas in general biology in which significant progress has been made towards an understanding of the mechanisms underlying living activities. For each of these fields, we have selected a sufficient number of classic papers to show the milestones in the advance of knowledge starting from raw observations and the first experimental gropings to quantitative physicochemical studies of the present day.

[v]

Inasmuch as our objective has been to convey something of what science is and the way in which science grows, we have tried to present connected sequences in a chain of discovery within a field, in preference to offering representative selections ranging over that entire subject. No attempt has been made to assess priorities; our choice has often been governed by simplicity of presentation, style, or other non-historical criteria.

Citations within the chronologies should be viewed as illustrative rather than definitive. If at times there does not seem to be a smooth, logical flow in the development of a concept, the chronology has served as a reminder that science does not advance by any master plan, but has always been, as Santayana remarked, ". . . a patient siege laid to the truth, which was approached blindly and without a general, as by an army of ants. . . ."

We are grateful to the members of the library staffs of Brooklyn College, the Brooklyn· Botanic Garden, and the Marine Biological Laboratory, Woods Hole, Mass., for cooperation in the use of their facilities and assistance in obtaining materials.

It is a pleasure to record our gratitude to Prof. Naphtali Lewis, Prof. Ethyle R. Wolfe, and Dr. Olga Janowitz for their assistance in the preparation of several translations.

We desire to acknowledge our indebtedness to the many authors and publishers who have kindly granted permission to reprint their publications. Each source will be found as a note preceding the article.

TABLE OF CONTENTS

Part Five

EMBRYOLOGY

The Germ Cell Theory

Embryonic Differentiation

Part Six

GENETICS

· Part Seven

EVOLUTION

GREAT EXPERIMENTS IN BIOLOGY

Part One

~~

THE CELL THEORY

CHRONOLOGY

590 B.C. Some properties of curved reflecting surfaces were investigated and recorded by Euclid.

65 A.D. Seneca reported that glass globules filled with water "will aid in seeing those difficult things that frequently escape the eye."

127–151 Ptolemy investigated the problem of magnification by means of curved surfaces.

1235 The invention of spectacles was announced by Roger Bacon in England.

1485 Da Vinci stressed the importance of using lenses for the study of small objects.

1590 Jans and Zacharias Janssen combined two convex lenses within a tube, thus constructing the forerunner of the compound microscope.

1656 Borel investigated the microscopic structure of red blood cells and accurately noted the regularity of stomatal movements.

1661 Malpighi conducted extensive investigations on the anatomy and embryology of plants and animals. He discovered the existence of capillaries—structures predicted to exist by Harvey some thirty years earlier.

1665 Hooke published the *Micrographia,* a collection of diverse essays dealing with the microscopic structure of familiar substances, among which the cellular structure of cork is fully described and illustrated.

1672 Grew published an extensively illustrated volume summarizing his detailed studies of plant anatomy.

1674 Leeuwenhoek further improved the art of polishing lenses of short focal length. He discovered and described protozoa, bacteria, rotifers, and the like.

1759 Wolff applied the microscope to the study of animal embryology and remarked that "the particles which constitute all animal organs in their earliest inception are little globules, which may be distinguished under a microscope."

1770 Hill introduced new techniques for macerating, preserving and staining woody materials. He employed alum, alcohol and carmine in preparing specimens for microscopic study.

1780 Adams and others devised slicing machines (microtomes) capable of cutting sections some $\frac{1}{2000}$ of an inch thick.

1802 Mirbel concluded from his numerous observations of plant structure that "the plant is wholly formed of a continuous cellular membranous tissue. Plants are made up of cells, all parts of which are in continuity and form one and the same membranous tissue."

1809 Lamarck investigated the microscopic structure of plants and animals. He remarked, "It has been recognized for a long time that the membranes which form the envelopes of the brain, of the nerves, of vessels, of all kinds of glands, of viscera, of muscles and their fibers, and even the skin of the body are in general the productions of cellular tissue. But no one, so far as I know, has yet perceived that cellular tissue is the general matrix of all organization and that without this tissue no living body would be able to exist, nor could it have been formed."

1824 Dutrochet further advanced the cell principle. He stated, "All organic tissues are actually globular cells of exceeding smallness, which appear to be united only by simple adhesive forces; thus all tissues, all animal (and plant) organs, are actually only a cellular tissue variously modified. This uniformity of finer structure proves that organs actually differ among themselves merely in the nature of the substances contained in the vesicular cells of which they are composed."

1830 Meyen reported his observations on algae, fungi and higher plants and concluded that ". . . each cell forms an independent, isolated whole; it nourishes itself, builds itself up, and elaborates raw nutrient materials, which it takes up, into very different substances and structures."

1831 Brown published his observations reporting the discovery and widespread occurrence of nuclei in cells.

1832 Dumortier observed the process of cell division in algae. The phenomenon had actually been reported some six years earlier by Turpin.

1835–1839 Von Mohl carefully described some details of mitosis. He recorded the appearance of the cell plate between daughter cells. He remarked, "Cell division is everywhere easily and plainly seen . . . in terminal buds and root tips."

1838 Schleiden published his *Beiträge zur Phytogenese,* an important contribution to understanding the genesis of plant tissues. He observed nucleoli but misinterpreted their significance in considering them as nuclei forming within nuclei. Schwann applied the same erroneous theory of cell formation to animal tissues but correctly emphasized that "cells are organisms and entire animals and plants are aggregates of these organisms arranged according to definite laws."

1845 Von Siebold recognized protozoa as single celled animals.

1845 Kölliker demonstrated that spermatozoa are cellular products of the organism. He also extended this finding to the ovum, from which the organism is derived by cell division.

1858 Virchow applied the cell theory to problems of pathology and disease and set forth the illuminating principle that the outward symptoms of disease are merely reflections of impairment at the level of cellular organization.

1861 Schultze established the protoplasm concept and, after noting the essential similarity between the cell contents of protozoa, plants and animals, concluded that "the cell is an accumulation of living substance or protoplasm definitely delimited in space and possessing a cell membrane and nucleus."

1880–1890 Flemming, Strasburger, Van Beneden, and others elucidated the essential facts of cell division and stressed the importance of the qualitative and quantitative equality of chromosome distribution to daughter cells.

1907 Wilson convincingly demonstrated the high level of cell individuality in phenomena of coalescence and regeneration in sponges.

1907 Harrison developed new techniques for culturing and studying isolated cells or tissue fragments apart from the intact whole organism.

The extensions flowing from the cell theory embrace the whole of modern biology. Because of their widely diverse and ramifying implications, however, they cannot be included in this section. The unifying character of the cell concept is repeatedly evidenced elsewhere in this book by the impetus and direction it has provided for the analysis of fundamental biological problems such as reproduction, sexuality, development, heredity, evolution, metabolism, coordination, growth, and a host of equally basic phenomena numerous beyond mention.

Of the Schematisme or Texture of Cork, and of the Cells and Pores of Some other such Frothy Bodies. ❧

by ROBERT HOOKE

From *Micrographia*, London: 1665

The term cell *is but one of the legacies left by the ingenious Robert Hooke. Among other accomplishments, Hooke investigated the problem of celestial mechanics, invented the vacuum pump used by Robert Boyle, and devised the forerunner of the balance spring of the modern watch. He was generally recognized as one of the foremost inventors and mechanically gifted individuals of his day. His Micro- graphia, a portion of which is reprinted here, is a large collection of diversified essays describing his observations ranging from the structure of cloth to the intimate morphology of the gnat.*

Throughout the following section concerning cork, it is interesting to note how Hooke persistently reinterprets the properties of cork in terms of the basic finding that it is of a porous or frothy nature. Especially note- worthy are his simple quantitative considerations on the number of cells. A direct count of some sixty cells per one eighteenth of an inch led him to the deduction that there must be well over a billion cells in a cubic inch of cork.

Though the term cell *remains with us today, it must be recalled that Hooke had actually observed only the walls of cells or the products of protoplasmic metabolism.*

I TOOK A GOOD CLEAR PIECE OF CORK, and with a Pen-knife sharpen'd as keen as a Razor, I cut a piece of it off, and thereby left the surface of it exceeding smooth, then examining it very diligently with a *Microscope,* me thought I could perceive it to appear a little porous; but I could not so plainly distinguish them, as to be sure that they were pores, much less what Figure they were of: But judging from the lightness and yielding quality of the Cork, that certainly the texture could not be so curious, but that possibly, if I could use some further diligence, I might find it to be discern- able with a *Microscope,* I with the same sharp Pen-knife, cut off from the former smooth surface an exceeding thin piece of it, and placing it on a black object Plate, because it was it self a white body, and casting the light on it with a deep *plano-convex Glass,* I could exceed- ing plainly perceive it to be all perfo- rated and porous, much like a Honey- comb, but that the pores of it were not regular, yet it was not unlike a Honey- comb in these particulars.

First, in that it had a very little solid substance, in comparison of the empty cavity that was contain'd between, for the *Interstitia,* or walls (as I may so call them) or partitions of those pores were neer as thin in proportion to their pores, as those thin films of Wax in a Honey- comb (which enclose and constitute the *sexangular cells*) are to theirs.

Next, in that these pores, or cells, were not very deep, but consisted of a great many little Boxes, separated out of one continued long pore, by certain *Dia- phragms.*[1] . . .

I no sooner discern'd these (which were indeed the first *microscopical* pores I ever saw, and perhaps, that were ever seen, for I had not met with any Writer or Person, that had made any mention of them before this), but me thought I had with the discovery of them, presently hinted to me the true and intelligible reason of all the *Phaenomena* of Cork; As,

First, if I enquir'd why it was so exceeding light a body? my *Microscope* could presently inform me that here was the same reason evident that there is found for the lightness of froth, an empty Honey-comb, Wool, a Spunge, a Pumice stone or the like: namely a very

[1] It is interesting to note that Hooke was keenly aware of the three dimensional nature of the material under study, despite the fact that it had been sectioned into rather thin slices. Today, even with microscopes of considerable refinement, students are prone to interpret their own observations as though the sections were geometrical planes of zero thickness.— *Editors.*

small quantity, of a solid body, extended into exceedingly large dimensions.

Next, it seem'd nothing more difficult to give an intelligible reason, why Cork is a body so very unapt to suck and drink in Water and consequently preserves it self, floating on the top of Water, though left on it never so long: and why it is able to stop and hold air in a Bottle, though it be there very much condensed and consequently presses very strongly to get a passage out, without suffering the least bubble to pass through its substance. For, as to the first, since our *Microscope* informs us that the substance of Cork is altogether fill'd with Air, and that that Air is perfectly enclosed in little Boxes or Cells distinct from one another. It seems very plain, why neither the Water, nor any other Air can easily insinuate it self into them, since there is already within them an *intus existens,* and consequently, why the pieces of Cork become so good floats for Nets, and stopples for Viols, or other close Vessels.

And thirdly, if we enquire why Cork has such a springiness and swelling nature when compress'd? and how it comes to suffer so great a compression, or seeming penetration of dimensions, so as to be made a substance as heavie again and more, bulk for bulk, as it was before compression, and yet suffer'd to return, is found to extend it self again into the same space? Our *Microscope* will easily inform us, that the whole mass consists of an infinite company of small Boxes or Bladders of Air, which is a substance of a springy nature, and that will suffer a considerable condensation (as I have several times found by divers trials, by which I have most evidently condens'd it into less then a twentieth part of its usual dimensions neer the Earth, and that with no other strength then that of my hands without any kind of forcing Engine, such as Racks, Leavers, Wheels, Pullies, or the like, but this onely by and by) and besides, it seems very proba-

ble that those very films or sides of the pores have in them a springing quality, as almost all other kind of Vegetable substances have, so as to help to restore themselves to their former position. . . .

But, to return to our Observation. I told [2] several lines of these pores, and found that there were usually about threescore of these small Cells placed end-ways in the eighteenth part of an Inch in length, whence I concluded there must be near eleven hundred of them, or somewhat more then a thousand in the length of an inch and therefore in a square inch above a million, or 1166400, and in a cubick inch, above twelve hundred Millions, or 1259712-000, a thing almost incredible, did not our *Microscope* assure us of it by ocular demonstration; nay, did it not discover to us the pores of a body, which were they diaphragm'd like those of Cork, would afford us in one Cubick Inch, more than ten times as many little Cells, as is evident in several charr'd Vegetables; so prodigiously curious are the works of Nature that even these conspicuous pores of bodies, which seem to be the channels or pipes through which the *Succus nutritus,* or natural juices of vegetables are convey'd, and seem to correspond to the veins, arteries and other vessels in sensible creatures, that these pores I say, which seem to be the vessels of nutrition to the vastest body in the World, are yet so exceeding small that the Atoms which *Epicurus* fancy'd would go neer to prove too bigg to enter them, much more to constitute a fluid body in them. . . .

But though I could not with my *Microscope,* nor with my breath, nor any other way I have yet try'd, discover a passage out of one of those cavities into another, yet I cannot thence conclude, that therefore there are none such,[3] by

---

[2] Counted.—*Editors.*

[3] A remarkably logical and prophetic deduction. The correctness of this view was amply verified by the abundant researches in the

which the *Succus nutritius,* or appropriate juices of Vegetables, may pass through them; for, in several of those Vegetables, whil'st green, I have with my *Microscope,* plainly enough discover'd these Cells or Holes fill'd with juices, and by degrees sweating them out: as I have also observed in green Wood all those long *Microscopical* pores which appear in charcoal perfectly empty of any thing but Air.

Now, though I have with great diligence endeavoured to find whether there

be any such thing in those *Microscopical* pores of Wood or Piths, as the *Valves* in the heart, veins, and other passages of Animals, that open and give passage to the contain'd fluid juices one way, and shut themselves, and impede the passage of such liquors back again, yet have I not hitherto been able to say any thing positive in it; though, me thinks, it seems very probable, that Nature has in these passages, as well as in those of Animal bodies, very many appropriated Instruments and contrivances, whereby to bring her designs and end to pass, which 'tis not improbable, but that some diligent observer, if helped with better *Microscopes,* may in time detect. . . .

period 1880–1930 that reported the widespread and probably universal occurrence of *plasmodesms,* i.e., intercellular protoplasmic bridges. —*Editors.*

The Structural Elements of Plants.

by R. J. H. DUTROCHET

From *Recherches Anatomiques et Physiologiques sur la Structure Intime des Animaux et des Végétaux et sur leur Motilité.* Paris: 1824. Translated by M. L. Gabriel for this volume.

Among the first clear statements to the effect that all living things are composed of cells was one made by Dutrochet in 1824, almost a decade and a half before the publications of Schleiden and Schwann. Some historians have developed the view that Dutrochet is something of a "forgotten man" in the history of the cell theory. As the chronology which heads this chapter makes clear, the emergence of a great scientific generalization is a historical social process and not the product of isolated flashes of insight. The attempt to assign credit for the cell theory to one individual or another, therefore, is apt to lead to a misunderstanding of the nature of scientific discovery. Nevertheless, Dutrochet, more than any other single investigator, is to be credited with the formulation of the cell concept as an outgrowth of his clear-cut observations and experimental dissociation of organized tissues. Though he did not recognize the existence of the nucleus, and though he did not realize that each cell has its own life cycle, he emphatically called attention to the individuality and independence of the cell as well as to its relationship to the structure and functioning of the organism as a whole. Applying this concept to the problem of form and structure of the whole organism, he pointed out that "growth results both from the increase in the volume of cells, and from the addition of new little cells. It is therefore evident that new, rudimentary cells are formed which, by increasing in size, finally become cells such as those which have preceded them in order of appearance and development." One would be hard pressed, even today, to find a more lucid statement on the nature of growth.

IF ANYTHING INDICATES the imperfect state of our knowledge of the intimate structure of plants, it is the divergence of opinion of naturalists on the subject. The source of this diversity of opinion lies in the extreme difficulty of observation, which cannot be done without the aid of the microscope, and which consequently is susceptible to manifold errors, practically impossible to avoid in using this instrument. To obtain a good idea of the form of an object, one must examine it on all sides; moreover, the sense of sight must be supplemented by touch. Now, with the microscope, one sees objects from one side only and the sense of touch is necessarily entirely lacking. A host of optical illusions increase the difficulties of investigation. Various refractions of light rays make parts that are really transparent appear opaque, and convey the impression of forms and structures that have no real existence. A space more transparent than the parts that surround it gives the appearance of an opening, and if the transparency is perfect, it is impossible to decide whether one is dealing with a free aperture or an opening closed by a transparent membrane.

In view of these difficulties of observation, it is not at all astonishing that there is so much dissent among observers regarding certain aspects of plant organization. The only means of ending these disagreements and determining the truth is to vary the forms of investigation. It is necessary to subject the elementary organs of plants to microscopic examination after having caused them to under-

go various modifications. Chemical reactions provide an invaluable aid in this regard: in some instances they render certain parts opaque while leaving others transparent; or they stain specific parts with particular colors which help to distinguish them; sometimes they dissolve certain parts while leaving others intact, and so forth. By microscopic examination of the elementary organs of plants thus variously prepared, we are able to recognize the errors that result, in certain cases, from optical illusions. Such comparative studies are indispensable for arriving at the truth. Anyone who follows only one method of investigation may be sure of falling into error in many respects. Now, the practice of always observing in the same manner is the fault of most investigators. The method most generally used in order to observe the elements of the plant organization microscopically consists of reducing the plant tissues to parts of great thinness either by sectioning with a very sharp instrument or by means of teasing out the tissue. The parts thus detached are more transparent the finer they are cut. Transparency may be increased by covering the preparation with a drop of water; then, with the aid of the microscope, one sees the form of the elementary organs that comprise the transparent fragment of tissue, through which light is passed by the reflecting mirror of the microscope. This method doubtless has its advantages, but it also has drawbacks. One has the benefit, by this method, of seeing the organs in place and in their natural relationships; but one has the disadvantage of never seeing these organs separated, and of not even knowing whether they *can* be isolated one from another. It was in this manner that M. de Mirbel was led to propose his first theory which considers the entire plant substance as formed by a membranous tissue, continuous throughout, the various folds and inflated portions of which form the *cells* and the *tubes*. According to this theory there exists, between two contiguous cells, only a single membrane forming the common wall of both. This opinion has not been shared by M. Link, who bases his opposition to it upon positive observations. He has seen that cellular tissue is composed of vesicles which are often separated from one another, especially in fruits, but are more often intimately cemented together in such a way that the cellular tissue appears to be continuous without any interruption. Between cells incompletely united to one another, he has furthermore noticed small gaps, previously seen by Hedwig, who named them *vasa revehentia,* and by Treviranus, who called them *meatus intercellulares* (intercellular passages).

M. Link resorted to boiling in water in order to separate cells which only weakly adhered to one another, such as those of bean pods, potatoes, parsley root, and the like. What M. Link accomplished only in these few cases by boiling in water, I have succeeded in doing as a general procedure, by means of nitric acid. I place a fragment of plant material, whatever it may be, in a glass tube closed at one end containing concentrated nitric acid; I then immerse the tube in boiling water. In five or six minutes, sometimes less, the tissue is separated more or less completely into its structural elements. The cells separate from one another, and it can be seen that the wall which separates two adjacent cells is double and not at all single, as M. de Mirbel's theory supposes. The tubes [fibro-vascular vessels] become isolated from one another and

are separated from the cells that adjoin them. All these elementary organs have their own walls and form individual enclosed cavities; they are vesicular organs of quite varied form which are contiguous to one another, sometimes cohering weakly, more often strongly joined together. Whatever causes their agglutination and adherence sometimes yields to boiling in water but always to boiling in nitric acid. These experiments, which confirm the value of comparative observations carried out by diverse procedures, prove that plant tissue is not in fact formed by a membranous tissue continuous throughout.

Nevertheless, M. de Mirbel has not at all regarded his theory as invalidated by the facts; he explains them thus: He maintains that two adjacent cells are separated by a single partition which serves as their common wall, and that this partition, having a certain density, remains soft in its middle, while the two parts which are immediately adjacent to the respective cavities of the two cells acquire solidity by desiccation, so that there takes place a shrinkage of substance from the middle towards the two surfaces, which produces the pulling apart which one sees in the thickness of the wall. *"If by means of boiling water or nitric acid,"* he says, *"one sometimes succeeds in isolating the cells, what does this prove, other than that the interior substance of the walls is less resistive to the action of these solvents than the superficial layer which limits the extent of each cavity?"*

The theory of M. de Mirbel was attacked by the facts; here he has defended it by a hypothesis,[1] but this hypothesis does not embrace all the facts. M. de Mirbel, in supposing that it is because of their desiccation on the interior that the walls of the cells sepa-

---

[1] This is an excellent illustration of the elastic hypothesis. One simply multiplies the assumptions *ad libitum* until all the observational data are harmonized.—*Editors.*

rate into two layers, has not realized that this hypothesis is only applicable to those cells which are filled with air, and not at all to those cells which are always full of liquid. In the case of the latter, it is not possible to assume the desiccation of the walls, and nevertheless these cells separate from each other, each preserving its own wall; besides, there are cells which, without the use of any solvent, appear to be separated from one another, or at least only weakly adherent, and only at a few points. Of this type are those globular or ellipsoidal cells which only touch their neighbors at one point, leaving large empty spaces between them elsewhere. M. Link has figured such cells in the plates of his *Researches on the Anatomy of Plants*. I have found similar ones in the endocarp or kernel of the apricot treated by boiling in nitric acid; I have found very large ellipsoidal cells, hardly adhering to one another at their points of contact, in the pulp of the plum where they are extremely abundant. They separate from one another without the use of any solvent. It is therefore certain that these little hollow organs are originally globular, and that in growing they are mutually compressed in the limited space

which surrounds them, and that it is because of this mutual pressure that they take on the polyhedral form in which we most often see them.[2] This theory, first proposed by Treviranus, then by Kieser, is adopted nowadays by all naturalists,-and by M. de Mirbel himself, who, convinced by his own observations on *Marchantia polymorpha,* has frankly acknowledged the truth of the theory which proposes that plant tissue is composed of juxtaposed vesicular organs and more or less strongly agglutinated together. Although I am not the first to have announced this truth, I flatter myself that it will be recognized that I have done more than anyone else to establish it upon a solid foundation as a general fact by means of the discovery I have made that boiling nitric acid has the power to dissociate, even in the hardest parts of the plant tissue, all the small hollow organs which, by their combination, constitute that tissue; this acid is the only one which produces this effect.

[2] Modern studies on bubbles in soap foam, on the shape of compressed spherical lead shot, and reconstructions from actual masses of plant and animal tissues show that the average number of sides or faces of a cell is fourteen (tetrakaidekahedron).—*Editors.*

The Organs and Mode of Fecundation in Orchideae and Asclepiadeae. ❧

by R. BROWN

From *Transactions of the Linnaean Society,* Vol. 16, No. 2, pp. 710–713 (1833).

Students of biological thought are virtually unanimous in crediting Brown with the discovery of the cell nucleus. His remarkable observations on the properties and behavior of the nucleus stand unmodified and without correction. That he was a skilled and careful observer is clear from his interpretation of the minute "areola" in pollen grains. Another observer might easily have mistaken these for nuclei, but Brown regarded them rather as points for the production of pollen tubes—they are in fact pollen grain micropyles. His description of protoplasmic streaming cannot help but command the respect and attention of the reader. In fact, from the descriptive viewpoint, it would be difficult to add to its completeness or accuracy. Today protoplasmic streaming or cyclosis is one of the important criteria by which the vitality of the cell is judged.

Brown is also credited with the discovery of what is now known as Brownian movement, a phenomenon that provides one of the principal arguments for molecular motion. Although he practiced medicine as a surgeon for five years, he later abandoned this and turned his efforts towards botanical science. In this area he distinguished himself in a series of studies on fertilization. He also demonstrated by comparative study that Gymnosperms, because they gave rise to naked seeds, were taxonomically distinct from the true flowering plants or Angiosperms.

I SHALL CONCLUDE MY observations on Orchideæ with a notice of some points of their general structure, which chiefly relate to the cellular tissue.

In each cell of the epidermis of a great part of this family, especially of those with membranaceous leaves, a single circular areola, generally somewhat more opake than the membrane of the cell, is observable. This areola, which is more or less distinctly granular, is slightly convex, and although it seems to be on the surface is in reality covered by the outer lamina of the cell. There is no regularity as to its place in the cell; it is not unfrequently however central or nearly so.

As only one areola belongs to each cell, and as in many cases where it exists in the common cells of the epidermis it is also visible in the cutaneous glands or stomata, and in these is always double,— one being on each side of the limb,—it is highly probable that the cutaneous gland is in all cases composed of two cells of peculiar form, the line of union being the longitudinal axis of the disk or pore.

This areola, or nucleus of the cell as perhaps it might be termed, is not confined to the epidermis, being also found not only in the pubescence of the surface,

particularly when jointed, as in Cypripedium, but in many cases in the parenchyma or internal cells of the tissue, especially when these are free from deposition of granular matter.

In the compressed cells of the epidermis the nucleus is in a corresponding degree flattened; but in the internal tissue it is often nearly spherical, more or less firmly adhering to one of the walls, and projecting into the cavity of the cell. In this state it may not unfrequently be found in the substance of the column, and in that of the perianthium.

The nucleus is manifest also in the tissue of the stigma, where, in accordance with the compression of the utriculi,[1] it has an intermediate form, being neither so much flattened as in the epidermis, nor so convex as it is in the internal tissue of the column.

I may here remark, that I am acquainted with one case of apparent exception to the nucleus being solitary in each utriculus or cell, namely in *Bletia Tankervilliæ.*

In the utriculi of the stigma of this plant I have generally, though not always, found a second areola apparently on the surface, and composed of much

[1] Old term for the cell content, apart from the cell wall.—*Editors.*

larger granules than the ordinary nucleus, which is formed of very minute granular matter, and seems to be deep seated.

Mr. Bauer has represented the tissue of the stigma in this species of Bletia, both before and as he believes after impregnation; and in the latter state the utriculi are marked with from one to three areolæ of similar appearance.

The nucleus may even be supposed to exist in the pollen of this family. In the early stages of its formation at least a minute areola is often visible in the simple grain, and in each of the constituent parts or cells of the compound grain. But these areolæ may perhaps rather be considered as merely the points of production of the tubes.

This nucleus of the cell is not confined to Orchideæ, but is equally manifest in many other Monocotyledonous families; and I have even found it, hitherto however in very few cases, in the epidermis of Dicotyledonous plants; though in this primary division it may perhaps be said to exist in the early stages of development of the pollen. Among Monocotyledones the orders in which it is most remarkable are Liliaceæ, Hemerocallideæ, Asphodeleæ, Irideæ, and Commelineæ.

In some plants belonging to this last-mentioned family, especially in *Tradescantia virginica* and several nearly related species, it is uncommonly distinct, not only in the epidermis and in the jointed hairs of the filaments,* but in

the tissue of stigma, in the cells of the ovulum even before impregnation, and in all the stages of formation of the grains of pollen, the evolution of which is so remarkable in those species of Tradescantia.†

---

nearly lenticular, and its granular matter is either held together by a coagulated pulp not visibly granular,—or, which may be considered equally probable, by an enveloping membrane. The analogy of this nucleus to that existing in the various stages of development of the cells in which the grains of pollen are formed in the same species, is sufficiently obvious.

3rdly. In the joint when immersed in water, being at the same time freed from air, and consequently made more transparent, a circulation of very minute granular matter is visible to a lens magnifying from 300 to 400 times. This motion of the granular fluid is seldom in one uniform circle, but frequently in several apparently independent threads or currents: and these currents, though often exactly longitudinal and consequently in the direction of the striæ of the membrane, are not unfrequently observed forming various angles with these striæ. The smallest of the threads or streamlets appear to consist of a single series of particles. The course of these currents seems often in some degree affected by the nucleus, towards or from which many of them occasionally tend or appear to proceed. They can hardly however be said to be impeded by the nucleus, for they are occasionally observed passing between its surface and that of the cell; a proof that this body does not adhere to both sides of the cavity, and also that the number and various directions of the currents cannot be owing to partial obstructions arising from the unequal compression of the cell.[2]

† In the very early stage of the flower bud of *Tradescantia virginica*, while the antheræ are yet colourless, their loculi are filled with minute lenticular grains, having a transparent flat limb, with a slightly convex and minutely granular semi-opake disk. This disk is the nucleus of the cell, which probably loses its membrane or limb, and, gradually enlarging, forms in the next stage a grain also lenticular, and which is marked either with only one transparent line dividing it into two equal parts, or with two lines crossing at right angles, and dividing it into four equal parts. In each of the quadrants [3]

---

* The jointed hair of the filament in this genus forms one of the most interesting microscopic objects with which I am acquainted, and that in three different ways:

1st. Its surface is marked with extremely fine longitudinal parallel equidistant lines or striæ, whose intervals are equal from about 1-15,000th to 1-20,000th of an inch. It might therefore in some cases be conveniently employed as a micrometer.

2ndly. The nucleus of the joint or cell is very distinct as well as regular in form, and by pressure is easily separated entire from the joint. It then appears to be exactly round,

[2] A description of cyclosis.—*Editors.*

[3] Each cell is a microspore, immediately following the two meiotic cell divisions. A small nucleus is visible; and even where one transparent line only is distinguishable, two nuclei

The few indications of the presence

may frequently be found in each semi-circular division. These nuclei may be readily extracted from the containing grain by pressure, and after separation retain their original form.

In the next stage examined, the greater number of grains consisted of the semicircular divisions already noticed, which had naturally separated, and now contained only one nucleus which had greatly increased in size.

In the succeeding state the grain apparently consisted of the nucleus of the former stage considerably enlarged, having a regular oval form, a somewhat granular surface, and originally a small nucleus. This oval grain continuing to increase in size, and in the thickness and opacity of its membrane, acquires a pale yellow colour, and is now the perfect grain of pollen. —*Editors.*

of this nucleus, or areola, that I have hitherto met with in the publications of botanists, are chiefly in some figures of epidermis, in the recent works of Meyen and Purkinje, and in one case in M. Adolphe Brongniart's memoir on the structure of leaves. But so little importance seems to be attached to it, that the appearance is not always referred to in the explanations of the figures in which it is represented. Mr. Bauer however, who has also figured it in the utriculi of the stigma of *Bletia Tankervilliæ,* has more particularly noticed it, and seems to consider it as only visible after impregnation.

Microscopical Researches. ❧

by T. SCHWANN

Excerpted from *Microscopische Untersuchungen über die Uebereinstimmung in der Struktur und dem Wachsthum der Thiere und Pflanzen.* Translated for the Sydenham Society by Henry Smith, London, 1847.

Of all biological concepts originating in the first half of the nineteenth century probably none has had such far-reaching consequences and widespread importance as the cell theory. Although no simple statement can encompass the manifold extensions and implications of the cell theory, it must be recognized primarily as a generalized, comprehensive declaration of fact. Conceptually, it embraces the findings that all living things are composed of cells, or of cells plus their products; that all cells are essentially alike in chemical constitution; that new cells are formed from preëxisting cells by a fundamental process of cell division; and that the activity of the organism as a whole is the sum of the activities and interactions of essentially independent cell units. In fact, as Karling [1] points out, "the cell concept is the concept of life, its origin, its nature and its continuity."

There can be little doubt that Schwann contributed significantly toward the establishment of the cell doctrine. However, to attribute the

[1] Karling, J. S., Schleiden's Contributions to the Cell Theory, *Biological Symposia,* vol. 1, 1940.

*origination of the doctrine to Schwann (or to Schleiden and Schwann),
as many present-day text writers have done, is contrary to a vast body of
well-authenticated documentary evidence. As historical retrospect repeatedly reveals, no single person can be credited with the establishment
of such a central concept. That others had antedated Schwann in the discovery of the cellular nature of living things, and that others had
correctly interpreted the fundamental mode of cell division where he had
not, are largely matters of historical interest. Perhaps Schwann's major
contribution is to be found in his clear recognition of cell phenomena as
being arbitrarily divisible into two classes; those having to do with
plastic, structural, or morphological changes, and those concerning physiological or metabolic changes, which result from chemical alterations in
the particles that compose the cells or in the materials surrounding the
cells. In the later pages of the selection presented here there is a clear
exposition of the viewpoint that metabolism is a highly selective process
and that its dynamics are largely dependent upon polarized, differentially
permeable cell membranes.*

THE VARIOUS OPINIONS entertained with respect to the fundamental powers of an organized body may be reduced to two, which are essentially different from one another. The first is, that every organism originates with an inherent power, which models it into conformity with a predominant idea, arranging the molecules in the relation necessary for accomplishing certain purposes held forth by this idea. Here, therefore, that which arranges and combines the mole-cules is a power acting with a definite purpose. A power of this kind would be essentially different from all the powers of inorganic nature, because action goes on in the latter quite blindly. A certain impression is followed of necessity by a certain change of quality and quantity, without regard to any purpose. In this view, however, the fundamental power of the organism (or the soul, in the sense employed by Stahl) would, inasmuch as it works with a definite individual pur-pose, be much more nearly allied to the immaterial principle, endued with con-sciousness which we must admit operates in man.

The other view is, that the funda-mental powers of organized bodies agree essentially with those of inorganic na-ture, that they work altogether blindly according to laws of necessity and irre-spective of any purpose, that they are powers which are as much established with the existence of matter as the physi-cal powers are. It might be assumed that the powers which form organized bodies do not appear at all in inorganic nature, because this or that particular combina-tion of molecules, by which the powers are elicited, does not occur in inorganic nature, and yet they might not be essenti-ally distinct from physical and chemical powers. It cannot, indeed, be denied that adaptation to a particular purpose, in some individuals even in a high degree, is characteristic of every organism; but, according to this view, the source of this adaptation does not depend upon each organism being developed by the opera-tion of its own power in obedience to that purpose, but it originates as in inorganic nature, in the creation of the matter with its blind powers by a ra-tional Being.[1] . . .

The first view of the fundamental powers of organized bodies may be called

---

[1] An alternative to this conclusion—that adaptations may arise through operation of a natural process—was formulated by Darwin in the theory of natural selection.—*Editors.*

the *teleological,* the second the *physical* view. An example will show at once, how important for physiology is the solution of the question as to which is to be followed. If, for instance, we define inflammation and suppuration to be the effort of the organism to remove a foreign body that has been introduced into it; or fever to be the effort of the organism to eliminate diseased matter, and both as the result of the "autocracy of the organism," then these explanations accord with the teleological view. For, since by these processes the obnoxious matter is actually removed, the process which effects them is one adapted to an end, and as the fundamental power of the organism operates in accordance with definite purposes, it may either set these processes in action primarily, or may also summon further powers of matter to its aid, always, however, remaining itself the "primum movens." On the other hand, according to the physical view, this is just as inadequate an explanation as it would be to say, that the motion of the earth around the sun is an effort of the fundamental power of the planetary system to produce a change of seasons on the planets, or to say, that ebb and flood are the reaction of the organism of the earth upon the moon.

In physics, all those explanations which were suggested by a teleological view of nature, as "horror vacui," and the like, have long been discarded. But in animated nature, adaptation—individual adaptation—to a purpose is so prominently marked, that it is difficult to reject all teleological explanations. Meanwhile it must be remembered that those explanations, which explain at once all and nothing, can be but the last resources, when no other view can possibly be adopted; and there is no such necessity for admitting the teleological view in the case of organized bodies. . . .

In any case it conduces much more to the object of science to strive, at least, to adopt the physical explanation. And I would repeat that, when speaking of a physical explanation of organic phenomena, it is not necessary to understand an explanation by known physical powers, such, for instance, as that universal refuge electricity, and the like; but an explanation by means of powers which operate like the physical powers, in accordance with strict laws of blind necessity, whether they be also to be found in inorganic nature or not.

We set out, therefore, with the supposition that an organized body is not produced by a fundamental power which is guided in its operation by a definite idea, but is developed, according to blind laws of necessity, by powers which, like those of inorganic nature, are established by the very existence of matter. As the elementary materials of organic nature are not different from those of the inorganic kingdom, the source of the organic phenomena can only reside in another combination of these materials, whether it be in a peculiar mode of union of the elementary atoms to form atoms of the second order, or in the arrangement of these conglomerate molecules when forming either the separate morphological elementary parts of organisms, or an entire organism. We have here to do with the latter question solely, whether the cause of organic phenomena lies in the whole organism, or in its separate elementary parts. If this question can be answered, a further inquiry still remains as to whether the organism or its elementary parts possess this power through the peculiar mode of combination of the conglomerate molecules, or through the mode in which the elementary atoms are united into conglomerate molecules.

We may, then, form the two following ideas of the cause of organic phenomena, such as growth, &c. First, that the cause resides in the totality of the organism. By the combination of the molecules into a systematic whole, such as the organism is in every stage of its development, a power is engendered, which enables such an organism to take up fresh material from without, and appropriate it either to the formation of new elementary parts, or to the growth of those already present. Here, therefore, the cause of the growth of the elementary parts resides in the totality of the organism. The other mode of explanation is, that growth does not ensue from a power resident in the entire organism, but that each separate elementary part is possessed of an independent power, an independent life, so to speak; in other words, the molecules in each separate elementary part are so combined as to set free a power by which it is capable of attracting new molecules, and so increasing, and the whole organism subsists only by means of the reciprocal * action of the single elementary parts. So that here the single elementary parts only exert an active influence on nutrition, and totality of the organism may indeed be a condition, but is not in this view a cause.

In order to determine which of these two views is the correct one, we must summon to our aid the results of the previous investigation. We have seen that all organized bodies are composed of essentially similar parts, namely, of cells; that these cells are formed and grow in accordance with essentially similar laws; and, therefore, that these processes must, in every instance, be produced by the same powers. Now, if we find that some of these elementary parts, not differing from the others, are capable of separating themselves from the organism, and pursuing an independent growth, we may thence conclude that each of the other elementary parts, each cell, is already possessed of power to take up fresh molecules and grow; and that, therefore, every ele-

mentary part possesses a power of its own, an independent life, by means of which it would be enabled to develop itself independently, if the relations which it bore to external parts were but similar to those in which it stands in the organism. The ova of animals afford us examples of such independent cells, growing apart from the organism. It may, indeed, be said of the ova of higher animals, that after impregnation the ovum is essentially different from the other cells of the organism; that by impregnation there is a something conveyed to the ovum, which is more to it than an external condition for vitality, more than nutrient matter; and that it might thereby have first received its peculiar vitality, and therefore that nothing can be inferred from it with respect to the other cells. But this fails in application to those classes which consist only of female individuals, as well as with the spores of the lower plants; and, besides, in the inferior plants any given cell may be separated from the plant, and then grow alone. So that here are whole plants consisting of cells, which can be positively proved to have independent vitality. Now, as all cells grow according to the same laws, and consequently the cause of growth cannot in one case lie in the cell, and in another in the whole organism; and since it may be further proved that some cells, which do not differ from the rest in their mode of growth, are developed independently, we must ascribe to all cells an independent vitality, that is, such combinations of molecules as occur in any single cell, are capable of setting free the power by which it is enabled to take up fresh molecules. The cause of nutrition and growth resides not in the organism as a whole, but in the separate elementary parts—the cells. The failure of growth in the case of any particular cell, when separated from an organized body, is as slight an objection to this theory, as it is an objection against the

---

* The word "reciprocal action" must here be taken in its widest sense, as implying the preparation of material by one elementary part, which another requires for its own nutrition.

independent vitality of a bee, that it cannot continue long in existence after being separated from its swarm. The manifestation of the power which resides in the cell depends upon conditions to which it is subject only when in connexion with the whole (organism).

The question, then, as to the fundamental power of organized bodies resolves itself into that of the fundamental powers of the individual cells. We must now consider the general phenomena attending the formation of cells, in order to discover what powers may be presumed to exist in the cells to explain them. These phenomena may be arranged in two natural groups: first, those which relate to the combination of the molecules to form a cell, and which may be denominated the *plastic* phenomena of the cells; secondly, those which result from chemical changes either in the component particles of the cell itself, or in the surrounding cytoblastema, and which may be called *metabolic* phenomena (implying that which is liable to occasion or to suffer change). . . .

These are the most important phenomena observed in the formation and development of cells. The unknown cause, presumed to be capable of explaining these processes in the cells, may be called the plastic power of the cells. We will, in the next place, proceed to determine how far a more accurate definition of this power may be deduced from these phenomena.

In the first place, there is a power of attraction exerted in the very commencement of the cell. . . . The power of attraction may be uniform throughout the whole cell, but it may also be confined to single spots; the deposition of new molecules is then more vigorous at these spots, and the consequence of this uneven growth of the cell-membrane is a change in the form of the cell.

The attractive power of the cells manifests a certain form of election in its operation. It does not take up all the substances contained in the surrounding cytoblastema, but only particular ones, either those which are analogous with the substance already present in the cell (assimilation), or such as differ from it in chemical properties. The several layers grow by assimilation, but when a new layer is being formed, different material from that of the previously-formed layer is attracted: for the nucleolus, the nucleus and cell-membrane are composed of materials which differ in their chemical properties.

Such are the peculiarities of the plastic power of the cells, so far as they can as yet be drawn from observation. But the manifestations of this power presuppose another faculty of the cells. The cytoblastema, in which the cells are formed, contains the elements of the materials of which the cell is composed, but in other combinations: it is not a mere solution of cell-material, but it contains only certain organic substances in solution. The cells, therefore, not only attract materials from out of the cytoblastema, but they must have the faculty of producing chemical changes in its constituent particles. Besides which, all the parts of the cell itself may be chemically altered during the process of its vegetation. The unknown cause of all these phenomena, which we comprise under the term metabolic phenomena of the cells, we will denominate the *metabolic power*. . . .

I think that, in order to explain the distinction between the cell-contents and the external cytoblastema, we must ascribe to the cell-membrane not only the power in general of chemically altering the substances which it is either in contact with, or has imbibed, but also of so separating them that certain substances appear on its inner, and others on its outer surface. The secretion of substances already present in the blood, as, for instance, of urea, by the cells with which the urinary tubes are lined, cannot be explained without such a faculty of the cells. There is, however, nothing so very hazardous in it, since it is a fact that different substances are separated in the decompositions produced by the galvanic pile. It might perhaps be conjectured from this peculiarity of the metabolic phenomena in the cells, that a particular position of the axes of the atoms composing the cell-membrane is essential for the production of these appearances.[2]

[2] The property of differential permeability and its dependence upon a polarized state of the plasma membrane are clearly recognized here.—*Editors.*

Coalescence and Regeneration in Sponges.

by H. V. WILSON

Reprinted from the *Journal of Experimental Zoology,* Vol. 5, No. 2, pp. 245–253 (1907), by permission.

According to Dutrochet's original formulation of the cell theory, the cell was thought to be the primary organic unit, or elementary organism. Each cell, it was held, had an independent existence or individuality, and the whole organism subsisted as a mosaic composite resulting from the reciprocal interactions of these primary single units. With Siebold's discovery (1845) that for many Protista the entire body consisted but of a single cell, many theoreticians soon came to believe that the multicellular organism represented, in effect, an assemblage or colony of single-celled individuals exhibiting a physiological division of labor.

In the case of germ cells, many algal and protozoan forms, amœboid lymphocytes, and metastasizing tumor cells, a high degree of cell independence is apparent. Again, in the case of some higher plants, it is well known that an entire organism can be regenerated from a small tissue fragment, or even a single cell.

A most convincing series of demonstrations illustrating the high degree of cellular individuality and independence is provided by experiments with sponges, hydroids, and polyps. In these experiments, an entire, highly differentiated, multicellular organism may be reassembled from cells that have been wholly detached one from another by experimental techniques. For the most part, the separate cells retain their specific character and reassemble without the occurrence of mitosis. These studies have had an important influence on a number of fundamental problems such as metabolic gradients, wound healing, organ replacement, and tissue differentiation.

IN A RECENT communication I described some degenerative and regenerative phenomena in sponges and pointed out that a knowledge of these powers made it possible for us to grow sponges in a new way. The gist of the matter is that silicious sponges when kept in confinement under proper conditions degenerate in such a manner that while the bulk of the sponge dies, the cells in certain regions become aggregated to form lumps of undifferentiated tissue. Such lumps or plasmodial masses, which may be exceedingly abundant, are often of a rounded shape resembling gemmules, more especially the simpler gemmules of marine sponges (Chalina, e. g.), and were shown to possess in at least one form (Stylotella) full regenerative power. When isolated they grow and differentiate producing perfect sponges. I described moreover a simple method by which plasmodial masses of the same appearance could be directly produced (in Microciona). The sponge was kept in an aquarium until the degenerative process had begun. It was then teased with needles so as to liberate cells and cell agglomerates. These were brought together with the result that they fused and formed masses similar in appearance to those produced in this species when the sponge remains quietly in aquarium. At the time I was forced to leave it an open question whether the masses of teased tissue were able to regenerate the sponge body.

During the past summer's work at the Beaufort Laboratory I again took up this question and am now in a position to state that the dissociated cells of silicious sponges after removal from the body will combine to form syncytial [1] masses that have power to differentiate into new sponges. In Microciona, the form especially worked on, nothing is easier than to obtain by this method hundreds of young sponges with well developed canal system and flagellated chambers. How hardy sponges produced in this artificial way are and how perfectly they will differentiate the characteristic skeleton, are questions that

[1] Multinucleate body with nuclei occupying a common cytoplasm.—*Editors*.

must be left for more prolonged experimentation.

Taking up the matter where it had been left at the end of the preceding summer, I soon found that it was not necessary to allow the sponge to pass into a degenerative state, but that the fresh and normal sponge could be used from which to obtain the teased out cells. Again in order to get the cells in quantity and yet as free as possible from bits of the parent skeleton, I devised a substitute for the teasing method. The method adopted is rough but effective.

Let me briefly describe the facts for Microciona. This species (M. prolifera Verr.) in the younger state is incrusting. As it grows older it throws up lobes and this may go so far that the habitus becomes bushy. The skeletal framework consists of strong horny fibers with embedded spicules. Lobes of the sponge are cut into small pieces with scissors and then strained through fine bolting cloth such as is used for tow nets. A square piece of cloth is folded like a bag around the bits of sponge and is immersed in a saucer of filtered sea-water. While the bag is kept closed with the fingers of one hand it is squeezed between the arms of a small pair of forceps. The pressure and the elastic recoil of the skeleton break up the living tissue of the sponge into its constituent cells, and these pass out through the pores of the bolting cloth into the surrounding water. The cells, which pass out in such quantity as to present the appearance of red clouds, quickly settle down over the bottom of the saucer like a fine sediment. Enough tissue is squeezed out to cover the bottom well. The cells display amœboid activities and attach to the substratum. Moreover they begin at once to fuse with one another. After allowing time for the cells to settle and attach, the water is poured off and fresh sea-water added. The tissue is freed by currents of the pipette from the bottom and is collected in the center of the saucer. Fusion between the individual cells has by this time gone on to such an extent that the tissue now exists in the shape of minute balls or cell conglomerates of a more or less rounded shape looking to the eye much like small invertebrate eggs. Microscopic examination shows that between these little masses free cells also exist, but the masses are constantly incorporating such cells. The tissue in this shape is easily handled. It may be sucked up to fill a pipette and then strewn over cover glasses, slides, bolting cloth, watch glasses, etc. The cell conglomerates which are true syncytial masses throw out pseudopodia all over the surface and neighboring conglomerates fuse together to form larger masses, some rounded, some irregular. The details of later behavior vary, being largely dependent on the amount of tissue which is deposited in a spot, and on the strength of attachment between the mass of tissue and the substratum.

Decidedly the best results are obtained when the tissue has been strewn rather sparsely on slides and covers. The syncytial masses at first compact and more or less rounded, flatten out becoming incrusting. They continue to fuse with one another and thus the whole cover glass may come to be occupied by a single incrustation, or there may be in the end several such. If the cover glass is examined at intervals, it will be found that differentiation is gradually taking place. The dense homogeneous syncytial mass first develops at the surface a thin membrane with underlying connective tissue (collenchyma). Flagellated chambers make their appearance in great abundance. Canals appear as isolated spaces which come to connect with one another. Short oscular tubes with terminal oscula develop as vertical projections from the flat incrustation. If the incrustation be of any size it produces several such tubes. The currents from the oscula are easily observed, and if the cover glass be mounted in an inverted position on a slide the movements of the flagella of the collar cells may be watched with a high power (Zeiss 2 mm.). This degree of differentiation is attained in the course of six or seven days when the preparations are kept in laboratory aquaria (dishes in which the water is changed answer about as well as running aquaria). Differentiation goes on more rapidly when the preparation is hung in the open harbor in a live-box (a slide preparation inclosed in a coarse wire cage is convenient). Sponges reared in this way have been kept for a couple of weeks. The currents of water passing through them are certainly active and the sponges appear to be healthy. In such a sponge spicules are present, but some of these have unquestionably been carried over from the parent body along with the squeezed out cells.

The old question of individuality may receive a word here. Microciona is one of that large class of monaxonid sponges which lack definite shape and in which the number of oscula is correlated simply with the size of the mass. While we may look on such a mass from the phylogenetic standpoint as a corm, we speak of it as an individual. Yet it is an individual of which with the stroke of a knife we can make two. Or conversely it is an individual which may be made to fuse with another, the two forming one. To such a mass the ordinary idea of the individual is not applicable. It is only a mass large or small having the characteristic organs and tissues of the species but in which the shape of the whole and the number of the organs are indefinite. As with the adult so with the lumps of regenerative tissue. They have no definiteness of shape or size, and their structure is only definite in so far as the histological character of the syncytial mass is fixed for the species. A tiny lump may metamorphose into a sponge, or may first fuse with many such lumps, the aggregate also producing but a single sponge although a larger one. In a word we are not dealing with embryonic bodies of complicated organization but with a reproductive or regenerative tissue which we may start on its upward path of differentiation in almost any desired quantity. A striking illustration of this nature of the material is afforded by the following experiment. The tissue in the shape of tiny lumps was poured out in such wise that it formed continuous sheets about one millimeter thick. Such sheets were then cut into pieces, each about one cubic millimeter. These were hung in bolting cloth bags in an outside live-box. Some of the pieces in spite of such rough handling metamorphosed into functional sponges.

Observations on the Living Developing Nerve Fiber.

by ROSS G. HARRISON

Reprinted from the *Proceedings of the Society for Experimentol Biology and Medicine*, Vol. 4, pp. 140–143 (1907), by permission of the author.

One of the most far-reaching implications of the facts embraced by the cell concept is that the metazoan cell, given appropriate conditions for survival, has the capacity for autonomously carrying on the whole complement of its metabolic processes. From the early studies of Dutrochet up to the present there has been a persistent search for methods and techniques that would permit the detailed study of single cells apart from the organismic mass as a whole. A first step in this direction was taken by Roux (1885) when he successfully cultured a fragment of chick embryo neural plate in warm saline solution. Though many improvements and modifications of this technique originated in subsequent years, it was not until 1907 that a reliable and definite technique for culturing cells outside of the body was reported by Harrison.

The following paper describes the elegantly simple hanging drop method wherein a fragment of tissue is affixed to the cover slip by clotting lymph fluid in which it is mounted. Further refinement of the methods, especially by A. Carrel and others, led to the establishment and uninterrupted culture of a chick embryo connective tissue strain for more than twenty-five years. To date, well over one thousand publications have been set forth in the literature on this subject. The techniques of tissue culture find wide applications in the cultivation of cells for grafting, maintaining tumor strains for research purposes, propagation of viruses, the study of allergenic and immunological reactions, and the effects of radiations or other mutagenic agents.

[*From the Anatomical Laboratory of the Johns Hopkins University.*]

THE IMMEDIATE OBJECT OF the following experiments was to obtain a method by which the end of a growing nerve could be brought under direct observation while alive, in order that a correct conception might be had regarding what takes place as the fiber extends during embryonic development from the nerve center out to the periphery.

The method employed was to isolate pieces of embryonic tissue known to give rise to nerve fibers, as for example, the whole or fragments of the medullary tube, or ectoderm from the branchial region, and to observe their further development. The pieces were taken from frog embryos about 3 mm. long, at which stage, *i. e.,* shortly after the closure of the medullary folds, there is no visible differentiation of the nerve elements. After carefully dissecting it out the piece of tissue is removed by a fine pipette to a cover slip upon which is a drop of lymph freshly drawn from one of the lymph sacs of an adult frog. The lymph clots very quickly, holding the tissue in a fixed position. The cover slip is then inverted over a hollow slide and the rim sealed with paraffine. When reasonable aseptic precautions are taken, tissues will live under these conditions for a week and in some cases specimens have been kept alive for nearly four weeks. Such specimens may be readily observed from day to day under highly magnifying powers.

While the cell aggregates, which make up the different organs and organ complexes of the embryo, do not undergo normal transformation in form, owing no doubt in part to the abnormal conditions of mechanical tension to which they are subjected, nevertheless the individual tissue elements do differentiate characteristically. Groups of epidermis cells round themselves off into little spheres or stretch out into long bands, their cilia remain active for a week or more and a typical cuticular border develops. Masses of cells taken from the myotomes differentiate into muscle fibers showing fibrillæ with typical striations. When portions of myotomes are left attached to a piece of the medullary cord the muscle fibers which develop will, after two or three days, exhibit frequent contractions. In pieces of nervous tissue numerous fibers are formed, though owing to the fact that they are developed largely within the mass of transplanted tissue itself, their mode of development cannot always be followed. However, in a large number of cases fibers were observed which left the mass of nerve tissue and extended out into the surrounding lymph clot. It is these structures which concern us at the present time.

In the majority of cases the fibers were not observed until they had almost completed their development, having been found usually two, occasionally three and once or twice four days after isolation of the tissue. They consist of an almost hyaline protoplasm, entirely devoid of the yolk granules, with which the cell-bodies are gorged. Within this protoplasm there is no definiteness of structure; though a faint fibrillation may sometimes be observed and faintly defined granules are discernible. The fibers are about $1.5-3\mu$ thick and their contours show here and there irregular varicosities. The most remarkable feature of the fiber is its enlarged end, from which extend numerous fine simple or branched filaments. The end swelling bears a resemblance to certain rhizopods and close observation reveals a continual change in form, especially as regards the origin and branching of the filaments. In fact the changes are so rapid that it is difficult to draw the details accurately. It is clear we have before us a mass of protoplasm undergoing amœboid movements. If we examine sections of young normal embryos shortly after the first nerves have developed, we find exactly similar structures at the end of the developing nerve fibers. This is especially so in the case of the fibers which are connected with the giant cells described by Rohon and Beard.

Still more instructive are the cases in which the fiber is brought under observation before it has completed its growth. Then it is found that the end is very active and that its movement results in the drawing out and lengthening of the fiber to which it is attached. One fiber was observed to lengthen almost 20 μ in 25 minutes, another over 25 μ in 50 minutes. The longest fibers observed were 0.2 mm. in length.[1]

When the placodal thickenings of the branchial region are isolated, similar fibers are formed and in several of these cases they have been seen to arise from individual cells. On the other hand, other tissues of the embryo such as myotomes, yolk endoderm, notochord and indifferent ectoderm from the abdominal region do not give rise to structures of this kind. There can therefore be no doubt that we are dealing with a specific characteristic of nervous tissue.

It has not yet been found possible to make permanent specimens which show the isolated nerve fibers completely intact. The structures are so delicate that the mere immersion in the preserving fluid is sufficient to cause violent tearing and this very frequently results in the tearing away of the tissue in its entirety from the clot. Nevertheless, sections have been cut of some of the specimens and nerves have been traced from the walls of the medullary tube, but they were in all cases broken off short.

In view of this difficulty an effort, which resulted successfully, was made to

obtain permanent specimens in a somewhat different way. A piece of medullary cord about four or five segments long was excised from an embryo and this was replaced by a cylindrical clot of proper length and caliber, which was obtained by allowing blood or lymph of an adult frog to clot in a capillary tube. No difficulty was experienced in healing the clot into the embryo in proper position. After two, three or four days the specimens were preserved and examined in serial sections. It was found that the funicular fibers from the brain and anterior part of the cord, consisting of naked axones without sheath cells, had grown for a considerable distance into the clot.

These observations show beyond question that the nerve fiber develops by the outflowing of protoplasm from the central cells. This protoplasm retains its amœboid activity at its distal end, the result being that it is drawn out into a long thread which becomes the axis cylinder. No other cells or living structures take part in this process. The development of the nerve fiber is thus brought about by means of one of the very primitive properties of living protoplasm, amœboid movement, which, though probably common to some extent to all the cells of the embryo, is especially accentuated in the nerve cells at this period of development.

The possibility becomes apparent of applying the above method to the study of the influences which act upon a growing nerve. While at present it seems certain that the mere outgrowth of the fibers is largely independent of external stimuli, it is of course probable that in the body of the embryo there are many influences which guide the moving end and bring about contact with the proper end structure. The method here employed may be of value in analyzing these factors.

---

[1] Behavior of tissue culture cells is easily studied today by a combination of phase contrast microscopy and the motion picture camera.—*Editors.*

Part Two

~~

GENERAL PHYSIOLOGY

ENZYMES

CHRONOLOGY

1752   Réaumur showed by experiments with a pet kite that gastric juice liquefied meat.

1783   Spallanzani extended these findings to other birds, small mammals, and finally to humans by using himself as an experimental animal. Digestion was clearly shown to be a chemical process rather than a mechanical grinding of the food.

1810   Planche observed that extracts of plant roots would turn alcoholic solutions of guaiacum blue. The agent responsible for this change was found to be water-soluble and thermolabile.

1815   Kirchhoff reported that a glutinous component of wheat is capable of converting starch to dextrin and sugar.

1830   Robiquet and Boutron, also Chalard, discovered the hydrolytic splitting of amygdalin by an extract of defatted bitter almonds. The agent was named *emulsin* by Liebig and Wohler in 1837.

1831   Leuchs described the diastatic action of salivary ptyalin.

1833   Payen and Persoz further described and isolated amylase in powder form from barley malt.

1836   Schwann reported the action of pepsin and described its properties. Putrefaction and fermentation were attributed to action of microorganisms.

1837   Berzelius classified fermentation as a catalyzed reaction.

1838   Cagniard-Latour attributed fermentation to yeast.

1839   Liebig maintained that non-living ferments cause fermentation. This began a controversy over the question whether fermentation was a vital or a chemical process.

1856   Corvisart described trypsin.

1857   Pasteur demonstrated that lactic acid fermentation is carried out by living bacteria.

1858   Pasteur noted that *Penicillium* molds fermented only dextro tartaric acid and did not attack the levo isomer. Thus he discovered a practical method for separating compounds which are identical but for the spatial arrangement of the substituent group.

1862   Danielewski experimentally separated trypsin from pancreatic amylase by differential adsorption.

1870   Liebig proposed a purely chemical theory of enzyme action.

1871   Pasteur conclusively demonstrated that yeast was necessary for fermentation as it could then be carried out. He distinguished two kinds of ferments, "organized ferments" such as yeast or lactic acid bacteria, and "unorganized ferments" like pepsin and amylase.

1878   Kuhne introduced the term *enzyme*.

1883   Duclaux introduced the custom of designating an enzyme by the name of the substrate on which its action was first reported and adding the suffix *ase*.

1894   Emil Fischer conducted an extensive series of investigations which still form the basis for our notions of enzyme specificity.

1897   Buchner settled the Pasteur-Liebig controversy by the discovery that cell-free yeast extracts can cause fermentation of sugars.

1897   Bertrand coined the term *co-enzyme* to designate inorganic substances which were necessary to activate certain plant enzymes.

1898   Croft-Hill announced the first enzymatic synthesis, that of iso-maltose.

1904   Harden and Young isolated the first organic co-enzyme. They clearly demonstrated that fermentation required the simultaneous presence of both a colloidal heat labile fraction and a diffusible, low molecular weight, heat stable co-enzyme.

1909   Sørensen pointed out the effect of pH on enzyme activity.

1913   Michaelis and Menten postulated the existence of an intermediate enzyme-substrate complex to explain enzyme action.

1926   Sumner prepared crystalline urease.

1930   Northrup crystallized pepsin.

1931   Northrup and Kunitz crystallized trypsin. Approximately thirty different enzymes have been crystallized at this writing.

1935–1936   Stern spectroscopically demonstrated the existence of an intermediate substrate-enzyme complex for the enzyme catalase, thus confirming the Michaelis-Menten hypothesis.

1943   Chance spectroscopically demonstrated the existence of an enzyme-substrate complex for catalase.

Memoir on Diastase, the Principal Products of its Reactions and their Applications to Industrial Arts. ❧

by MM. PAYEN and PERSOZ

Abridged from *Annales de Chimie et de Physique*, Vol. 53, pp. 73–92 (1833). Translated by M. L. Gabriel for this volume.

The general phenomenon of catalysis was first discovered in 1811–1814 by G. S. C. Kirchhoff, who reported the existence of a glutinous component of wheat that had the capacity of digesting starch. Some twenty years later Payen and Persoz undertook the heroic task of isolating this active plant principle. They attempted this without any prior knowledge of the chemical nature of the agent or its properties. In fact, the only guide to the presence of the elusive substance at any particular stage of the isolation procedure was its digestive effect upon the starch substrate. Despite these serious obstacles, Payen and Persoz early recognized that their digestive principle was destroyed by heat. It is also clear that they were aware of the fact that the enzyme they sought existed in extremely low concentrations. For this reason, their persistent attempts at purification by means of fractional precipitation with alcohol, lead acetate, or controlled heating are especially noteworthy. These procedures, still useful in modern enzyme studies, were in a large measure responsible for the successful isolation of diastase at this early date.

The interest of this paper is not, however, limited to the authors' technical success in isolating the enzyme. Payen and Persoz concluded their report by calling attention not only to the applicability of enzyme action for the analysis of starch products and the industrial production of dextrins and sugars from starch, but also to the theoretical importance of diastases in such problems of plant metabolism as the synthesis, storage, and translocation of carbohydrate reserves. Considering the primitive state of chemical concepts of the day, their grasp of the implications of their work is indeed remarkable.

SINCE WE MADE the announcement to the Academy of Sciences about a new method of preparing dextrin by separating and removing the envelopes of starch by direct action, we have sought the agent that produces this singular reaction.

This substance, which we have succeeded in isolating, contains proportionally less nitrogen the closer it comes to a state of purity. In addition it has the following properties: it is solid, white, amorphous, insoluble in alcohol, soluble in water and dilute alcohol; its aqueous solution is neutral and without any pronounced taste; it is not precipitated by lead acetate; left by itself it changes more or less quickly according to the atmospheric temperature, and becomes acid; heated to 65°—75° with starch, it has the remarkable property of promptly detaching the envelopes from the modified internal substance, the dextrin, which readily dissolves in water, while the insoluble coatings either float to the top or are precipitated, according to the movements of the liquid. This singular separating property has prompted us to give the substance that possesses it the name of *diastase,* which exactly expresses this fact.[1]

The operation, which is readily carried out, gives a purer dextrin preparation than any hitherto prepared. The material displays in a high degree its characteristic power of rotation [of polarized light], which is not obtainable to an equal extent by any other method of preparation. Nevertheless, the solution of diastase, in the presence of dextrin, converts the latter gradually into sugar, which is not precipitated either by baryta [barium hydroxide] or by lead acetate. It is necessary that the temperature be maintained at 65°—75° during the contact, for if the diastase solution is heated to boiling it loses the capacity to act upon starch or dextrin.

Diastase is present in germinated seeds of barley, oats, and wheat, in the germs [embryos] of germinated grains, but not in the radicles; it is not present in either the shoots or the roots of sprouted potatoes, but only in the tuber near and around its point of insertion. . . .

Cereals or potatoes before germination contain no diastase; it can be extracted from germinated barley by the following procedure—the yield is greater when the germination has been carried out uniformly, and when the development of the plumule is most nearly equal in length to that of the grains.

After the mixture of water and germinated barley has been macerated in cold water for several minutes, it is put into a filter, or better, it is put under strong pressure and the solution is filtered; the clear liquid is heated in a water bath to 70°. This temperature coagulates most of the nitrogenous matter, which must then be separated by another filtration; the filtrate contains the active principle plus a small amount of nitrogenous matter, colored substance, and a quantity of sugar proportionate to the degree of germination. In order to separate the latter, alcohol is added to the liquid until no more precipitate is formed; diastase being insoluble in alcohol, it forms an insoluble flocculent deposit which can be collected and dried at a low temperature. In order to avoid producing any alteration it is necessary to keep from heating it while moist to a temperature of 90–100°; to obtain it in still purer state, it should be dissolved in water and reprecipitated with alcohol; these solutions and precipitations may even be repeated twice. Diastase free from nitrogenous matter [2] may also be obtained without coagulating the latter by raising the temperature, but solely by several precipitations with alcohol. After each precipitation, less of this substance dissolves, and the diastase becomes more and more white and pure. . . .

The diastase solution, whether pure or containing sugar, separates the dextrin from all kinds of starchy substances and thus permits the direct analysis of flours, rice, bread, and the like. When the extraction of this new agent has been

---

[1] Greek: *diastasis*—separation.—*Editors.*

[2] Diastase, being a protein, is of course not "free from nitrogenous matter." But the fact that enzymes are protein was not proven until nearly a hundred years later, when Sumner crystallized urease in 1926.—*Editors.*

carried out carefully, its activity is such that one part by weight is enough to render soluble in hot water the internal substance of two thousand parts of dry starch, with subsequent conversion of the dextrin into sugar. These reactions are more easily accomplished, and the first takes place more promptly, if a great excess of diastase is used. Thus, by doubling the dose to one per thousand, the solution of starch can be carried out in ten minutes. . . .

Crude dextrin is in general composed of three substances (not counting certain teguments): The first is insoluble in cold water, soluble in hot water, colorable with iodine, and identical with the internal material of starch. The second is soluble in cold and hot water and in dilute alcohol, it cannot be colored with iodine, and it is analogous to gum. The third is a sugar which is soluble in water and in alcohol at 35 degrees, it cannot be colored by iodine, and it is fermentable.

The prolonged action of diastase evidently reduces these three substances to the last two by completing the transformation of the first. . . .

The new principle, more or less pure, will be especially useful in the analysis of starches, flour, bread, and other starchy substances. This is one of the most elegant procedures in organic analysis.

Solutions containing diastase will provide an agent for manufacturing commerical dextrin and sugar of dextrin, operations already carried out with great precision and reduced to their simplest expression.

This agent affords the means of obtaining the teguments of starch free from all of the substance colored by iodine, and of obtaining the latter abundantly, or converting it, at will, into two other substances—a sugar and a gum. This agent also serves to explain the passage of the products of starch through the sap—it is significant to recall that we have found the active principle near the points where the starch is diminished in the plant. . . .

There remains before us a vast field of researches to be traversed as to the existence of diastase in the various parts of the vegetable organization, its atomic weight, its elementary composition, its combinations,[3] and the products of its markedly specific reaction on vegetables that contain starch.

---

[3] More difficult tasks than the authors could have guessed! The chemistry of enzymes and the structure of proteins still present research problems a century and a quarter later.— *Editors.*

Alcoholic Fermentation Without Yeast Cells.

by EDUARD BUCHNER

Abridged from *Berichte deutsche Chemische Gesellschaft,* Vol. 30, pp. 117–124 (1897). Translated by M. L. Gabriel for this volume.

The date of publication for the paper that follows is 1897. For nearly sixty years prior to this date a heated controversy raged in the pages of scientific journals. By a series of ingenious experiments, one of which is reprinted in another section of this volume, Pasteur demonstrated that the chemical alterations accompanying fermentation occurred only in the presence of living organisms. By his time it had been recognized that a number of bio-chemical reactions were mediated by wholly extracellular enzymes, such as diastase, pepsin, or trypsin. In no sense could these be considered living organisms or "organized ferments." This difficulty was erased by the simple expedient of giving different names to the different ferments. Thus biologists and chemists alike were forced to wrestle with two conceptions of catalytically active substances—"organized" and "unorganized" ferments.

The incorrectness of this dualism was accidentally resolved by Eduard Buchner. In the course of a series of experiments designed to test various fractions of yeast extracts for their medicinal values, Buchner found that when he attempted to preserve his extracts by the simple household procedure of adding large quantities of sugar, vigorous fermentation occurred in his cell-free yeast extracts. It was clear that it was not yeast cells themselves, but rather the materials which could be separated from them that were the actual ferments. Buchner designated this albuminoid, water-soluble, heat-labile principle as zymase.

During the last forty years zymase has been shown to be a complex of several enzymes. Our current notions of fermentation assume the participation of at least twelve distinct enzymes catalyzing at least fourteen or more reactions. Most of these enzymes are associated with cytoplasmic particles known as mitochondria.

SEPARATION OF THE fermentation process from living yeast cells has up to now not been successfully accomplished; in the following communication an experiment is described that solves this problem.

One thousand grams of brewer's yeast, cleaned as for pressing into cakes, but without the addition of potato starch, is carefully mixed with an equal weight of quartz sand * and 250 grams of diatomaceous earth, and then ground until the mass becomes moist and plastic. To this dough, 100 gms of water are added and the dough is wrapped in a cloth and gradually brought under a pressure of 4–500 atmospheres. Three hundred ccm of juice are thus obtained.

The remaining cake is once again ground, strained and mixed with 100 gms of water. Subjected once more to the same pressure in the hydraulic press, it yields 150 cc more of juice. Therefore, out of a kilogram of yeast one obtains 500 cc of juice which contains about 300 cc of cellular material. To remove a slight remaining turbidity, the juice is finally shaken up with 4 gms of fuller's earth and filtered through filter paper, the first part of the filtrate being refiltered repeatedly.

The juice thus obtained has the appearance of a clear but opalescent yellow liquid with a pleasant yeasty smell. . . .

The most interesting property of the juice is the fact that it is capable of fermenting carbohydrate. When it is mixed with an equal volume of a con-

---

* Glass powder, because of its mild alkaline reaction, is less suitable.

centrated cane sugar solution a steady evolution of carbon dioxide begins in as little as ¼—1 hour, and continues for days. Exactly the same results are obtained with glucose, fructose, and maltose; on the other hand, no fermentation takes place in mixtures of juice with saturated lactose or mannitose, just as these substances are not fermented by living brewer's yeast cells. Mixtures of juice and sugar solution that have been allowed to ferment for several days and placed in an ice chest gradually become turbid, without giving evidence of the presence of any microscopic organisms; on the other hand, at a magnification of 700 times, a fairly large number of particles of albuminoids are visible, the formation of which is probably due to the acid arising during the course of fermentation. Saturation of the mixture of juice and saccharose solution with chloroform does not inhibit the fermentation, but it leads prematurely to the separation of a small amount of albumin. Neither is the power of fermentation destroyed by filtration of the juice through a sterilized Berkefeldt filter of diatomaceous earth, which certainly retains all yeast cells; a mixture of a quite clear filtrate with sterilized cane sugar solution begins to ferment, although with a delay of about one day, even at the temperature of the ice chest. If a parchment paper bag filled with juice is suspended in thirty-seven per cent cane sugar solution, the outer surface of the bag becomes covered after several hours with innumerable tiny gas bubbles; naturally an active evolution of gas could also be observed in the inner surface as a consequence of the inward diffusion of sugar solution. Further experiments will be necessary to decide whether the agent responsible for fermentation has the capacity to diffuse through parchment paper, as would seem to be the case. The fermenting capacity of the juice is gradually lost in time—juice kept for five days in ice water in half-full flasks proved to be inactive toward saccharose. It is remarkable that, on the other hand, juice which has been mixed with cane sugar and is therefore actively fermenting retains its capacity for fermentation in the ice chest for at least two weeks. The most likely explanation is that the carbon dioxide formed by the fermentation has a favorable influence by keeping out the oxygen of the air. It is also possible, however, that the easily assimilated sugar contributes to the preservation of the agent.

Up to the present only a few experiments have been carried out to elucidate the nature of the active substance in the juice. Upon warming the juice to 40°–50° there occurs first the production of carbon dioxide, then gradually the separation of coagulated albumin. After an hour the juice was filtered with repeated pouring back of the filtrate. The clear filtrate still possessed a slight capacity for fermentation of cane sugar in one experiment, and none in another experiment; accordingly it would seem that the active substance either loses its activity at this surprisingly low temperature or else that it coagulates and precipitates out. Later 20 ccm of juice were suspended in three volumes of absolute alcohol, the precipitate was sucked off and dried over sulphuric acid in a vacuum; two grams of dry substance were obtained which on being resuspended in water was only slightly soluble. The filtrate obtained from this was incapable of fermenting cane sugar. These experiments should be repeated—especially the isolation of the active substance by means of ammonium sulphate should be attempted.

The following conclusions may be drawn with respect to the theory of fermentation. In the first place it has been demonstrated that for the production of the fermentation process no such complicated apparatus is necessary as is represented by the yeast cell. It is much more likely that the agent of the juice which is active in fermentation is a soluble substance, doubtless an albuminoid substance; this may be designated as zymase.

The view that an albuminoid substance of a specific nature derived from the yeast cells is responsible for fermentation was already expressed in 1858 by M. Traube as the enzyme or ferment theory, and later was especially defended by F. Hoppe-Seyler. However, the separation of such an enzyme from the yeast cell has heretofore never been accomplished.

The question now remains whether zymase is to be considered as one of the long well-known enzymes.[1] As C. von Nägeli has already pointed out, there are important differences between fermentation and the action of ordinary enzymes. The latter are merely hydrolyzing agents which can be imitated by the simplest chemical means. Although A. von Baeyer has given us a closer understanding of the chemical processes involved in alcoholic fermentation, tracing it to fairly simple principles, nevertheless the breakdown of sugar into alcohol and carbon dioxide still is one of the more complicated reactions; it involves the breaking of carbon bonds, something that has not been attained to so complete an extent by other means. The temperature relations also constitute a significant difference.

[1] I.e., what are now called extracellular enzymes.—*Editors*.

Invertin may be extracted by means of water from yeast cells that have been killed by dry heat (heating one hour to 150°) and isolated by precipitating with alcohol as a powder slightly soluble in water. The material active in fermentation cannot be obtained by a similar procedure. It is no longer present in yeast cells heated this much; if we may draw a conclusion from the experiment cited above, it becomes modified by precipitation in alcohol into a water-insoluble substance. One would therefore hardly go astray in assuming that zymase belongs to the genuine albuminoid substances and is much closer to the living protoplasm of the yeast cell than is invertin.[2]

It is possible that the fermentation of the sugar by the zymase takes place inside the yeast cells; it is more probable though that the yeast cells secrete this albuminoid substance into the sugar solution, where it causes the fermentation. If so, the process in alcoholic fermentation is perhaps to be regarded as a physiological act only insofar as it is living yeast cells that secrete the zymase.

[2] The logic of this argument is undeniably valid, but the inference is incorrect nevertheless. Zymase, a complex of several enzymes, will cease to function in fermentation as soon as the most heat-sensitive member of the complex is inactivated. Invertase does happen to be one of the most heat stable enzymes known, but like all other protein enzymes it can be irreversibly inactivated if it is sufficiently heated. —*Editors*.

On Cytochrome, a Respiratory Pigment, Common to Animals, Yeast, and Higher Plants. ❧

by D. KEILIN

Abridged from *Proceedings of the Royal Society of London*, Series B, Vol. 98, pp. 312–329 (1925). Reprinted by permission of the author and The Royal Society.

In a communication to The Royal Society dated 1886 C. A. MacMunn reported several important and novel discoveries. Examining a variety of tissues from different organisms by means of microspectroscopy, he found a series of absorption bands that varied but little from organism to organism, or from tissue to tissue. In the concluding section of the paper MacMunn remarked,

"Thus from Echinoderms to man throughout the animal kingdom, we find in various tissues a class of pigments whose spectra show a remarkable resemblance to each other; they are allied to the haemochromogens, the bands of which are closely imitated by the histohaematins. . . . Their bands are intensified by reducing agents and enfeebled by oxidizing agents; they accordingly appear to be capable of oxidation and reduction and are therefore respiratory. . . . They combine with the oxygen conveyed to them in the blood, and hold it for the purposes of metabolism, parting with the carbon dioxide in exchange for the oxygen. . . . These observations appear to me to point out the fact that the formation of carbon dioxide and the absorption of oxygen takes place in the tissues themselves and not in the blood."

These findings were severely criticized by Hoppe-Seyler, one of the most influential biochemists of the day, and by others, who argued that MacMunn's histohaematin and myohaematin were essentially decomposition products of hemoglobin. MacMunn acknowledged these criticisms and pointed out that though his pigments and the hemoglobin derivatives had similar spectra, they were not identical. Moreover, he also reported the existence of these pigments in such organisms as yeast and insects which do not possess hemoglobin at any time in their life cycles. Hoppe-Seyler never replied to this evidence and closed further discussion on the matter by appending an editorial note to MacMunn's work stating that any further discussion was unnecessary and superfluous. Though the original findings were recorded in the cumulative literature of science, their significance was soon forgotten by contemporary workers.

In 1925 these same cellular pigments, now designated as cytochromes,

*were rediscovered by Keilin. MacMunn's findings were amply verified
and extended to all aerobic organisms. In his original work Keilin
recognized that the spectroscopic evidence indicated that cytochrome was
a mixture of related iron-porphyrin compounds rather than a single substance. Three chemically related substances were described by Keilin and
further research has indicated that there are at least seven such iron-
porphyrin proteins. One of them, cytochrome a3, is apparently identical
with the Atmungsferment, or cytochrome oxidase, discovered by Warburg. The cytochromes are macromolecules with molecular weights approximating 16,000. In cellular metabolism they function as terminal
intermediates for the transfer of hydrogen or electrons to cytochrome
oxidase. Thus, they are regarded as reversibly oxidizable or reducible
substances, or hydrogen or electron carriers, in the long chain of
enzymatically catalyzed reactions leading from substrate to molecular
oxygen.*

UNDER THE NAMES myohæmatin and histohæmatin MacMunn (1884–1886) described a respiratory pigment, which he found in muscles and other tissues of representatives of almost all the orders of the animal kingdom. He found that this pigment, in the reduced state, gives a characteristic spectrum, with four absorption bands occupying the following positions: 615—593/567.5—561/554.5—546/532—511/. When oxidized, the pigment does not show absorption bands. In 1887 MacMunn described a method by which it can be extracted in a "modified form" from the muscles of birds and mammals. He found the pectoral muscle of a pigeon to be the most suitable material for the extraction of "myohæmatin," in the belief that it was the sole colouring matter of the muscles in a pigeon bled to death. From this "modified myohæmatin" he also obtained other derivatives, such as acid hæmatin and hæmatoporphyrin, and he finally arrived at the conclusion that myo- and histohæmatin are respiratory pigments different and independent from hæmoglobin and its derivatives.

In 1889 Levy carefully repeated MacMunn's experiments in extracting myohæmatin from muscles of birds and mammals and obtained the substance described by MacMunn as "modified myohæmatin." But he regarded this substance as an ordinary hæmochromogen, derived from hæmoglobin.

Levy's paper was soon followed by a reply from MacMunn (1889), and by a discussion between this author and Hoppe-Seyler [1] (1890), who fully supported Levy and refused to take into consideration the presence of myohæmatin in invertebrates devoid of hæmoglobin. As to the four-banded absorption spectrum of myohæmatin, which, according to MacMunn, can be seen in a fresh muscle of mammal or bird, Hoppe-Seyler explained it as a mere superposition of bands of oxyhæmoglobin on the surface of the muscle with the bands of reduced hæmoglobin of the deeper layer, and possibly also with the bands of a small amount of hæmochromogen. Hoppe-Seyler finally dealt with the CO compound which he had obtained from MacMunn's "modified myohæmatin" present in the extracted fluid. This compound, which is in all respects similar to the compound obtained from ordinary hæmochromogen, Hoppe-Seyler brings as conclusive evidence against the ex-

[1] A distinguished figure in scientific circles and participant in numerous controversies. He was the editor of a prominent biochemical journal, which is still published today and bears his name.—*Editors.*

istence of myohæmatin as a separate respiratory pigment.

In 1890 MacMunn tried once more to defend his position, but his defence was not even replied to by Hoppe-Seyler, who merely appended to MacMunn's paper a short editorial note, stating that he considered all further discussion as superfluous, MacMunn not having brought any fresh evidence in support of his views. Hoppe-Seyler's note ended the discussion and MacMunn's new respiratory pigment was gradually forgotten. The term myohæmatin still made occasional appearances in the literature, but authors mentioning it have seldom seen the pigment or even read MacMunn's original papers; those who have seen the pigment have misunderstood its properties, and have not failed to show that they were aware of Hoppe-Seyler's criticisms, with which they were in full agreement.

Methods.—For the spectroscopic examination of living organisms, cells, tissues, or their extracts, two instruments have been used—the microspectroscopic ocular of Zeiss and the Hartridge reversion spectroscope. Zeiss's microspectroscope was mainly used for the detection of the pigment when its concentration was very low, and for the examination of opaque tissues, portions of organism, suspensions of cells or turbid fluids. It was also used for examination of rapid oxidation and reduction of the pigment in cells or complete living organisms. For the precise determination of the position of absorption bands, the Hartridge reversion spectroscope gave exceptionally good results. It was, however, slightly modified by Dr. Hartridge for use with the microscope. The main modification consisted in inserting in front of the slit a double-image Wollaston prism. Calibration of this instrument was obtained by a determination of 14 sharp lines of emission spectra, giving a straight line when plotted. A strong source of light such as the Nernst lamp was used with both microspectroscopes.

DISTRIBUTION OF CYTOCHROME.

In the course of my study on the respiration of parasitic insects and worms, I have found that the pigment myo- or histohæmatin not only exists, but has much wider distribution and importance than was ever anticipated even by MacMunn. Considering that this pigment is not confined to muscles and tissues, but exists also in unicellular organisms, and further, that there is no evidence that it is a simple hæmatin in the proper sense of the term, the names myo- and histohæmatin, given to it by MacMunn, are misleading. In fact, as we shall see later, there is ample evidence that this pigment is not a simple compound, but a complex formed of three distinct hæmochromogen compounds, the nature of which is not yet completely elucidated. I propose therefore to describe it under the name of *Cytochrome,* signifying merely "cellular pigment," pending the time when its composition shall have been properly determined. This name, which expresses also its intracellular nature, does not, however, relegate the pigment to any definite compound, an important consideration inasmuch as the properties of various compounds cannot hereafter be ascribed to it without good evidence.

I have found cytochrome in the cells and tissues of a great number of individuals of the following groups and species of animals: —Turbellaria: *Dendrocœla lactea;* Oligochætes: *Allolobophora chlorotica, Helodrilus caliginosus;* Nematodes: *Ascaris megalocephala, Ascaris suis;* Molluscs: *Limnaea peregra, L. stagnalis, Helix nemoralis, H. aspersa;* Crustacea: *Oniscus sp., Asellus aquatilis, Cancer pagurus;* Myriapods: *Lithobius forficatus, Geophilus sp.;* Arachnids: *Epeira diademata.* Most of the orders of insects, 40 species of which have been examined. . . .

The study of this pigment in verte-brates required more complicated manipulation, such as perfusion of their circulatory system, and was therefore confined to a few examples: frogs, pigeons, guinea-pigs and rabbits.

The number and wide range of systematic distribution of the species which show this pigment clearly, and which have been enumerated either by Mac-Munn or myself, is so great that it may safely be concluded that cytochrome is one of the most widely distributed respiratory pigments. Moreover, cytochrome is not confined to animal cells alone. I have found it, and in great concentration, in cells of bacteria, those of ordinary bakers' yeast, and also in some of the cells of higher plants. To avoid all confusion in the terms which will be used in this paper it is important to mention beforehand that cytochrome

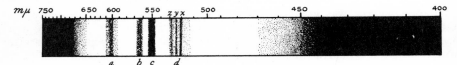

FIG. 1.—Absorption spectrum of cytochrome in thoracic muscles of a bee.

(= myohæmatin = histohæmatin) is a pigment distinct both from blood hæmoglobin and from muscle-hæmoglobin (= myochrome of Mörner = myoglobin of Günther) or their derivatives. In many cells cytochrome may, however, coexist with hæmoglobin.

GENERAL CHARACTERS OF ABSORPTION SPECTRUM OF REDUCED CYTOCHROME.

Cytochrome in Animal Tissues.—The best material for the study of the absorption spectrum of cytochrome is provided by the thoracic muscles of the honey bee. Specimens of bees frozen at $-7°$ C. are allowed rapidly to thaw. The head and abdomen are cut off, and by compressing the thorax laterally with the fingers the thoracic muscles are expelled in one mass through the anterior opening of the thorax. The muscles of 2 or 3 bees, compressed between a slide and coverslip and examined with the Zeiss microspectroscope, show clearly a very characteristic absorption spectrum (fig. 1) composed of four bands (a, b, c, d), the position of which can be determined only with the Hartridge microspectroscope. For each band I have taken an average of 10 readings and although the

pigment was examined *in situ*, the variations between individual readings were only about 7 Ångström units. The position of maximum intensity of the bands in the bees is as follows:—a, 6046; b, 5665; c, 5502; d, 5210. The relative width and intensity of the bands, in other words, the general aspect of the spectrum, varies naturally with the thickness of the layer of tissue examined. . . . The absorption spectrum of cytochrome in other organisms differs very little from that of the honey-bee (fig. 2). . . . It is impossible at this stage to decide whether the small differences observed in the position of the bands of cytochrome in different organisms correspond to a real difference in the composition of this pigment, or are only of the nature of an experimental error, caused by the presence of small amounts of other pigments, such as lipochromes or hæmoglobin.

Cytochrome in yeast cells.—A slightly wetted fragment of bakers' yeast, compressed between two slides to the thickness of 0.6 mm., and examined with the Zeiss' microspectroscope, shows very clearly the characteristic spectrum of cytochrome, with its four bands: a, b, c, d, very similar to those of the thoracic

	610 605 600 595 590 585 580 575 570	565 560 555 550 545 540 535 530 525 520 mμ

Organism	a	b	c	d
Bee: wing muscles	6046	5665	5502	5210
Dytiscus: wing muscles	6038	5664	5495	5205
Galleria: wing muscles	6046	5657	5495	5200
Helix: radula muscles	6035	5650	5495	5200
Frog: heart muscle	6040	5660	5500	5205
Guinea pig: heart muscle	6045	5662	5500	5205
Yeast cells	6035	5645	5490	5190

FIG. 2.—Positions of the four main absorption bands of cytochrome (*a, b, c,* and *d*) in various organisms.

muscles of a bee. . . . We can say, therefore, that cytochrome, in spite of its great range of distribution, shows a very characteristic, easily recognisable and uniform absorption spectrum. This uniformity of the spectrum indicates, moreover, the great similarity in the chemical composition and the properties of this pigment whatever may be its origin.

The four absorption bands of cytochrome are of unequal intensity: thus band *c* is usually the strongest, then come *a* and *b,* and finally *d,* which is faint, and, when the concentration of pigment is low, may easily be overlooked. It is important to note, that this relative intensity of the four bands, although very general, is not so constant as the position of the bands. In some tissues bands *b* or *a* are almost as strong as the band *c*.

When a tissue showing clearly all the four bands is gradually compressed between two slides, the bands become faint and disappear in inverse order to their intensity. During this process the tissue shows a succession of spectra with 3, 2, or 1 absorption bands. This observation shows that the reduction in number of the bands of cytochrome which may be found in tissues of different organisms denotes only a lower concentration of the pigment. Moreover, in the great majority of those cases, the remaining absorption bands can be detected on increasing the depth of tissue examined. This naturally applies to tissues devoid of all pigments other than cytochrome.

OXIDIZED AND REDUCED CYTOCHROME.

The absorption spectrum with four characteristic bands corresponds to the reduced state of cytochrome, while the spectrum of the pigment in its oxidized state, at least in the concentration found in the tissues, shows no distinct absorption bands, but only a very faint shading extending between 520–540 and 550–570 μμ. The oxidation and reduction of the pigment can be easily observed in yeast. If a shallow tube (30 mm. high) is half-filled with a suspension of bakers' yeast in water (20 per cent.), and the suspension then examined with the Zeiss microspectroscope, the four absorption bands may be clearly seen; but when the air is rapidly bubbled through the suspension the cytochrome becomes oxidized and the bands disappear. If the current of air is stopped the pigment becomes reduced and the four bands rapidly reappear.

A similar result can be obtained by shaking a 5 c.c. yeast-emulsion in a test-tube and examining it with the microspectroscope. When, instead of air, a current of N_2 is passed through the yeast emulsion, or when the latter is shaken with N_2, the cytochrome remains in a reduced state, showing all the time its characteristic four absorption bands. Similar results are obtained with the thoracic muscles of bees or the striated muscles of a guinea-pig. But in these cases the oxidation and reduction are better seen in the broken-up muscles, which may be spread on a slide. When the muscle is exposed to air the cytochrome is seen in its oxidized form, but when the slide is covered with another slide and the space around the muscle filled with glycerin, the cytochrome becomes reduced and the four bands appear. In these experiments, cytochrome is oxidized by O_2 of the air and reduced by the tissue itself. The oxidation of a reduced cytochrome can easily be obtained without shaking with air, by adding to the tissue a small quantity of potassium ferricyanide or of H_2O_2. On the other hand, when the reducing power of the tissue has been destroyed, cytochrome, which then becomes easily oxidized with air, can be readily reduced by adding to the tissue a small quantity of a reducer such as $Na_2S_2O_4$. . . .

ACTION OF NARCOTICS ON CYTOCHROME.

When a drop of weak solution of KCN is added to the suspension of yeast, no matter how actively this suspension is shaken with air or pure O_2, the cytochrome remains completely reduced, and continues to show the characteristic bands, which do not differ in the slightest degree from the bands of an ordinary reduced cytochrome. The concentration of KCN which stops oxidation of cytochrome is about $n/10,000$, and a much lower concentration, such as $n/100,000$, inhibits to a great degree the oxidation power of the pigment.

Further and more important, when a drop of KCN is added to the suspension of yeast, kept at a low temperature and previously oxidized by a current of air,

the cytochrome becomes immediately reduced, just as if KCN was acting as a powerful reducing agent. In fact, KCN does not act as a reducer, but inhibits the oxidation of cytochrome, while it does not inhibit other oxidation processes which may accompany the reduction of our pigment.

The action of sodium pyrophosphate is similar to that of KCN. It also inhibits the oxidation of cytochrome only, while it does not arrest the reduction of this pigment. Other substances, such as formaldehyde, ethyl alcohol, acetone, and ethyl urethane, act in a very different way. All these substances, even in concentrations which kill the cells of yeast, do not inhibit the oxidation of cytochrome. On the contrary, in such a concentration they completely stop the reduction of cytochrome, which then remains oxidized indefinitely.* In lower concentrations they delay the reduction of oxidized cytochrome, though they do not completely stop it.

If a suspension of yeast in ethyl urethane is shaken with air until the cytochrome becomes completely oxidized, and KCN solution is then added to this suspension, the cytochrome does not become reduced. It remains oxidized because the reducing action of the cells is inhibited, or even destroyed, by urethane, while KCN has no effect on oxidized cytochrome. When the reducing power of the cells is not completely destroyed by the action of urethane, on adding KCN to such suspension a gradual but slow reduction of cytochrome can be observed.

The facts given above show clearly that in relation to the oxidation process

---

* The oxidation of cytochrome in this case differs slightly from ordinary oxidation. In ordinary oxidation all the four bands fade away more or less simultaneously. In presence of urethane or formaldehyde band c disappears the first, while the other three bands remain and band b seems to be even intensified. On shaking the emulsion for a long time with air, all the bands disappear, band b being the last to go.

in cells in which cytochrome is involved all the inhibitors of oxidation can be separated into two distinct categories, the actions of which are fundamentally different. To one category belong KCN and sodium pyrophosphate; to the other such substances as alcohols, urethane, and aldehydes. The first category (A) inhibits the oxidation of cytochrome, the second (B) inhibits its reduction. Diagrammatically this can be represented in the following way:—

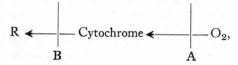

$$R \longleftarrow \text{Cytochrome} \longleftarrow O_2,$$
$$\qquad\quad B \qquad\qquad\qquad A$$

R being the substances which reduce the oxidized cytochrome, B and A indicating the places of rupture in the oxidation system produced respectively by the substances of the corresponding category of inhibitors. This seems to indicate that, at least for oxidation systems similar to that of cytochrome, the problem of the action of narcotics needs further investigation and existing theories require careful revision.

THE NATURAL BEHAVIOUR OF CYTOCHROME IN LIVING ORGANISMS.

We have previously seen that in a compressed fragment of bakers' yeast or in an emulsion of yeast, cytochrome is usually found in a reduced state. Yet we can hardly speak of natural conditions of life in the case of yeast, which is an organism highly modified by long and constant selection. We have found, however, that while in bakers' yeast the concentration of cytochrome is very high, in brewers' yeast it is very low. This is undoubtedly correlated with the different modes of life of these two categories of yeasts.

In the dissected muscles of a perfused guinea-pig, cytochrome is usually found in a completely, or almost completely

oxidized form, and the reduction takes place when the muscles are excluded from the air, e.g., pressed between two slides. The thoracic muscles of insects, on the other hand, even when they are rapidly taken out from the body and immediately examined, almost always show the reduced form of the pigment.

In both these cases we are dealing with portions of tissues excised from an organism and therefore not examined in natural conditions. To understand the function of this pigment it is important to find out in what state this pigment is present in a normal living organism. The main difficulty in answering this question consisted in finding suitable material for such an investigation. One insect, however, the common wax-moth (*Galleria mellonella*) answered the purpose. Several active specimens of this moth were selected out of a large stock bred in the Laboratory, and the thorax of each was carefully cleaned from scales. These specimens were then attached by the ventral surface to a slide (by means of small droplets of gum arabic) and the thorax carefully examined with Zeiss microspectroscope and a strong light.†

The following are the results of these observations:—

(1) Female of *Galleria* remained very quiet, except for the occasional expulsion of an egg and a somewhat rhythmic movement with ovipositor. The thorax being of a yellow colour showed better the long-wave portion of the spectrum, but no absorption band could be detected.

(2) In specimens of males and females which began to struggle constantly, vibrating their wings in efforts to detach themselves from the slides, the bands of cyto-

---

† In this condition the insects remained alive for long periods, and even after three hours the females, in spite of being attached to the slide, went on ovipositing.

chrome gradually appeared, band *a* being very clear, and bands *b* and *c* appeared as almost fused into one band.

(3) When these specimens ceased to move and stopped the vibration of the wings, the bands became very faint and hardly detectable.

(4) In a specimen which showed no absorption bands (the cytochrome being oxidized) a slight pressure exercised upon the thorax made the bands of a reduced cytochrome to appear.

(5) Specimens of *Galleria* fixed to the glass bottom of a special airtight gas-chamber and examined spectroscopically showed no absorption bands. When N_2 or coal gas was passed through the chamber all the four bands of reduced cytochrome appeared very rapidly. When N_2 was cleared with air, the bands rapidly disappeared.

(6) When a specimen with oxidized cytochrome was exposed for a few seconds to vapours of KCN all the four bands rapidly appeared and the insect became motionless.

(7) The same specimen being brought back into fresh air, the absorption bands of reduced cytochrome gradually faded away and the insect began to show signs of life.

The absorption bands of cytochrome shown by *Galleria* after exertion, still less after intense vibration with the wings, are never so strong as they appear in specimens exposed to pure N_2 or to the vapours of KCN. This fact indicates that in natural conditions cytochrome is in the oxidized form, and that during exertion, however great, cytochrome becomes only partially reduced.

The above experiments with *Galleria* and the previous observations on yeast show that cytochrome acts as a respiratory catalyst, which is functional in oxidized as well as in a partially reduced form. The oxygen is constantly taken up by this pigment and given up to the cells. In the living organism the state of the cytochrome as seen spectroscopically denotes only the difference between the rates of its oxidation and reduction. . . .

DERIVATIVES OF CYTOCHROME AND NATURE OF THIS PIGMENT.

Several attempts have been made to extract this pigment in unmodified state from cells of yeast and the thoracic muscles of bees, where this pigment is the only colouring substance seen spectroscopically. Up to the present, however, all attempts have completely failed.[2] The pigments extracted showed marked differences from cytochrome both in the absorption bands and in other properties and can only be considered as its derivatives. . . .

[2] It turned out that cytochrome was a complex mixture of at least seven chemically similar though distinct substances. Keilin succeeded in purifying cytochrome c in 1930. In this work he established the existence of at least three compounds.—*Editors*.

The Enzyme Problem and Biological Oxidations. ⟿

by OTTO WARBURG

Reprinted from *Bulletin of the Johns Hopkins Hospital*, Vol. 46, pp. 341–358 (1930), by permission of the editors, the publishers, and the author.

The importance of heavy metal catalysis in protoplasmic oxidation was first discovered by Warburg. In particular, he elucidated the role of iron in living systems. In his studies on respiration of sea urchin eggs, he found that added iron stimulated the respiration as determined by measurement of the rate of oxygen consumption. It developed, as Warburg himself later realized, that this was but another instance where the "happy accident" furthered the development of scientific information. Actually, most cells do not respond to added iron, but sea urchin eggs apparently contain an excess of organic materials that can unite with iron to form an effective enzyme.

Part of Warburg's experimental attack on the problem of cellular respiration involved the development and study of simple model systems. He found that hemin charcoal (a hemoglobin derivative heated to incandescence) could effectively catalyze a number of oxidative processes in vitro. He further discovered that the simple charcoal model responded to narcotics, cyanide, hydrogen sulfide, and carbon monoxide in much the same way that the respiration of living cells is affected by these reagents. Not only did these studies firmly establish the importance of heavy metals in oxidative catalysis, but they also provided a strictly physico-chemical foundation for the interpretation of enzyme "poisoning." Cyanide exerted its effects by displacing reactive materials from the catalyst surface. Carbon monoxide, on the other hand, formed a firm chemical bond with the iron of the hemin charcoal.

The crucial experiments leading to the discovery of the respiratory enzyme, or cytochrome oxidase [1] as it is currently designated, were based on spectrophotometric studies of the light reversible inhibition of cellular respiration by carbon monoxide. Oxidations catalyzed by heavy metals or aerobic cellular respiration are inhibited by carbon monoxide in the dark. However, when the system is illuminated, the inhibition is reversed and the inactive complex is photochemically decomposed into carbon monoxide and the active enzyme.

Although cytochrome oxidase is widespread in its occurrence, it is not

---

[1] Also known as *Atmungsferment*, indophenol oxidase, and *respiratory enzyme*.

found in all living cells. For those cells which ordinarily utilize oxygen or which are not destroyed by its presence, cytochrome oxidase is the primary agent that binds oxygen in the course of protoplasmic oxidation. The oxidase itself does not act on the initial metabolic substrates (such as carbohydrates, fat, or protein). Rather, the oxidizable substrate yields electrons to a long chain of interlocking intermediate enzymes analogous to a conveyor belt system of which cytochrome oxidase is only the terminal enzyme. Here, free protons, the transmitted electrons, and activated molecular oxygen are chemically united on the enzyme surface to form metabolic water.

Warburg's conclusions were based on entirely indirect experiments. In all the early work which led to the demonstrated existence of an auto-oxidizable enzyme in aerobic cells, its chemical nature, and cellular concentration, there was no attempt to isolate the enzyme. Many workers have subsequently attempted to isolate cytochrome oxidase. Although highly active cell-free preparations have been obtained, it has been found that the enzyme is firmly bound to cytoplasmic particles with molecular weights approximating several millions.

Warburg is widely recognized as one of the most imaginative and prolific contributors to modern biology. He was awarded the Nobel Prize in 1931 for his monumental contribution to the understanding of cellular metabolism.

IN 1820 EDMUND DAVY discovered that ethyl alcohol when passed over platinum black in the presence of molecular oxygen is oxidized to acetic acid. This experiment caused a great sensation. Alcohol, which is otherwise stable in the presence of molecular oxygen, here was oxidized to acetic acid at as low a temperature as in acetic acid bacteria. Berzelius, under the influence of Davy's experiment, wrote: "The fermentations are possibly brought about by forces like those brought about by platinum black." For Schönbein the catalytic action of platinum black was the prototype of all fermentations. Bredig called the finely divided platinum metals inorganic enzymes.

With the development of organic chemistry Davy's experiment lost much of its interest. The similarity of action of both platinum black and enzymes was no longer taken too seriously. Platinum was inorganic, the enzymes belonged to organic chemistry.

I. NEWER DEVELOPMENT

The newer development of the enzyme problem began with a chance discovery. In experiments on the respiration of sea urchin's eggs, the production of carbon dioxide was determined by displacing it with tartaric acid. It was then noted that tartaric acid, when in contact with the egg substance, was rapidly oxidized by the oxygen of the air. The cell substance therefore contained a catalyst which caused the oxidation of the otherwise stable tartaric acid. This catalyst proved to be resistant to boiling, even resistant to incandescence, and was nothing else than iron which occurs in traces in the sea urchin's egg.

Attention was thus called to iron, and work was undertaken to investigate whether physiological oxidation had any relation to iron.

It was found that traces of iron added to the sea urchin's egg substance accelerated the physiological oxidation. Doubling the normal iron content doubled the rate of oxidation, that is, the rate of oxidation was even proportional to the iron content.

Many favorable circumstances occurred which furthered these experiments. Free iron salt has no remarkable catalytic effect, but iron is effective only when it is in complex linkage. Such a complex-forming substance happened to be present in excess in the sea urchin's egg. But generally it is *not* present in excess. Therefore, generally, with the usual physiological material, the described experiments do not work; the addition of iron to the cell substance has *no* effect on the rate of oxidation.

One can always demonstrate, however, the action of iron on the cell substance by cultivating the cells in solutions containing very small amounts of iron. When the iron in the solutions is used up, the development ceases. If iron is added, the development starts again. I fully realize that these experiments are too ambiguous to prove a relation between iron and enzyme action. Nevertheless, they should come first in all considerations referring to the biological significance of iron.

II. THE HEMIN CHARCOAL MODEL

The consequence of the experiments upon the sea urchins' eggs was that the production of artificial respiration by means of iron was tried, that is, the production of what we call a respiration model. In such a model molecular oxygen must oxidize physiological combustible substances under physiological conditions.

If one brings hemin, the colored component of hemoglobin, to incandescence, a charcoal is formed containing nitrogen and iron. The iron here is linked to the nitrogen. This nitrogen-linked iron acts as a powerful catalyst towards physiological combustible substances. On adding hemin charcoal to aqueous solutions of amino-acids and shaking at body temperature with molecular oxygen, the

latter is absorbed and transferred to the amino-acids. Leucine gives valeric aldehyde, ammonia and carbon dioxide. Cysteine gives ammonia, carbon dioxide, sulfuric acid and other unknown products of incomplete combustion. Thus we have here reactions in which, as in the combustion of protein in living cells, molecular oxygen is absorbed and ammonia, carbon dioxide and sulfuric acid are produced.

Narcotics inhibit the respiration of the hemin model, because they displace the amino-acids from the surface of the hemin charcoal. On the other hand, the narcotics are stable on the charcoal surface, so that by removing the amino-acids from the charcoal surface all oxygen absorption is caused to cease. In this way the model reacts exactly as do living cells. The hemin model therefore served to relate narcosis to a simple physical phenomenon: the displacing of reacting substances from surfaces.

The hemin charcoal model has a second property of living cells; traces of hydrocyanic acid render it inactive. As contrasted with the case of narcosis this is brought about by a specific chemical reaction. Hydrocyanic acid combines with the active iron of the hemin charcoal, forming a dissociating chemical component which is catalytically inactive. Traces of hydrocyanic acid are sufficient for this, because the active iron is present only in traces in the hemin charcoal. Thus the hemin charcoal model has served to explain a second fundamental property of living cells, this time chemically.[1]

III. PLATINUM AND IRON CATALYSES

Davy's platinum model was the first respiration-model; the hemin charcoal model was the second respiration-model

[1] From the impersonal style of writing it is not apparent that Warburg himself was largely responsible for the development of the fruitful hemin-charcoal model.—*Editors.*

given us by science. The second model is superior to the first, because it replaces platinum, which never occurs in cells, by a metal which occurs in all cells and which is necessary to life. Common to both models is the heavy metal capable of change of valence. If iron is, as we shall see, the active atom of the respiration enzyme, then we understand the analogy which seemed so remarkable to Berzelius. This analogy was by no means formal; on the contrary, it is deeply founded in the chemical nature of both model and enzyme.

Davy's model satisfied the scientific mood of its time. But the ideas on enzyme action changed, and the hemin charcoal model was contrary to the scientific feeling of its time. Nearly all leading scientists working on enzyme action opposed it and preferred to see in it only formal or incidental similarities with enzyme action. But the younger generation thought that if the phenomena agree, the substances must agree, and concentrated its attention on iron.

Many catalyses of physiological importance were discovered in this way. It was found that cysteine, the only apparently auto-oxidizable [2] cell component, is not really auto-oxidizable, but is oxidized only in the presence of heavy metals. The SH-group of cysteine links iron, copper and manganese to complex components. What seemed to be the auto-oxidation of cysteine is nothing else than the valency change of these complex-linked heavy metals. Thus a main position of the purely organic enzyme theory was lost. . . .

IV. THE INHIBITION OF RESPIRATION CAUSED BY CARBON MONOXIDE

There are three heavy-metal reagents which inhibit the respiration of living cells: hydrocyanic acid, hydrogen sulfide

and carbon monoxide. The most important of the three is carbon monoxide. Indeed the experiment which decided in favor of the iron theory was performed with carbon monoxide.

Carbon monoxide reacts as an indifferent gas towards organic substances free from heavy metals. On the other hand, carbon monoxide is bound reversibly by many simple and complex heavy metal salts. The analytical chemist uses copper salt in gas analysis for the absorption of carbon monoxide. The biologist knows carbon monoxide as the gas which displaces oxygen from the iron of hemoglobin.

Eighty years ago Claude Bernard, the discoverer of carbon monoxide hemoglobin, investigated whether carbon monoxide reacts in the body with hemoglobin only or also with the cells. He did not find any action on the cells and thereafter carbon monoxide was considered as the typical blood poison. Later an experiment of John Haldane seemed to confirm this point of view. Haldane added to the air breathed by mice so much carbon monoxide that it displaced all the oxygen from the hemoglobin. The animals died from suffocation. If, however, the oxygen pressure of the respired air was increased from one-fifth of an atmosphere to two atmospheres, the animals did *not* die, though all the oxygen was displaced from the hemoglobin by carbon monoxide. At the higher oxygen pressure the blood *plasma* contained sufficient dissolved oxygen to supply the cells of the body. So it seemed finally proved that only the transport of the oxygen was inhibited by carbon monoxide, but not at all the respiration of the cells.

All those experiments are exact, and yet carbon monoxide does inhibit cell respiration. However, one must not attack the question with the preconceived idea that the same low pressure of carbon monoxide which expels oxygen from hemoglobin is able to inhibit the

---

[2] Spontaneous, direct combination with oxygen—not enzymatically catalyzed.—*Editors*.

respiration of the cells. To displace oxygen from hemoglobin the addition of a few tenths per cent of carbon monoxide to the respired air is sufficient. But to inhibit the respiration of the cells a carbon monoxide pressure of the order of magnitude of *one atmosphere* is needed. That is the reason why Claude Bernard, who had become accustomed by his hemoglobin experiments to work with low pressures of carbon monoxide, overlooked the effect of carbon monoxide on cell respiration.

Important for the mechanism of the inhibition of respiration by carbon monoxide is the fact that it depends not only on the carbon monoxide pressure but also on the oxygen pressure. The lower the oxygen pressure, the more pronounced is the inhibition of the respiration at the same carbon monoxide pressure.

The law of distribution of hemoglobin between oxygen and carbon monoxide is well known. It is

$$\frac{HbO_2}{HbCO} \times \frac{CO}{O_2} = K$$

According to the same law the respiration enzyme is distributed between carbon monoxide and oxygen, as was found by respiration measurements at different pressures of carbon monoxide and oxygen. Let FeO_2 and $FeCO$ be the concentrations of the enzyme linked to oxygen and carbon monoxide, respectively. Then the distribution of the enzyme between the two gases is determined by the law

$$\frac{FeO_2}{FeCO} \times \frac{CO}{O_2} = K$$

Because carbon monoxide inhibits respiration anticatalytically, it must combine with the catalyst of respiration. Because this inhibition is reversible, the linkage between the catalyst and carbon monoxide is reversible. These facts prove that the active part of the respiration enzyme is a heavy metal. Carbon monoxide and oxygen compete for this heavy metal as follows from the law of distribution. Just as carbon monoxide displaces the oxygen from the iron of hemoglobin, it displaces the oxygen from the heavy metal of the respiration enzyme. This is the chemically clear mechanism of the effect of carbon monoxide on cell respiration.

V. THE EFFECT OF LIGHT

The great importance of the action of carbon monoxide on cell respiration is due to a strange property of carbon monoxide-iron compounds.

In 1891, Mond and Langer discovered that iron pentacarbonyl splits off carbon monoxide when illuminated. A few years later, in 1897, John Haldane observed that carbon monoxide hemoglobin is split into carbon monoxide and hemoglobin by light. A third case, the photochemical dissociation of carbon monoxide pyridine haemochromogen has been described recently by H. A. Krebs. A fourth case was discovered this year by W. Cremer: the photochemical dissociation of carbon monoxide ferrocysteine, that is, the carbon monoxide compound which is formed when carbon monoxide is passed through a solution of cysteine containing iron. Dewar also worked on the photochemical dissociation of carbon monoxide metal compounds and observed that nickel carbonyl, in contrast to iron carbonyl, is not photosensitive. The general experience is that the photochemical dissociation is confined to the *iron* compounds of carbon monoxide. No other heavy metal compound has so far been found which splits off carbon monoxide in the light.

Imagine now a complex iron compound used as a catalyst in some transfer of oxygen. If carbon monoxide combines with the iron, such catalytic reaction will be inhibited by carbon monoxide in the dark. But in the light the action of carbon monoxide will disappear because light will set free the catalyst from carbon monoxide.

The experiment has been made with iron porphyrin and iron cysteine as catalysts. Figure 1 represents the porphyrin experiment carried out by Dr. H. A. Krebs. The oxygen transferred is plotted as ordinate, and the time as abscissa. The slope of the curve measures the rate of oxidation. At intervals of 10 minutes the solution was illuminated and darkened, and from the slope of the lower curve one can see that the rate of oxidation increases in the light and falls in the dark. The upper curve represents the rate of oxidation in a carbon-monoxide-free atmosphere, and here we have, as expected, *no* influence of light.

Cell respiration behaves exactly like this simple catalytic system. If we inhibit cell respiration by carbon monoxide and illuminate the inhibited cells, then the inhibition disappears. Figure 2 represents the experiment with living cells. As in the model experiment with iron porphyrin, the absorbed oxygen is plotted as ordinate and the time as abscissa. The slope of the curve measures the respiration. At intervals of 20 minutes the cells were alternately illuminated and dark-

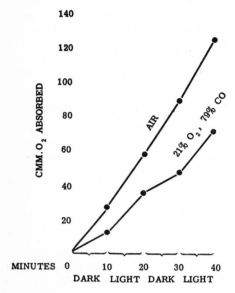

FIG. 1.—Effect of Carbon Monoxide upon the catalytic action of Hemoporphyrin (dark and light).

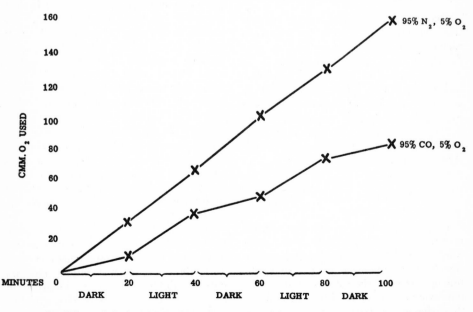

FIG. 2.—Effect of Carbon Monoxide upon the respiration of yeast cells (dark and light).

ened, and from the slope of the lower curve one can see that the respiration increases in the light and decreases in the dark. The upper curve represents the respiration in a carbon-monoxide-free atmosphere, and here we have no influence of light at all.

As has been said, only the *iron* compounds of carbon monoxide dissociate in the light. Hence it follows from the light experiment with living cells that the heavy metal of the respiration enzyme is *iron*.

The effect of carbon monoxide and light on the cell respiration was discovered in experiments with yeast cells. Later it was found that most cells behave like yeast. I might mention bacteria, plant seeds, liver, chorion, retina, embryos of chicken and rat, tumors of rat, blood-leucocytes, blood-platelets and so on. All these different cells react in the same way with carbon monoxide. Their respiration enzyme reacts with carbon monoxide reversibly. The enzyme is distributed between carbon monoxide and oxygen according to the law of distribution. The enzyme is sensitive to light when linked to carbon monoxide. That is, in all these cells there is an iron compound which takes up and transfers the oxygen in the process of respiration.

VI. CONCENTRATION OF THE ENZYME IN THE CELL

We now proceed to the question: what is the chemical constitution of this iron compound?

It is well known that complex iron compounds occur in the cell. As F. G. Hopkins discovered, nearly all cells contain cysteine which combines with iron salt to form the complex iron-cysteine. As MacMunn discovered [3] and Keilin recently confirmed, nearly all cells contain iron-porphyrins, *e.g.,* the histohaematin of MacMunn, which is identical with Keilin's cytochrome.

[3] An account of this is given in the previous paper by Keilin.—*Editors.*

Iron-cysteine *does* combine with carbon monoxide and the carbon monoxide compound is sensitive to light. But the affinities of iron-cysteine to carbon monoxide and the sensitiveness to light are so different from the enzyme that it seems very unlikely that the enzyme is an iron cysteine compound. MacMunn's histohaematin does *not* combine with carbon monoxide nor with oxygen, and therefore can not be the enzyme. In addition, histohaematin occurs in such large quantities in the cells that one can see it with the spectroscope—the way in which it was discovered. But the concentration of the enzyme in the cells is almost infinitely small. Indeed one can calculate that 100 million grams of yeast contain only *one* gram of enzyme iron.

From this figure you see that there is not much hope of isolating the enzyme by the methods of analytic chemistry. Moreover, the enzyme is unstable and is quickly destroyed if separated from the cells.

It seems therefore that the old difficulties of the enzyme problem render advance impossible — the instability of the enzyme and its nearly infinitely low concentration. Only a method which is independent of the quantity of the enzyme and which does not require its separation from the cell can overcome these difficulties.

VII. ABSORPTION SPECTRUM OF THE ENZYME:—METHOD

There is such a method. Imagine illuminated cells whose respiration is inhibited by carbon monoxide. Then, as we already know, the respiration increases on account of the dissociation of the carbon monoxide compound of the enzyme. According to the principle of conservation of energy this can take place only if the carbon monoxide compound of the enzyme absorbs the light which dissociates it.

The source of light in the described experiment was a metal filament lamp. The light was a mixture of all the wavelengths emitted by the metal filament. Now substitute for the metal filament lamp sources of light which emit lines, isolate the lines and illuminate the cells monochromatically. The effect of 15 lines has been examined. These lines were situated in a region which extends from the ultraviolet line, 254 $\mu\mu$, to the red line, 660 $\mu\mu$. Each of the 15 lines were found to be efficient, each of these lines is therefore absorbed by the enzyme.

But the photochemical efficiency of the different lines was not equal. The efficiency of different lines of equal intensity [4] dependent upon the wavelength of the light. The greatest efficiency was found in the blue. The blue line, 436 $\mu\mu$, acted 10 times more strongly than the ultra-violet line, 254 $\mu\mu$, and 200 times more strongly than the red line, 660 $\mu\mu$. The obvious explanation lay in selective absorption.

A general remark on the relation between the *action* of light and the *absorption* of light may be inserted here.

From the light quantum theory of Planck and Einstein, it follows for photochemical dissociation that the number of dissociated molecules must be equal to the number of absorbed light quanta. For gas reactions this simple law has been verified in many cases by Emil Warburg but in aqueous solutions it does not always hold true. For photochemical reactions in aqueous solutions in every new case the relation between the *action* of light and the *absorption* of light must be determined.

This has been done for various carbon-monoxide iron compounds, especially for carbon-monoxide hemochromogen and carbon-monoxide ferrocysteine. Aqueous solutions were irradiated, the absorbed light energy and the carbon monoxide split off were determined. The result

was that the photochemical dissociation of carbon-monoxide iron compounds follows Einstein's law very closely. In the whole region of the spectrum which has been examined one quantum of light decomposes one iron-carbonyl group.

The relation between the *action* of light and the *absorption* of light being thus determined quantitatively, we can calculate by the action of different lines the absorption spectrum of the enzyme. The simple experiment is this: The respiration of cells is inhibited by carbon monoxide in the dark. The cells are then illuminated with different lines of light, whose intensity is measured. From the *action* of light, by means of Einstein's law, the *absorption* of light is calculated.

Here it makes no difference whether the cells contain besides the enzyme other substances which absorb light as long as the total light absorption remains small. Neither MacMunn's histohaematin nor any other accompanying substance, even if it is sensitive to light, disturbs the method. Regardless of what other substances are present, the method gives the absorption spectrum of that substance, the photochemical dissociation of which is measured, that is, in this case, the carbon monoxide compound of the enzyme.

VIII. ABSOLUTE ABSORPTION SPECTRUM OF THE ENZYME:—METHOD

With the described method we obtain the relative absorption spectrum of the enzyme, that is, the positions of the absorption bands and the ratio of the intensities of these bands. But the possibilities of the method are not yet exhausted. It is possible to develop it in such a way as to give also the absolute values of the absorption coefficients. The principle involved is this:

Imagine again cells the respiration of which is inhibited by carbon monoxide in the dark. If we illuminate them, the respiration does not immediately go up. It takes some time, but quite a short

---

[4] A highly important experimental variable, the control of which is essential for a valid photochemical study.—*Editors.*

period, till the carbon monoxide compound of the enzyme is split by the light. Even without calculation one can understand that the time required to split off the carbon monoxide must be related to the absolute light absorption by the enzyme. If the absorption by the enzyme is strong, then the time required will be short and vice versa.

It is possible to measure this time. We can measure, for example, how long it takes for half of the carbon monoxide compound of the enzyme to be decomposed by a given intensity of light. With this time and the light intensity used, we can calculate the absolute absorption coefficient for every wave-length. Experimentally, the device is about the same

as in the experiment already described. But while in the determination of the relative spectrum the illumination is *continuous*, in the determination of the absolute spectrum *intermittent* illumination is used.

The absolute absorption coefficient of the enzyme for the blue mercury line 436 $\mu\mu$ has been found to be 3.6×10^8 cm^2 per gram atom Fe. This order of magnitude may be illustrated as follows: If *one* gram-molecule of the enzyme be dissolved in one litre, a layer of $\frac{2}{1,000,000}$ (2×10^{-6}) of a centimetre of this solution will decrease the intensity of light to one half. The light absorption power of the enzyme is, as

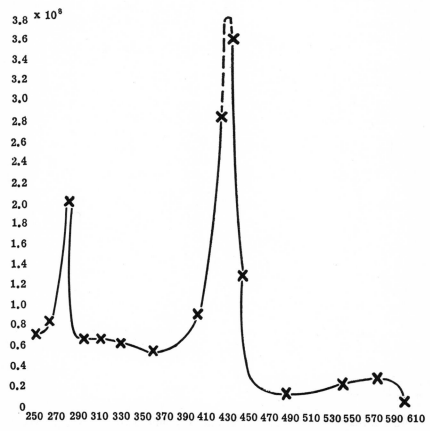

FIG. 3.—Spectrum of the CO compound of the respiration ferment.

you see, very high indeed, of the order of magnitude of our strongest dyestuffs. That it is still impossible to see the enzyme in the cell is due only to its infinitely low concentration.

IX. ABSOLUTE ABSORPTION SPECTRUM OF THE ENZYME

In Figure 3 the absolute absorption spectrum of the carbon monoxide compound of the enzyme is plotted. Fifteen points were determined: Seven wavelengths in the ultraviolet and eight in the visible part of the spectrum.

To indicate the apparatus used I shall give you for each wave-length the light source out of which it was isolated:

WAVE-LENGTH	COLOR	SOURCE OF LIGHT
$\mu\mu$		
254	Ultraviolet	Mercury lamp
265	Ultraviolet	Mercury lamp
283	Ultraviolet	Magnesium spark
300	Ultraviolet	Mercury lamp
313	Ultraviolet	Mercury lamp
332	Ultraviolet	Zinc spark
366	Ultraviolet	Mercury lamp
405	Violet	Mercury lamp
427	Blue	Carbon dioxide aureole of the tungsten spark
436	Blue	Mercury lamp
448	Sky blue	Magnesium spark
492	Bluish green	Mercury lamp
546	Green	Mercury lamp
578	Yellow	Mercury lamp
603	Orange	Carbon arc containing calcium

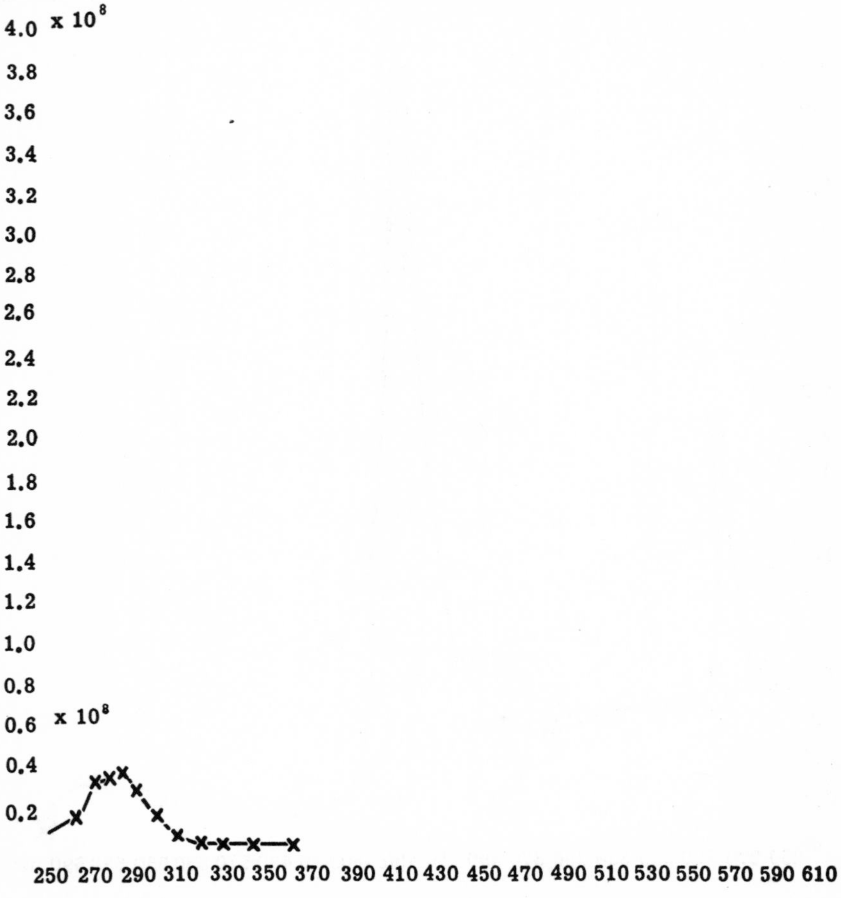

FIG. 4.—The absorption spectrum of the CO compound of Iron Cysteine.

We will now compare this spectrum with those of the complex iron compounds of which we know that they occur in all cells. They are iron cysteine and iron porphyrin.

The absolute spectra of these compounds are also measured, not with the indirect method as in the case of the enzyme, but with direct physical methods. The direct absorption measurement with the photoelectric cell of Elster und Geitel is very suitable for this purpose. It is sensitive between 250 and 600 $\mu\mu$, which is the range of interest in this case and surpasses in exactness the photographic method.

In Figure 4 the absolute absorption spectrum of the carbon monoxide compound of iron cysteine is plotted. The scale is the same as in the figure of the enzyme spectrum. The positions of the bands as well as the absolute values of the absorption coefficients show that iron cysteine and enzyme are different substances.

In Figure 5 the absolute absorption spectrum of carbon monoxide hemin is plotted. The scale is again the same as in the figure of the enzyme spectrum. The concordance of this spectrum with that of the enzyme (Fig. 3) is remarkable, both in the positions of the bands and in the absolute values of the absorption coefficients. The closeness of this agreement may be shown with a few figures.

A minimum of absorption lies in both cases around 490 $\mu\mu$. The absolute absorption coefficients here are:

For carbon monoxide hemin

$$0.12 \times 10^8 \frac{cm.^2}{gram\ atom\ Fe}$$

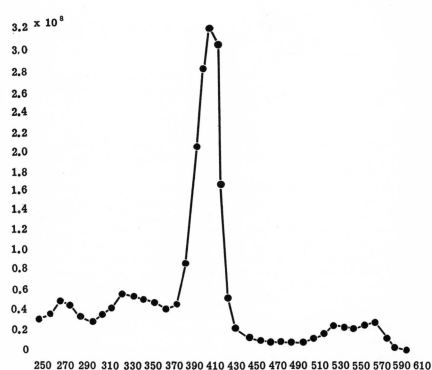

FIG. 5.—The absorption spectrum of Carbon Monoxide Hemin.

For carbon monoxide enzyme

$$0.13 \times 10^8 \frac{cm.^2}{gram\ atom\ Fe}$$

The maximum of absorption lies in both cases in the blue. The absolute absorption coefficients in the maximum are:

For carbon monoxide hemin

$$3.2 \times 10^8 \frac{cm.^2}{gram\ atom\ Fe}$$

For carbon monoxide enzyme

$$3.6 \times 10^8 \frac{cm.^2}{gram\ atom\ Fe}$$

From this quantitative agreement it follows that the enzyme is an iron-porphyrin compound, which was expected from the experiments with iron-porphyrin as catalyst. But now it is proved.

If at this point we look back, we see that in many respects the hemin charcoal has been more than a model. It is true that in the hemin charcoal the porphyrin is destroyed by the heat of incandescence, but still there is the nitrogen of the porphyrin and the linkage of the iron to the nitrogen. Iron linked to nitrogen is the catalyst in both, in the artificial respiration of the hemin charcoal model and the respiration of living cells.

The Isolation and Crystallization of the Enzyme Urease. ✖

by JAMES B. SUMNER

Reprinted from the *Journal of Biological Chemistry*, Vol. 69, pp. 435–441 (1926), by permission of the author and editors.

Progress in unraveling the mechanisms of biological oxidation and protoplasmic synthesis is proceeding at an accelerated pace today. Current research data indicate that enzyme pathways of considerable length are common to both respiration and photosynthesis, the two fundamental cell processes. In avant garde circles of modern enzymology one frequently hears statements to the effect that the total structure and function of cells are understandable purely in terms of the concentration, activation, and spatial organization of the enzymes that compose them. This view is a marked contrast to the neo-vitalism of the late 19th century.

As late as 1900 the world-famous chemist Willstätter and his school maintained that although enzymes were probably bound to proteins, they could not themselves be protein in character. Equally prominent leaders in scientific thought held that enzymes either represented an altogether unknown class or classes of unknown substance, or that they could not be understood in ordinary chemical terms.

As knowledge of protein structure and behavior accumulated, however, added impetus was given to the understanding of proteins and their properties by the brilliant studies of Emil Fischer. He devised new methods for the analysis and synthesis of polypeptides, thus establishing the manner in which proteins were constructed of amino acid residues. Meanwhile, evidence for the protein nature of enzymes mounted steadily. The final and decisive step, accomplished by Sumner and co-workers, was reported in 1926. Urease, one of earliest enzymes to be recognized, had been prepared in a pure crystalline form. Such preparations are characteristically homogeneous by all known physical criteria including electrophoretic mobility, antigenicity, and repeated recrystallization.

Since Sumner's epochal triumph more than thirty different enzymes have been obtained in crystalline form. That the activity of these crystalline preparations is actually due to the protein, and not to some constituent impurity or adsorbed compound, is clearly evidenced by the fact that loss of enzyme activity is strictly proportional to protein denaturation, and that the reversal of denaturation is accompanied by a proportional gain in activity. In recognition of his achievement Sumner was awarded the Nobel Prize in 1940.

It is a strange coincidence that urea was the first organic compound to be synthesized [Wöhler, 1828] and that urease, which acts on no known substance other than urea, was the first enzyme to be characterized chemically. The doctrine of an "essential vital force" remained unchallenged until Wöhler was led by chance observation to the discovery that organic compounds can arise without the agency of any organism. Wöhler repeated his experiment many times before publishing. When he was satisfied with the evidence he recognized in it a clear refutation of the postulated "vital force." In a letter to Berzelius, contemporary authority on catalysis and a gifted chemist, who maintained that the synthetic production of organic compounds was beyond the realm of possibility, he wrote,

"I can prepare urea without requiring a kidney or an animal, either man or dog."

At the present moment we can prepare neither proteins nor enzymes by any known or unknown series of chemical reactions in vitro. This remains a wholly unexplored area for which the "great experiments" are still unprojected.

AFTER WORK BOTH by myself and in collaboration with Dr. V. A. Graham and Dr. C. V. Noback that extends over a period of a little less than 9 years, I discovered on the 29th of April a means of obtaining from the jack bean a new protein which crystallizes beautifully and whose solutions possess to an extraordinary degree the ability to decompose urea into ammonium carbonate. The protein crystals have been examined through the kindness of Dr. A. C. Gill, who reports them to be sharply crystallized, colorless octahedra, belonging by this definition to the isometric system. They show no double refraction and are from 4 to 5 μ in diameter.

While the most active solutions of urease prepared in this laboratory by Sumner, Graham, and Noback and by Sumner and Graham possessed an activity of about 30,000 units per gm. of protein present, the octahedra, after washing away the mother liquor, have an activity of 100,000 units per gm. of dry material. In other words, 1 gm. of the material will produce 100,000 mg. of ammonia nitrogen from a urea-phosphate solution in 5 minutes at 20°C. At this temperature the material requires 1.4 seconds to decompose its own weight of urea.

The crystals, when freshly formed, dissolve fairly rapidly in distilled water, giving a water-clear solution after centrifuging from the slight amount of insoluble matter that is present. The solution coagulates upon heating and gives strongly the biuret, xanthoproteic, Millon, Hopkins and Cole, ninhydrin, and unoxidized sulfur tests.[1] The phenol reagent of Folin and Denis gives a strong color, while the uric acid reagent gives none. The material can be entirely precipitated by saturating with ammonium sulfate. The Molisch test is negative and Bial's test is negative also. The absence of pentose carbohydrate, as shown by Bial's test is especially pleasing as we have experienced a great deal of trouble in the past in freeing jack bean proteins from this substance.

The octahedral crystals, when freshly prepared, are very soluble in dilute alkali or dilute ammonia, and are either dissolved or coagulated by dilute mineral and organic acids, depending upon the concentration of acid. Even so weakly acid a substance as primary potassium phosphate is capable of causing an irreversible coagulation. Although the crystals dissolve in distilled water I am inclined to regard the material as globulin inasmuch as a precipitate is formed when carbon dioxide is passed into its solution and this precipitate immediately redissolves upon the addition of a drop of neutral phosphate solution.

Owing to the fact that I have not had large enough amounts of the material to work with I am unable to give accurate

[1] These are standard qualitative chemical test for proteins.—*Editors*.

figures for its nitrogen content at the present time, but this can be stated to be not far from 17 per cent, as shown by micro-Kjeldahl determinations made on several preparations. The content of ash is certainly low, so low that a considerable amount of material will have to be used to obtain this figure. Determination of the enzyme activity of the crystals has been somewhat interfered with, owing to the fact that dilute solutions of the crystals produce less ammonia from urea than one would calculate from results obtained from more concentrated solutions. If this effect is real, rather than apparent, it may be due to the instability of the enzyme at great dilutions. When in concentrated solution the activity is not lost very rapidly, provided the material is kept in the ice chest.

When old the crystals are entirely insoluble in distilled water, salt solutions, and dilute ammonia. In this condition the enzyme activity is almost nil. I have made several attempts to purify the fresh crystals by a second crystallization but have never succeeded in obtaining more than traces of crystals and these have been insoluble in water and inactive.

It may be worth noting that practically all of our previous ideas concerning the nature of urease appear to be confirmed by the discovery of the octahedral crystals and by study of their properties. I undertook the task of isolating urease in the fall of 1917 with the idea that it might be found to be a crystallizable globulin, in which case the proof of its isolation would be greatly simplified. Other reasons for choosing urease were that the quantitative estimation of urease is both rapid and accurate, that urease can be reasonably expected to be an individual enzyme, rather than a mixture of enzymes, and that the jack bean appears to contain a very large amount of urease, if it is permissible to draw a parallelism between the urease content of the jack bean and the amounts of other enzymes found in other plant and animal materials.

In previous work in collaboration with Graham and Noback and in unpublished work of my own it has been found that urease is very completely precipitated, together with the jack bean globulins, by cooling its 35 per cent alcoholic solution to —5 to —10°C., provided the reaction is sufficiently acid. We have found that urease can be precipitated by neutral lead acetate and neutralized cadmium chloride and that most of the urease can be re-extracted by decomposing the precipitate with potassium oxalate; that urease can be precipitated by tannic acid without very much inactivation and that urease can be rendered insoluble, with loss of a part of its activity, by the action of dilute alcohol or very dilute acid.

Although the literature contains numerous references to a coenzyme of urease, I believe that no specific coenzyme exists. My evidence rests upon the fact that the loss of activity that occurs when the octahedral crystals are separated from a jack bean extract is almost exactly equal to the activity obtained when these crystals are washed with dilute acetone and then dissolved in water. If anything could separate an enzyme from its coenzyme crystallization might be expected to do so. The proteins in impure urease solutions doubtless exert a protective action as buffers and both proteins and polysaccharides may exert protective colloidal action.

I present below a list of reasons why I believe the octahedral crystals to be identical with the enzyme urease.

1. The fact that the crystals can be seen by the microscope to be practically uncontaminated by any other material.

2. The great activity of solutions of the crystals.

3. The fact that solvents which do not dissolve the crystals extract little or no urease and that to obtain solutions of urease one must dissolve the crystals.

4. The fact that the other crystallizable jack bean globulins, concanavalin A and B, carry with them very little urease when they are formed from solutions that are comparatively rich in urease.

5. The unique crystalline habit of the octahedra and their ready denaturation by acid.

6. The fact that the crystals are purely protein in so far as can be determined by chemical tests, combined with evidence from previous work to the effect that urease behaves like a protein in its reactions towards heavy metals, alkaloid reagents, alcohol, and acids.

7. The fact that the crystals are nearly free from ash and the fact that we have previously prepared solutions of urease that contained neither iron, manganese, nor phosphorus.

The method which I have used to obtain the crystals is extremely simple. It consists in extracting finely powdered, fat-free jack bean meal with 31.6 per cent acetone and allowing the material to filter by gravity in an ice chest. After standing overnight the filtrate is centrifuged and the precipitate of crystalline urease is stirred with cold 31.6 per cent acetone and centrifuged again. The crystals can be now dissolved in distilled water and centrifuged free from insoluble and inactive matter that has passed through the filter during the filtration. Of the urease extracted from the meal as much as 47 per cent may be present in the crystals. If one uses coarsely ground jack bean meal that has not been freed from fat the crystals are still obtained, but in traces only. I have carried out the process described above about fifteen times since first discovering the crystals and have always had success. The method is described in the experimental part of this paper in detail. . . .

HORMONES

CHRONOLOGY

Like many other concepts of modern biology, the origin of the principle of chemical coordination, or hormonal mediation of biological function, is difficult to trace. In part, the difficulty lies in the large number of highly diversified investigations that have contributed to the development of this concept. As can be seen from the chronology that follows, bits of information stemming from unrelated studies grew, within a span of less than one hundred years, into an enormously complex maze of accumulated fact and experience. Our current notions of hormone production, structure, and function represent a flowing together of generalizations drawn from animal experiments, studies of chemical structure and techniques of isolation, clinical studies on the course of various diseases, the detailed investigation of the modifying effect of glandular extracts and preparations on the various diseases, studies of insect development, plant growth responses, and problems of nerve impulse transmission.

1849   Berthold demonstrated by extirpation and transplantation that the testis produces a blood-borne substance conditioning sexual characteristics.

1855   Bernard maintained that all organs liberated into the tissue fluids special substances which assisted in maintaining the constancy of the internal environment.

1855   Addison described the syndrome associated with the deterioration of the human adrenal cortex. This is beyond question the first major achievement of clinical endocrinology.

1856   Vulpian applied a solution of ferric chloride to slices of the adrenal glands and noted that the medulla stained green while the cortex did not. He also noted that the same reaction was given by samples of venous blood leaving the adrenal, but not by arterial blood entering the gland. To account for these observations, he assumed that the medulla synthesized a substance that was liberated into the circulation.

1869   Langerhans, studying the structure of the pancreas, noted specialized groups or islands of cells that were especially well supplied with microscopic blood vessels.

1871   Fagge concluded that degeneration, atrophy, or loss of the thyroid gland resulted in cretinism.

1874   Gull recognized and described the disease known as myxoedema, which he regarded correctly as the adult form of cretinism.

1878   Balfour observed that the medullary region of the adrenal gland was derived from ectodermal rudiments that also gave rise to parts of the sympathetic nervous system, while the cortex arose from mesodermal buds.

1886   Horsley induced both cretinism and myxoedema in monkeys by experimentally removing the thyroid gland.

1886   Marie fully described the constellation of symptoms termed acromegaly.

1887   Minkowski associated the acromegalic syndrome with a hyperfunctional state of the pituitary gland.

1889   Brown-Séquard injected macerated testes from other animals into his own body and believed he obtained rejuvenating effects. Though erroneous, these conclusions were influential in inaugurating the administration of endocrine gland extracts as an experimental technique.

1889   Von Mering and Minkowski duplicated the symptoms of diabetes in the dog by experimental excision of the pancreas. They further obtained presumptive evidence for the endocrine function of the islets of Langerhans in 1893.

1891   Murray prepared emulsions of dried sheep thyroid in glycerine. He used these with considerable success on patients suffering from hypothyroidism.

1895   Magnus-Levy found by means of direct calorimetric measurements that persons with myxoedema have a lowered heat production. He also found that administration of thyroid preparations to normal or myxoedematous patients raised the metabolic level.

1895   Oliver and Schaefer prepared potent extracts of the adrenal medulla which upon injection into normal animals produced a striking elevation in blood pressure.

1896   Baumann reported that the thyroid gland contained an appreciable concentration of iodine in organic combinations. He also reported that persons inhabiting coastal areas contained more thyroid iodine than persons living further inland.

1897   Ostwald clearly demonstrated that the iodine of the thyroid is firmly bound to a globulin-like protein and introduced the term *thyroglobulin*.

1901   Aldrich and Takamine isolated a substance with hormone activity from the adrenal medulla.

1902   Abel independently isolated a crystalline chemical derivative prepared from adrenal medulla extracts. The substance was designated as *epinephrine*.

1902   Bayliss and Starling discovered *secretin,* a hormone produced by the intestinal mucosa which acted principally on the pancreas.

1904   Stoltz determined the chemical formula for epinephrine and achieved a total chemical synthesis of the substance.

1905   Starling introduced the word *hormone*.

1910   Boysen-Jensen established the existence of phyto-hormones or auxins which were responsible for the chemical transmission of growth responses of higher plants.

1912   Schaefer coined the term *insulin* for the active principle of the pancreas.

1914   Kendall completed the final isolation of crystalline thyroxine, the active substance produced by the thyroid gland.

1920   Loewi ingeniously demonstrated the release of stimulating and inhibitory substances at the terminal branches of nerve fibers. This discovery led to the concept of nerve impulse transmission across junctions by means of chemical mediators.

1921   Banting and Best isolated insulin and further studied its physiological properties.

1922   Kopec first demonstrated that pupation in an insect is conditioned by an agent in the body fluid.

1925   Koller, by means of blood transfusions, obtained evidence of the presence of hormone-like substances regulating the activity of chromatophores in crustaceans.

To record the hundreds and possibly thousands of significant contributions in this and related fields is outside the scope and intent of this volume. In fact, it will be noted that the chronology is arbitrarily terminated at the year 1925. The reason for this is not the closure of research frontiers in hormone study, but rather the contrary. The rate of publication and degree of specialization have been so intensified in the last thirty years that only specialists can hope to master the fund of knowledge in this expanding field. Among the numerous achievements of this latter period we might single out a few, such as the identification and synthesis of some 26 steroidal hormones of the adrenal cortex and gonads, and the separation of six or more physiologically active protein hormones produced by the anterior lobe of the pituitary gland. Several of these, including the follicle-stimulating hormone, the luteinizing hormone, the thyrotrophic hormone, the adrenocorticotrophic hormone and prolactin, have been isolated as crystalline proteins. Although our understanding of hormones is rapidly expanding, vast areas of ignorance still remain. At the present moment, for example, almost nothing is known about the mechanisms by which hormones are synthesized by cells, or what specific hereditary and environmental factors determine their precisely balanced interrelationships.

Endocrinology stands out today as a well-defined branch of medical practice. Its ramifications extend to widely diverse problems such as malignancy, growth and ageing, personality development, commercial milk, beef, and fowl production, weed and brush control. The impact of the hormone concept on society is clearly evidenced by the fact that the chemical industry concerned with the isolation, synthesis, distribution, and sale of hormones or hormone products represents a multi-million dollar aspect of our economy.

Transplantation of the Testes. ❧

by A. A. BERTHOLD

From *Archiv für Anatomie Physiologie und Wissenschaftliche Medizin*, 1849, p. 42. Translated by M. L. Gabriel for this volume.

The phenomenal progress in our understanding of endocrine function during the last seventy-five years has depended to a large extent upon the development of adequate experimental methods. As long as the biologist was restricted to mere observation, insight into problems of hormonal control of body function, or discovery of hormones themselves was seriously retarded. Obviously, what was required was some series of manipulative techniques that would enable the investigator to alter the normal physiological relations and then, by comparing the experimentally treated group with a suitable control, to draw inferences concerning the normal or abnormal functions. "The modern experimentalist surgically removes or transplants organs, cultures tissues in vitro, denervates localized areas, deprives specific parts of blood, collects and analyzes secretions, determines the action of known materials injected into the system, produces local temperature changes, graphically records muscular movements, administers various anaesthetics, determines the consumption of oxygen, and so on." [1] Endocrinology started on the route to becoming an exact science when early investigators adopted the technique of animal experimentation for the elucidation of biologic problems.

The general principle that diffusible blood-borne substances can modify the development and behavior was first demonstrated by Berthold in 1849. In Berthold's report, which is reprinted here, the essential techniques of surgical removal, denervation, and organ transplantation are clearly emphasized. The behavioral consequences following these experimental alterations led Berthold to postulate the existence of a testicular product, other than spermatozoa, that modified and conditioned the voice, reproductive drive, belligerency, growth of the comb, wattles, and spurs in fowl. The report itself is an excellent illustration of scientific reporting as well as experimental design. In all, six animals were employed. Careful study of the way in which each animal was utilized will doubtless suggest that Berthold's experiments were more extensive than this report indicates.

The first biologically effective testicular extract was prepared by McGee in 1927. A lipoid concentrate of fresh bull testis was found to

---

[1] Turner, C. D., *General Endocrinology*, p. 6, Philadelphia, 1948.

induce measurable growth of the capon's comb and to repair the castrate atrophic effects in the guinea pig and rat. By 1929 many workers had shown that extracts of human urine produced similar effects on suitable test organisms. Butenandt, Ruzicka, and others in the period from 1931–1935 succeeded in isolating two distinct androgenic substances in urinary concentrate. After these steroidal substances were isolated in crystalline form they were found to be physiologically less effective per unit than testis concentrate. Also they differed from the fresh testis preparations with respect to alkali-lability. It was therefore inferred that still a third androgen must be present in the testis extracts. The new androgen was finally obtained in crystalline form and isolated in 1935. It was designated as testosterone. Testosterone is the most potent androgen yet obtained and most workers regard it as identical with the hormone produced by the testis. Several different lines of evidence, including histochemical observations, cytological findings, and also the course of testicular degeneration in cases of cryptorchidism, strongly indicate that the major site of testosterone production is the interstitial tissue cells of the testis.

ON AUGUST 2 OF last year [1848], I caponized six young cockerels, of which *a, b,* and *c* were three months old, and *d, e,* and *f* were two months old. In none of these animals were the wattles, the combs, or the spurs removed. In cockerels *a* and *d* both testes were removed. These animals later showed the typical characteristics of capons: Their behavior was timid, they engaged only seldom in brief, listless fighting with other cocks, and gave voice to the well-known single-toned cry of capons. Combs and wattles were pale and poorly developed; the head remained small. When these animals were killed on the 20th of December there was found at the position occupied by the testes an insignificant, barely perceptible scar. The spermatic ducts were recognizable as thin, delicate threads.

Cockerels *b* and *e* were castrated in the same manner, except that only one testis was removed from the body cavity, and the other one was allowed to lie isolated in the body cavity. In cockerels *c* and *f,* on the other hand, both testes were extracted from the body cavity and then one testis from cockerel *c* was inserted into the body cavity of cockerel *f,*

and one testis from cockerel *f* was inserted into the body cavity of cockerel *c,* among the intestines.

These four roosters (*b, e, c, f*) in their general behavior displayed the nature of uncastrated animals; they crowed quite normally, frequently became involved in battles with one another and with other young cocks, and displayed the usual attraction to hens; also their combs and wattles developed as in normal roosters.

Cockerel *b* was killed on October 4th; one testis had healed in place in its original location, had increased more than half in circumference, was provided with numerous blood vessels, showed the seminal tubules very clearly, and upon being cut through, yielded a whitish liquid containing larger and smaller cells among which, however, no spermatozoa could be recognized.

On the same day, the fairly well-developed combs and wattles were cut off from cockerels *c, e, f* and the body cavity was opened in order to examine the testes. In cockerel *e* I found the testis in the normal location just as in cockerel *b;* I cut it loose, removed it from the body cavity and found it similar in condition to that of rooster *b*. The abdominal incision was soon healed and comb and wattles became scarified, but did not regenerate again. Instead of crowing as heretofore the animal emitted the usual capon cry. From now on it was indifferent to the hens, it did not become involved in fights with other roosters, remained apart from them, and in general displayed the nature of a true capon.

In cockerels *c* and *f* no trace of testes was to be found in the location where they had been previously present. The combs and wattles regenerated, the animals retained their rooster-like nature, crowed as previously, and continued their previous behavior towards hens and other cocks. These two roosters were killed on January 30, 1849. No trace of testes was evident at the normal location; however, in rooster *c* the testis was found growing on the dorsal surface of the colon, flanked on either side by the ends of the caeca, without however adhering to the latter. In cockerel *f* the same condition was present, but the point of adhesion of the testis was somewhat further posterior, opposite the middle of the caeca. The testis in both individuals had an oval form, a length of 15 lines, a width of 8, and a thickness of 6 [i.e., about $34 \times 18 \times 14$ mm]. Well-developed branches of the mesenteric blood vessels supplied the testes, penetrating their interior in numerous places, and traceable to the seminal tubules. When I cut the testes open, a whitish, milky fluid flowed out, which had quite the characteristics and the odor of normal rooster semen. Under the microscope I recognized in this fluid very numerous smaller and larger cells of $\frac{1}{450}$—$\frac{1}{150}$ lines [i.e., about 5-15 microns] in diameter and in addition numerous spermatozoa with the most beautiful flagellar movements which became far more active upon the admixture of a drop of water.

The following general results of phys-iological interest emerge from these experiments:

(1) The testes are transplantable organs; they are able to heal back after they have been removed from the body; indeed the testis may be transplanted from one individual into another, and the healing succeeds as well at the location from which the testis had been removed as in a completely foreign location, namely on the walls of the intestines.

(2) The transplanted testis continues to grow, even in a quite different location, with its characteristic properties as a seminal organ; the seminal tubules expand and enlarge and fulfill their normal function in that they secrete a quite normal semen containing spermatozoa. We have here quite the same condition as in plants, where the graft scion continues to grow in its specific manner on the parent stock, and produces fruit of its own type and not of that of the parent stock.

(3) It is a well-known fact that severed nerves grow together with one another and that in parts whose nerves have been cut through, sensitivity and movement return again after healing. When such healing takes place nerve fibers other than those properly corresponding can also unite, as is proven by the healing of skin grafts transplanted from one part of the body to another.[1] From observation of the rehealing of separated testes in foreign locations in the body, namely on the intestine, whereby the testis continues to develop as a semen-producing organ and manufactures true semen, one is able to conclude that there are no specific seminal nerves, and this is a cogent argument against the hypothesis that there are specific trophic nerves, which up to

[1] An erroneous idea. Actually, when a nerve is cut, the fibers distal to the cut degenerate, and only those nerve fibers proximal to the cut and still connected to the nerve cell bodies are capable of regeneration. Berthold's experiments, in fact, proved more than he knew.—*Editors*.

the most recent times the sympathetic nervous system has been thought to contain.

(4) The remarkable consensual [involuntary activity correlated with voluntary activity] and antagonistic relationship between the life of ‘the individual and the life of the species, as it sets in especially at the time of puberty and continues into advanced age, persists when the testes are removed from their original position and from their nerves and healed into a quite different position in the body. With regard to the voice, the reproductive drive, belligerency, the growth of the comb and of

the wattles, animals upon which such operations have been performed remain true roosters. Since, however, testes which have been transplanted to foreign locations can no longer be connected with their original nerves, and since, as (3) makes clear, there are no specific nerves responsible for secretion, it follows that this combination of characteristics must be conditioned by the productive relationships of the testis, i.e., through its influence upon the blood, and then through corresponding influences of the blood upon the organism in general, of which, to be sure, the nervous system constitutes a very essential part.

The Mechanism of Pancreatic Secretion. ~

by W. M. BAYLISS and E. H. STARLING

Abridged from *The Journal of Physiology*, Vol. 28, pp. 325–353 (1902). Reprinted by permission of the editors.

Claude Bernard was the first to propose, in 1872, that substances present in the intestine produced a stimulating effect on the external pancreatic secretion. Bernard, Pavlov, and others who studied secretion in animals having a pancreatic fistula attributed the effect to a wholly nervous reflex mechanism. On the other hand, similar results obtained by Wertheimer and Lepage in their studies of parabiotically joined animals indicated that blood-borne chemical mediators rather than nervous mechanisms controlled glandular activity in the intact organism. It was against this background of thought and experience that Bayliss and Starling reported their momentous discovery in 1902.

The active agent of pancreatic secretion was released, according to these authors, by the intestinal mucosa after it had been acted upon by hydrochloric acid from the stomach. It was further held that the intestinal principle was absorbed directly into the blood stream and exerted a specific effect on the pancreas. Convincing as the initial demonstrations were, they could not be regarded as decisive, since reflex mechanisms were not entirely excluded. The final demonstration leading to the eventual abandonment of the "nervous control hypothesis" was indeed simple. The crucial experiments involved the use of intravenously injected scrapings from the intestinal mucosa; this was the experimental basis for the discovery of secretin.

In 1933 Hammarsten and co-workers reported the isolation of several secretin derivatives in pure crystalline form. Secretin is a substance of relatively low molecular weight to which the tentative empirical formula C_3H_3ON has been assigned. It is not affected by proteolytic enzymes or prolonged heating. Highly purified secretin is widely employed in clinical tests of pancreas function and other tests essential to proper diagnosis and treatment.

I. HISTORICAL.

IT HAS LONG BEEN known that the activity of the pancreas is normally called into play by events occurring in the alimentary canal. Bernard found that the pancreatic secretion could be evoked by the introduction of ether into the stomach or duodenum, and Heidenhain studied the relation of the time-course of the secretion to the processes of digestion going on in the stomach and intestines.

Our exact knowledge of many of the factors determining pancreatic secretion we owe to the work of Pawlow and his pupils, who have shown that the flow of pancreatic juice begins with the entry of the chyme into the duodenum and is not excited directly by the presence of food in the stomach itself. The exciting influence of the chyme is due chiefly to its acidity, and a large secretion can be brought about by the introduction of 0.4% hydrochloric acid into the stomach, whence it is rapidly transferred to the duodenum. Pawlow found, however, that other substances, *e.g.* water, oil, introduced into the stomach had a similar, though less pronounced, effect. In each case the effect was produced only when the substances had passed into the duodenum. Pawlow has, moreover, drawn attention to a remarkable power of adaptation presented by the pancreas, the juice which is secreted varying in composition according to the nature of the food which has passed into the duodenum. Thus, with a diet of meat the tryptic ferment is present in relatively largest amount, while a diet of bread causes the preponderance of the amylolytic ferment, and a diet of milk or fat that of the fat-splitting ferment.

Pawlow regards the secretion evoked by the presence of acid in the duodenum as reflex in origin, and ascribes the varying composition of the juice in different diets to a marvellous sensibility of the duodenal mucous membrane, so that different constituents of the chyme excite different nerve-endings, or produce correspondingly different kinds of nerve-impulses, which travel to the gland, or its nerve-centres, and determine the varying activity of the gland-cells.

In searching for the channels of this reflex, Pawlow has shown that, if proper precautions be taken, it is possible to excite a secretion of pancreatic juice by excitation of the divided vagus or splanchnic nerves. The vagus nerves, also, according to him, contain inhibitory fibres.

The question as to the mechanism by which a pancreatic secretion is evoked by the introduction of acid into the duodenum has been narrowed still further by the independent researches of Popielski and of Wertheimer and Lepage. These observers have shown that the introduction of acid into the duodenum still excites pancreatic secretion after section of both vagi and splanchnic nerves, or destruction of the spinal cord, or even after complete extirpation of the solar plexus. Popielski concludes, therefore, that the secretion is due to a peripheral reflex action, the centres of which are situated in the scattered ganglia found throughout the pancreas, and ascribes special importance to a large collection of ganglion cells in the head of the pancreas close to the pylorus. Wertheimer and Lepage, while accepting Popielski's explanation of the secretion excited from the duodenum, found that secretion could also be induced by injection of acid into the lower portion of the small intestine, the effect, however, gradually diminishing as the injection was made nearer the lower end of the small intestine, so that no effect at all was produced from the lower two feet or so of the ileum. Secretion could be excited from a loop of jejunum entirely isolated from the duodenum. They conclude that, in this latter case, the reflex centres are situated in the ganglia of the solar plexus, but they did not perform the obvious control experiment of injecting acid into an isolated loop of jejunum after extirpation of these ganglia. They showed that the effect was not abolished by injection of large doses of atropin, but compared with this the well-known insusceptibility to this drug of the sympathetic fibres of the salivary glands.

The apparent local character of this reaction interested us to make further experiments on the subject, in the idea that we might have here to do with an extension of the local reflexes whose action on the movements of the intestines we have already investigated. We soon found, however, that we were dealing with an entirely different order of phenomena, and that the secretion of the pancreas is normally called into play not by nervous channels at all, but by a chemical substance which is formed in the mucous membrane of the upper parts of the small intestine under the influence of acid, and is carried thence by the blood-stream to the gland-cells of the pancreas.

II. EXPERIMENTAL METHODS.

All our experiments were made on dogs which had received a previous injection of morphia, and were anæsthetized with A.C.E. mixture during the course of the experiment. In order to keep the animals' condition constant, artificial respiration was usually employed, a procedure which is especially necessary when both vagi are divided, the anæsthetic bottle being introduced in the course of the blast of air from the pump. The animals had received no food for a period of 18 to 24 hours previously. In the earlier experiments, where a considerable degree of preliminary operative manipulation was required in the abdominal cavity, the animals were placed during the remainder of the experiment in a bath of warm physiological saline, the level of the fluid being above that of the abdominal wound. This method was found to keep them in such good condition throughout a long experiment that it was adopted as a routine practice in all cases. The arterial pressure was always recorded by means of a mercurial manometer connected with the carotid artery in the usual way. The pancreatic juice was obtained by placing a cannula in the larger duct which enters the duodenum on a level with the lower border of the pancreas. To the cannula was connected a long glass tube filled at first with physiological saline; the end of this tube projected over the edge of the bath so that the drops of the fluid as they were secreted fell upon a mica disc cemented to the lever of a Marey's tambour, which was in connection, by means of rubber tubing, with another tambour which marked each drop upon the smoked paper of the kymograph.

III. THE EFFECT OF THE INJECTION OF ACID INTO THE DUODENUM AND JEJUNUM.

It is unnecessary to describe at length the results obtained under this heading.

We are able to confirm the statements made by our predecessors. The result of injecting from 30 to 50 c.c. of 0.4% hydrochloric acid into the lumen of the duodenum or jejunum is to produce, after a latent period of about two minutes, a marked flow of pancreatic juice. Further, this effect is still produced after section of both vagi, section of the spinal cord at the level of the foramen magnum, destruction of the spinal cord, section of the splanchnic nerves, or extirpation of the solar plexus, or any combination of these operations. . . .

Our experiments, therefore, confirm those of previous observers in so far as we find that after exclusion of all nerve-centres, except those in the pancreas itself, a secretion of pancreatic juice is obtained by the introduction of acid into the duodenum. But, as pointed out above, the *experimentum crucis* of taking an isolated loop of intestine, dividing the mesenteric nerves supplying it, and then injecting acid into it, had not been performed.

It is plain that this experiment cannot be performed on the duodenum for anatomical reasons. Fortunately, however, as Wertheimer and Lepage have shown, the jejunum, separated by section from the duodenum, is also capable of exciting the pancreas to activity, when acid is introduced, and in this case the centre for the "reflex" must be in the cœliac or mesenteric ganglia. The possibility of our crucial experiment is given here, and the results are contained in the next section.

IV. THE CRUCIAL EXPERIMENT.

On January 16th, 1902, a bitch of about 6 kilos weight, which had been fed about 18 hours previously, was given a hypodermic injection of morphia some 3 hours before the experiment, and during the experiment itself received A.C.E. in addition. The nervous masses around the superior mesenteric artery and cœliac axis were completely removed and both vagi cut. A loop of jejunum was tied at both ends and the mesenteric nerves supplying it were carefully dissected out and divided, so that the piece of intestine was connected to the body of the animal merely by its arteries and veins. A cannula was inserted in the large pancreatic duct and the drops of secretion recorded. The blood-pressure in the carotid was also recorded in the usual way. The animal was in the warm saline bath and under artificial respiration.

The introduction of 20 c.c. of 0.4% HCl into the duodenum produced a well-marked secretion of 1 drop every 20 secs. lasting for some 6 minutes; this result merely confirms previous work.

But, and this is the important point of the experiment, and the turning-point of the whole research, *the introduction of 10 c.c. of the same acid into the enervated loop of jejunum produced a similar and equally well-marked effect.*

Now, since this part of the intestine was completely cut off from nervous connection with the pancreas, the conclusion was inevitable that the effect was produced by some chemical substance finding its way into the veins of the loop of jejunum in question and being carried in the blood-stream to the pancreatic cells. Wertheimer and Lepage have shown, however, that acid introduced into the circulation has no effect on the pancreatic secretion, so that the body of which we were in search could not be the acid itself. But there is, between the lumen of the gut and the absorbent vessels, a layer of epithelium, whose cells are as we know endowed with numerous important functions. It seemed therefore possible that the action of acid on these cells would produce a body capable of exciting the pancreas to activity. The next step in our experiment was plain, viz. to cut out the loop of jejunum, scrape off the mucous membrane, rub it up with sand and 0.4% HCl in a mortar, filter through cotton-wool to get rid of lumps and sand, and inject the extract into a vein. The first effect is a considerable fall of blood-pressure, due, as we shall show later, to a body distinct from that acting on the pancreas, and, after a latent period of about 70 secs. a flow of pancreatic juice at more than twice the rate produced at the beginning of the experiment by introduction of acid into the duodenum. We have already suggested the name "secretin" for this body, and as it has been accepted and made use of by subsequent workers it is as well to adhere to it.

In the same experiment we were able to make two further steps in the elucidation of the subject. In the first place the acid extract was boiled and found undiminished in activity; secretin is therefore not of the nature of an enzyme. In the second place, since Wertheimer and Lepage have shown that the effect of acid in the small intestine diminishes in proportion as the place where it is introduced approaches the lower end, so that from the last 6 inches or so of the ileum no secretion of the pancreas is excited, it was of interest to see whether the distribution of the substance from which secretin is split by acids is similar in extent. . . . [Upon] injecting an extract from the lower 6 inches of the ileum, made in the same way as the jejunum extract, the fall of blood-pressure is present, but there is no effect on the pancreas. Another preparation from the ileum just above this one also had no effect on the pancreas. A preparation from the jejunum below the previous one had a marked effect, but less than that of the loop above. The distribution of "prosecretin," as we have proposed to call the mother-substance, corresponds therefore precisely with the region from which acid introduced into the lumen excites secretion from the pancreas.

The Internal Secretion of the Pancreas. ~

by F. G. BANTING and C. H. BEST

Abridged from the *Journal of Laboratory and Clinical Medicine*, Vol. 7, No. 5, February, 1922, pp. 251–266. Reprinted by permission of the author.

Diabetes mellitus has been known to man since the early days of the Roman Empire. However, it was not correlated with functional defect of the pancreas until 1889. Von Mering and Minkowski, by means of improved surgical techniques, successfully removed the pancreas from several dogs. These experimental animals soon developed symptoms remarkably similar to those characteristic of human diabetes and died within three or four weeks. Parallel chemical studies revealed the striking finding that although sugar was absent in the urine of control or sham operated animals, it was abundantly present in the urine of experimentally altered animals. From these findings it was soon realized that diabetes is essentially a defect of carbohydrate metabolism. Investigators were quick to attempt the preparation of pancreas extracts that might ultimately be used for the specific treatment of the disease. These attempts were uniformly unsuccessful. The principal difficulty lay in the apparent destruction of the hormone by powerful proteolytic enzymes produced in the exocrine portions of the pancreas.

Reprinted in the following paper are the detailed methods employed by Banting and his collaborators which ultimately led to the preparation of extracts sufficiently potent to relieve the symptoms of experimentally produced diabetes. Crucial to the successful demonstration of the hormone, and its partial isolation in the form of active extracts, was the application of an improved surgical technique leading to degeneration of the exocrine portion of the pancreas but without effect upon the islet tissue responsible for the synthesis of insulin. In recognition of these accomplishments Banting and his former teacher, Professor Macleod, were awarded the Nobel Prize in 1923.

Five years after Banting's revolutionary findings were published, Abel and his associates reported the isolation of crystalline insulin. Various analytical studies since that time indicate that insulin is a protein molecule, though one of the smallest. In 1954, the Cambridge University biochemist Frederick Sanger and his colleagues, after a decade of intensive research, succeeded in describing its molecular structure. Insulin thus became the first protein for which a structural formula could be written.

THE HYPOTHESIS underlying this series of experiments was first formulated by one of us in November, 1920, while reading an article dealing with the relation of the isles of Langerhans to diabetes. From the passage in this article, which gives a résumé of degenerative changes in the acini [sac-like chambers] of the pancreas following ligation of the ducts, the idea presented itself that since the acinous, but not the islet tissue, degenerates after this operation, advantage might be taken of this fact to prepare an active extract of islet tissue. The subsidiary hypothesis was that trypsinogen or its derivatives was antagonistic to the internal secretion of the gland. The failures of other investigators in this much-worked field were thus accounted for.

The feasibility of the hypothesis having been recognized by Professor J. J. R. Macleod, work was begun, under his direction, in May, 1921, in the Physio-

logical Laboratory of the University of Toronto.

In this paper no attempt is made to give a complete review of the literature. A short résumé, however, of some of the outstanding articles which tend to attribute to the isles of Langerhans the control of carbohydrate metabolism, is submitted.

In 1889 Mering and Minkowski found that total pancreatectomy in dogs resulted in severe and fatal diabetes. Following this, many different observers experimented with animals of various species and found in all types examined, a glycosuria [sugar in the urine] and fatal cachexia [poor physical condition] after this operation. The fact was thus established that the pancreas was responsible for this form of diabetes. In 1884, Arnozan and Vaillard had ligated the pancreatic ducts in rabbits and found that within twenty-four hours the ducts become dilated; the epithelial cells begin to desquamate; and that there are proto-plasmic changes in the acinous cells. On the seventh day there is a beginning of round-celled infiltration. On the four-teenth day the parenchyma was mostly replaced by fibrous tissue. Sscobolew in 1902 noted in addition to the above, that there was a gradual atrophy and sclerosis of the pancreas with no glucosuria. However, in the later stages, from thirty to one hundred and twenty days after ligation of the ducts, he found involve-ment of the islets and accompanying glucosuria.

Lewaschew believed that the islets were modified acinous cells. Laguesse, an anatomist, first suggested that the islets might be the organ of pancreatic internal secretion. He showed that there were comparatively more islets in the fetus and the newborn than in the adult animal. Opie and Sscobolew independ-ently furnished the first clinical founda-tion for the belief that the islets were involved in pancreatic diabetes.

W. G. MacCallum, in 1909, ligated the ducts draining the tail third of the pancreas. After seven months he excised the remaining two-thirds. This was fol-lowed by a mild glucosuria. Three weeks later he removed the degenerated tail third. This second operation resulted in an extreme and fatal glucosuria. Kirkbridge, in 1912, repeated and cor-roborated MacCallum's findings and, by the use of Lane's method of staining, proved that the atrophic tissue contained healthy islets.

Kamimura in 1917, working on rab-bits, traced the degenerative changes in the parenchymatous tissue of the pan-creas after ligation of the ducts, and found that the islets remained normal and that the animal did not develop glucosuria as long as the islets were left intact.

The first attempt to utilize the pan-creas in defects of carbohydrate metabo-lism was made by Minkowski. This worker tried the effect of pancreatic feeding, with no beneficial results. Up to the present time only useless or even harmful effects have been obtained from repeated attempts to use this method.

Knowlton and Starling, in 1912, pub-lished experiments which showed a marked decrease in the power of using sugar of a diabetic heart perfused out-side the body, as compared with a normal heart under similar conditions. Macleod and Pearce, using eviscerated animals, were unable to confirm the above results. Patterson and Starling subsequently pointed out that a serious error was involved in the early experiments due to (1) excess glycogen present in diabetic hearts, and (2) to the irregular disap-pearance of glucose from the lungs.

Murlin prepared an alkaline extract of pancreatic tissue and after injection of this solution, secured a reduction in sugar excreted in a diabetic animal. Kleiner has pointed out that the reduc-tion secured by Murlin might be due to the alkali *per se*. Kleiner himself has shown that "unfiltered-water extracts of fresh pancreas diluted with .90 per cent NaCl when administered slowly usually resulted in a marked decrease in blood sugar." There was no compensating in-crease in urine sugar, but rather a decrease, which Kleiner suggests may be partly due to a temporary toxic renal effect. Hemoglobin estimations made during the experiment showed that the reduction in blood sugar was not a dilu-tion phenomenon. Paulesco has recently demonstrated the reducing effect of whole gland extract upon the amounts of sugar, urea and acetone bodies in the blood and urine of diabetic animals. He states that injections into peripheral veins produce no effect and his experi-ments show that second injections do not produce such marked effect as the first.

From the work of the above-men-tioned observers we may conclude: (1) that the secretion produced by the aci-nous cells of the pancreas are in no way connected with carbohydrate utilization;

(2) that all injections of whole gland extract have been futile as a therapeutic measure in defects of carbohydrate utilization; (3) that the islands of Langerhans are essential in the control of carbohydrate metabolism. According to Macleod there are two possible mechanisms by which the islets might accomplish this control: (1) the blood might be modified while passing through the islet tissue, i.e., the islands might be detoxicating stations and (2) the islets might produce an internal secretion.

We submit the following experiments which we believe give convincing evidence that it is this latter mechanism which is in operation.

In the ten-week interval which we considered necessary for complete degeneration of the acinous tissue, we secured records of dogs depancreatized by the Hédon method.

METHODS

The procedure is as follows: under general anesthesia an upper right rectus incision is made through the abdominal wall. The duodenum is delivered through the abdominal wound, and the pancreas traced to the tail portion. The mesentery beyond is cut between clamp and ligature. Vessels from spleen are then isolated, ligated and divided. Little dissection is then required until the duodenum is reached. The superior pancreatico-duodenal vessels are located and great care is exercised to avoid damaging them. The pancreas is stripped from the duodenum by dry dissection. The vessels to the uncinate process are ligated and divided, and the process freed from its mesenteric attachments. The larger duct of the pancreas is then ligated close to its entry into the duodenum and the pancreas is removed. Special care must be exercised to preserve the splenic vessels. The superior pancreatico-duodenal vessels must be left intact. Failing this, duodenal ulcer is a frequent development. If this procedure is carried out the whole gland with the exception of the portion in contact with the duodenum is covered with mesentery. The abdominal wound is closed layer by layer with catgut. A collodion dressing is used. The urethral orifice is exposed by a midline incision of the perineum and the edges of the wound drawn together to facilitate healing.

We have found that animals between eight and sixteen months old are the most suitable for this operation. At this age the pancreas is not so firmly fixed as it becomes later.

We first ligated, under general anesthesia, the pancreatic ducts in a number of dogs. (Blood sugar estimations on these animals were recorded from time to time. We have no record of a hyperglycemia).

The extract was prepared as follows: The dog was given a lethal dose of chloroform. The degenerated pancreas was swiftly removed and sliced into a chilled mortar containing Ringer's solution. The mortar was placed in freezing mixture and the contents partially frozen. The half frozen gland was then completely macerated. The solution was filtered through paper and the filtrate, having been raised to body temperature, was injected intravenously.

We have never found it necessary to cut down on a vein under general or local anesthetic. The skin surface above the vein is shaved and the needle inserted into the vein which is dilated by compression. The dogs make very little resistance to this procedure and after the first few punctures lie quietly during the operation. Sugar injections (100 c.c. of fluid) as well as the numerous administrations of extract were conducted by this method.

We performed several experiments with the object of exhausting the zymogen granules of the pancreas. Prolonged secretin injections and vagus stimulation below the diaphragm were practiced. Fortune favored us in the first experiment. In subsequent attempts we were never able to exhaust the gland sufficiently to obtain an extract free from the disturbing effects of some constituent of pancreatic juice.

The blood sugar estimations were made by the Myers-Bailey modification of the Lewis-Benedict method. The results of this method were corroborated by the Schaffer-Hartman method at high and low percentages of blood sugar. The former method gave results which were consistently slightly higher (.01 per cent) than those obtained by the Schaffer-Hartman method. We find the average normal blood sugar, from observations on thirty normal dogs, to be .090 per cent.

Hemoglobin estimations were made by the carbon-monoxide saturation method, using the du Boscq colorimeter.

RESULTS

[*The authors here present many detailed protocols, of which we reprint only the following excerpts.*]

At 6 P.M., September 8, we administered ten c.c. of extract of degenerated pancreas *per rectum*. There was no reduction in blood sugar at 7 P.M. when we gave 12 c.c. of extract of exhausted gland intravenously. [The blood sugar rapidly fell from .30 per cent to .21 per cent; subsequent injections of the same material produced a further drop in blood sugar to .07 per cent.] At 6 A.M., September 10, [the blood sugar having returned to .27 per cent] we administered 15 c.c. of extract of exhausted gland per rectum. There was no effect. At 8 A.M., September 10, fifteen c.c. of extract of exhausted gland were injected intravenously. The drop in blood sugar [to .13 per cent] was very marked. Twenty c.c. of exhausted gland extract, made 1 per cent alkaline with NaOH, were incubated three hours at body temperature with 10 c.c. of active pancreatic juice. This solution was neutralized and injected intrave-

nously at 7 P.M. September 10. No reduction in blood sugar resulted, At 2 P.M. September 11, 20 c.c. of acid extract incubated for three hours at 37.5° F. were injected. [There followed a] drop in blood sugar. On September 13 at 9 A.M. and 2 P.M. extracts from the partially exhausted gland of a cat [were administered.] This extract produces a pronounced general reaction.

We observe that extracts prepared from these more or less exhausted glands, while retaining to some extent the reducing effect upon blood and urine sugar, produce many symptoms of toxicity which are absent after injections of extracts from completely degenerated glands. . . .

A short, but very interesting experiment again demonstrates the remarkable effect of the extract of degenerated pancreas upon the power of a diabetic animal to retain sugar. On Nov. 8 at 11 A.M. (blood sugar .35 per cent), 10 gm. of sugar were injected intravenously. [In one hour the blood sugar rose to .40 per cent.] In the four hours following the injection, 10.88 gm. of sugar were excreted. From 3 to 9 P.M. 78 c.c. of dilute extract were injected in 13 c.c. doses. [The blood sugar fell to .09 per cent.] At 9 P.M. (b.s. .09 per cent), 10 gm. of sugar were injected. [At 10 P.M. the blood sugar had risen to .22 per cent.] Hemoglobin estimations before and after administration of extract were identical.[1] Duodenal ulcer was the cause of the early termination of the experiment.

A more detailed description of the histologic sections obtained during our experiments will be included in a subsequent communication. Suffice it here to note that the pancreatic tissue removed after seven to ten weeks' degeneration shows an abundance of healthy islets, and a complete replacement of the acini with fibrous tissue.

---

[1] Evidence that the fall in blood sugar is not a dilution phenomenon.—*Editors.*

In the course of our experiments we have administered over seventy-five doses of extract from degenerated pancreatic tissue to ten different diabetic animals. Since the extract has always produced a reduction of the percentage sugar of the blood and of the sugar excreted in the urine, we feel justified in stating that this extract contains the internal secretion of the pancreas. Some of our more recent experiments, which are not yet completed, give, in addition to still more conclusive evidence regarding the sugar retaining power of diabetic animals treated with extract, some interesting facts regarding the chemical nature of the active principle of the internal secretion. These results, together with a study of the respiratory exchange in diabetic animals before and after administration of extract, will be reported in a subsequent communication.

We have always observed a distinct improvement in the clinical condition of diabetic dogs after administration of extract of degenerated pancreas, but it is very obvious that the results of our experimental work, as reported in this paper, do not ~at present justify the therapeutic administration of degenerated gland extracts to cases of diabetes mellitus in the clinic.[2]

---

[2] The history of insulin has spectacularly exceeded these cautious expectations. It is estimated that 90 billion units of insulin are used annually in the treatment of America's half million or more diabetics. The life expectancy of diabetics has increased remarkably since pre-insulin days, particularly for younger patients. Before 1913 a thirty-year old diabetic could expect to die in four years; today he can expect to live to sixty. In the pre-insulin era, diabetic children were doomed to die in a year or two; today they can live to middle-age or beyond and their death rate is only 0.3% above that of the general population.—*Editors.*

On the Humoral Transmission of the Action of Heart Nerves. ❧

by OTTO LOEWI

From *Pflüger's Archiv*, Vol. 189, pp. 239–242 (1921), by permission of the author. Translated by M. L. Gabriel for this volume.

In the brief paper that follows we find a simple, elegant, forcefully convincing demonstration that the vagus nerve produces its effects on the frog's heart by liberating a chemically definable inhibitor substance. The hormone concept is thus extended to embrace the general problems of protoplasmic irritability and conduction and throws a new light on the stubborn problem of nerve impulse transmission.

By a method which is now a classic of experimental physiology, Loewi showed that following vagal stimulation a substance accumulated in the fluid filling an isolated amphibian heart. When this fluid was applied to a second heart, entirely isolated from the first, effects identical to those obtained by vagus stimulation were observed. Although Loewi and

Navratil identified the substance released by the vagus nerve as acetylcho-line in 1926, a considerable degree of uncertainty still remains concern-ing the in vivo mechanisms of its liberation, synthesis, propagation and destruction. It is of some interest to note that acetylcholine had been prepared by the organic chemists some sixty years prior to Loewi's work. And, despite the fact that a good deal of literature had accumulated concerning the powerful physiological effects of acetylcholine (easily detectable effects being produced by a dose as low as one ten millionth of a milligram), its importance could not be appreciated without Loewi's pioneering achievement. In recognition of his notable discovery Loewi was awarded the Nobel Prize in 1936.

THE MECHANISM OF action of the nerve stimulus is unknown. In view of the fact that certain drugs act almost identically with the stimulation by specific nerves, the possibility exists that under the influence of nerve stimulation substances might be formed which in turn would produce the effects of stimulation. Under the conditions existing with experimenta-tion on the intact animal, it is quite hopeless to solve this problem. The only possibility lies in experiments upon the isolated organ. Of studies in this direc-tion there is only the work of Howell, according to which the activity of the vagus is supposedly conditioned by a liberation of potassium during the stimu-lation; these experimental results have, however, been refuted.

METHODS

I chose the heart of a cold-blooded animal because here the possibility exists that under suitable experimental condi-tions any substances originating as a result of stimulation may be allowed to accumulate in a small amount of fluid medium, and thus be made demonstrable.

The method chosen was the heart-cannula procedure of Straub with the modification that the vagus was dissected out [with the heart], its attachment to the sinus was retained, and it was laid over an electrode. If the nerve is kept moist and the stimulation is occasionally interrupted, even briefly, it often remains excitable for many hours.

The Ringer's fluid contained 0.6% NaCl, 0.01% KCl, 0.02% CaCl$_2$·6H$_2$O, 0.05% NaHCO$_3$. Oxygen was continuously supplied. The experiments were carried out in February and March on mostly freshly caught *Rana esculenta* (10 experiments), *R. temporaria* (4 experiments), and common toads (4 experiments).

EXPERIMENTS

All experiments yielded the same results.

1. Experiments with inhibitory action of vagus stimulation.

After the heart had been rinsed several times with Ringer's solution to remove the remaining blood, the Ringer's solution was not changed for a certain time, and at the end of this period (normal period) it was pipetted off and preserved. Then the vagus was electri-cally stimulated with short interruptions for an equal length of time. The result with frogs was the well-known ino- and chronotropic response. [A decrease in amplitude and rate of the heart beat.] The fluid medium of the period of vagal stimulation was also pipetted off and kept. When the heart had recovered from the vagal stimulation, it was im-mersed alternately in the fluids of both periods. The fluid of the normal period acted no differently than fresh Ringer's; in other words, it had no effect. But when the Ringer's of the period of vagal stimulation was poured on, a clear negative inotrope [decrease in amplitude] consistently occurred, and sometimes a negative chronotrope [decrease in rate] as well. The latter was scarcely to be expected, since the sinus, under the experimental conditions used, hardly came in contact with the fluid medium. The effect is promptly abolished by atropine.

2. *Experiments with stimulating effects of vagus excitation.*

The obvious thought—to test whether in the atropinized frog vagal stimulation would perhaps lead to secretion of an "accelerator substance" in consequence of the intermingling of accelerator fibers not paralyzed by atropine—could not be carried out up to now because of lack of frog material. I was therefore obliged to use toads. At the present time of year these react to vagal stimulation with an extreme increase in pulse amplitude and frequency. These experiments were carried out as described above. Whereas the perfusion fluid of the normal period is quite ineffectual, that of the accelerator stimulation period leads to an extreme increase in pulse volume. In this connection it is very significant that the perfusion fluid of the period of accelerator stimulation was obtained 3½ hours after the beginning of the experiment, in other words, after the heart had been washed countless times and the accelerator nerve had already been stimulated for one hour. In view of this long preceding treatment of the heart, it seemed desirable to test the efficacy of the perfusion fluid on a quite fresh toad heart. The effect was nearly the same in a fresh heart as in the one previously utilized.

DISCUSSION OF THE RESULTS

The experiments show that under the influence of the nerves inhibiting and accelerating the heart, substances having effects similar to stimulation of the respective nerves become demonstrable in the solution perfusing the heart. Under the influence of the nerve stimulation these substances therefore are either formed, or liberated, or they were previously formed and the cells have only now become permeable to them. As to the significance of these substances, two possibilities exist: On the one hand, they may arise directly under the influence of the nerve stimulation independently of the manner of heart action, and in turn they may cause the specific reaction of the heart to the nervous stimulation, which thus would be effective only indirectly. If their activity under the experimental conditions used falls short quantitatively of the nerve stimulation, this should not be surprising, since it may be assumed that only a minute part of the material formed or liberated by the cell passes into the fluid, which moreover causes a great dilution. On the other hand, the possibility exists that the substances are only products of the special kind of heart action caused by the nervous stimulation; in this case they are to a certain extent only by chance identical in their effect with the nerve stimulation.

As regards the problem of the nature of the substances, we can at present only exclude the possibility that the product of vagus stimulation is potassium, since an increased activity due to potassium cannot be abolished by atropine, which has been effective in our experiments.

As soon as I have suitable animal material at my disposal, I intend to work on the problem of the nature of these substances, as well as other problems which have arisen in connection with the experiments here reported.

VITAMINS

The vitamin concept grew out of numerous observations concerning the effects of habitually restricted diets in man and domesticated animals. Deficiency diseases were recognized and described in great detail long before anything was known about their nature, cause, and cure. If the vitamin intake falls below a certain threshold requirement, which differs from organism to organism and from vitamin to vitamin, metabolic alterations, characteristic lesions, or modifications of body structure are consistently observed. At the present writing a considerable number of vitamins have already been identified and nearly twenty can be obtained in a chemically pure, crystalline state.

CHRONOLOGY

First Period (1750–1895): Recognition of the connection between dietary deficiencies and particular diseases.

1752   Lind called attention to the value of fresh fruits in preventing scurvy.

1795   Lime and lemon juice were introduced into the British navy rations to control scurvy.

1882   Takaki reduced the incidence of beriberi in the Japanese navy by dietary improvements.

1895   Theobald Smith produced a hemorrhagic deficiency disease in guinea pigs deprived of leafy foods.

Second Period (1897–1926): Recognition that the deficiency disease is related to lack of a *specific substance.*

1897   Eijkman produced experimental polyneuritis in fowls by feeding them polished rice, and called attention to rice hulls as containing the preventive agent of human beriberi.

1906   Eijkman found the anti-beriberi agent to be a water-soluble component of rice polishings.

1910   Fraser and Stanton showed that alcoholic extracts of rice polishings had a curative effect in beriberi.

1911   Funk isolated crystalline "antineuritis vitamine" (actually B-complex) and coined the word "vitamine" (later changed to "vitamin").

1913   Osborn and Mendel showed that rats developed xerophthalmia on diets in which lard supplied the fat; the condition was cured by substitution of butter-fat.

1917   McCollum and Simmonds showed that xerophthalmia is due to lack of a fat-soluble substance which they named vitamin A.

1919   Drummond named vitamin C.

1919–1920 Steenbock demonstrated the relationship between vitamin A activity and the plant pigment carotene.

1919   Mellanby produced experimental rickets in puppies.

1922   McCollum et al showed that experimental rickets was caused by lack of a new food factor, vitamin D.

Third Period (1926–1935): The isolation and chemical characterization of vitamins.

1926   Jansen and Donath isolated crystalline thiamin—vitamin B_1.

1927   Ergosterol was identified by Windaus and others as the parent substance of vitamin D.

1928   Euler prepared pure carotene and demonstrated its high vitamin A activity.

1928   Szent-Györgyi isolated hexuronic acid, $C_6H_8O_6$ from adrenal cortex, oranges, and cabbage.

1930–1931 Askew et al crystallized calciferol, vitamin D.

1932   Waugh and King isolated vitamin C in crystallized form.

1932–1933 Svirbeli and Szent-Györgyi showed that hexuronic acid was identical with vitamin C and proposed the name ascorbic acid.

1936   Williams and Cline synthesized thiamin.

Fourth Period (1935–   ): Elucidation of the rationale of deficiency diseases: identification of the metabolic role of vitamins.

1932   Warburg and Christian isolated a yellow conjugated protein from yeast: the yellow enzyme of respiration.

1935   Kuhn et al identified lactoflavin (riboflavin) as the prosthetic group of Warburg and Christian's yellow enzyme.

1935   Wald suggested that vitamin A is a metabolic precursor of visual purple.

1937   Lohmann and Schuster isolated cocarboxylase and showed that it is the diphosphate of thiamin (vitamin B_1).

Since present knowledge of vitamin structure and function is both complex and extensive, this section will be devoted to considering the single vitamin thiamin, or vitamin B_1. Although the selection is somewhat arbitrary, it illustrates the thinking and procedures underlying the aquisition of new knowledge in this area and reveals a fundamental change in the status of the vitamin concept.

An Attempt to Combat Beriberi. ❧

by C. EIJKMAN

From *Virchow's Archiv*, Vol. 149, pp. 187–194 (1897). Translated by Olga Janowitz and M. L. Gabriel for this volume.

It was during the early seventeenth century that a practical cure was found for the debilitating, hemorrhagic disease scurvy. The empirical cure effected by the consumption of citrus fruits did not, however, lead to a more meaningful insight into the nature of such diseases. The first steps in this direction arose from observations connected with the human disease beriberi and similar animal diseases. A clue to the nature of this degenerative and paralytic condition was provided by the Japanese physician, Takaki. He noted that beriberi did not occur among naval crews, if they received barley instead of rice, and especially if this were supplemented by meat, fresh vegetables, and fish.

A few years later the Dutch government sent a commission to the East Indies to investigate the ancient Oriental crippling disease. Two years were wasted in a search for some causative micro-organisms. However, it must be recalled that this was the period during which Pasteur's influence dominated the scientific scene, and bacteria were widely regarded as the sole cause of disease.

Eijkman, a member of the Dutch commission, observed that experimental chickens, maintained on food scraps consisting mainly of polished rice accidentally dropped in the kitchen and dining area, soon developed polyneuritis and paralytic symptoms akin to human beriberi. Further experiments later revealed that if unpolished rice, or rice husks, were included in the diet, the pathology, without exception, could be prevented entirely. In attempts to identify the active principle in rice husks, he found it extractable by both water and alcohol, and further demonstrated by dialysis experiments that it was a diffusable, low molecular weight, non-colloidal substance.

The Eijkman paper reprinted here is concerned with evidence collected during a public health survey of penal institutions. These data led to the conclusion that human beriberi is not a germ disease, but is rather the direct consequence of a dietary deficiency. For the most part, beriberi is associated with the wholesale consumption of polished rice, upon which the bulk of the world's population depends for its survival.

SINCE LAST YEAR research has been carried out on the island of Java with regard to a possible connection between the main dietary component and the incidence of beriberi in the native prisons. These tests were initiated by the results of my studies on a chicken disease similar to beriberi. I was able to establish that that disease is caused by feeding certain grains, especially rice. Only polished rice (raw or boiled) proved to be harmful; unpolished rice was tolerated quite well by the chickens and the same is true of half-polished rice, i.e., with the grains freed from the hulls, but still covered by the cuticles. From these experiments I drew the conclusion that the cuticles probably contain a substance or substances which neutralize the harmful influence of the starchy nutriment. . . .

From this point of view the polished rice diet has first claim on our attention. That beriberi mainly, if not exclusively, occurs among rice-eating nations may be assumed to be known, as well as that the rice diet has been causally connected with this disease by many. As Balz reports, in Japan the navy and later the army have replaced a part of the rice ration by barley and bread, but at the same time the general hygiene has been improved as much as possible. Since that time beriberi has almost entirely disappeared among the sailors and it has also been reduced extraordinarily in the army. To what extent the nutritional change has contributed to this effect, and how much other factors are responsible, is still doubtful, according to Balz.

Already prior to this, apparently favorable results had been obtained with sailors in the Dutch East Indies by giving the native men, who represent the majority of the diseased people, a ration approximately similar to that of the Europeans. For reasons unknown to me these experiments have not been pursued further.

In any case, it is a difficult undertaking to change the diet to which people have been accustomed from childhood, and for this reason we first tried out the half-polished rice diet which had given such excellent results with chickens. I knew that the natives in some parts of Java still subsist on such rice, particularly the variety that is called *bras merah* (red rice) because of the color of the cuticle. It therefore seemed advisable to find out whether the nutrition of half polished rice had a beneficial effect on beriberi.

Two ways were open to us.

First the half-polished rice could be introduced as a main item of diet into institutions in which beriberi appears among the inmates and one could then observe whether the number of disease cases was reduced. Such experiments have been carried out on Java since last year and the preliminary results are encouraging, indeed. So far, these experiments have been carried out on too small a scale to give a positive proof. However, the results might at once have been unfavorable, and thus the falsehood of our expectations would have been proved; it is therefore valuable to state that this was not the case.

The other available way has been taken successfully by Herr Vorderman. As a supervisor of the Civil Health Department of Java, he knew that according to local customs, in some parts polished rice, in other parts half-polished rice was given to the native prisoners as a main diet. Therefore it was ascertainable whether there existed a connection between the type of diet and the occurrence of beriberi in the prisons. For this purpose, Vorderman began to send letters to the local authorities asking them to give information on the pertinent points. The reports received covered about 100 prisons on Java and on the small neighboring island of Madura, a number which seems to be sufficient to obtain accurate statistics. It was found that beriberi cases occurred in only one among 27 prisons where red rice was eaten as against 36 (or more than 50%) prisons where the main diet, according to the authorities, consisted of white rice.

This result was so surprising that the Dutch-Indian government at my suggestion appointed Herr Vorderman to check the correctness of the statements at their place of origin and to examine further what other factors could have an influence on the occurrence of beriberi in the native prisons. This inspection trip took place from May to September 1896 and it is the result of this survey which I will report here. . . .

On investigation of the rice samples it was found that the distinction between polished and "half-polished" rice was not sufficient because in not a few cases the grains were only partly freed of the cuticles. The rice samples were therefore classified into three groups:

(1) Half-polished rice: The cuticles entirely or at least 75% preserved.

(2) Mixture of 1 and 3.

(3) Polished rice: The cuticles entirely or at least 75% removed.

It was found that beriberi occurs:

1. (half-polished rice) in 1 out of 35 prisons, i. e., ... 2.7%
2. (mixture) in 6 out of 13 prisons, i.e., 46.1%
3. (polished rice) in 36 out of 51 prisons, i. e., ... 70.6%

The influence of the kind of rice diet shows up even more clearly than in the first inquiry. In full agreement with my observations on the chicken disease, the results are more favorable the more the bran material (cuticle) has been preserved. This is true also of the disease incidence. In the single prison of group 1

in which beriberi cases had occurred, the number of cases was only 0.16%. In the second group, somewhat higher numbers were found, though all of them were still less than 1%. Finally, in the third group, the morbidity in two-thirds of the prisons affected by beriberi was greater than 1%, often over 10%, and in one case (Prison for Women Convicts at Surabaja) it reached the extremely high number of 37%.

The average number of those affected by beriberi was:

In group 1: 1 of 10,000 prisoners
In group 2: 1 of 416 prisoners
In group 3: 1 of 39 prisoners

These statistics cover a total of 279,-629 prisoners.

Those who have looked for the cause of beriberi in the rice diet have attributed harmful effects to old rice, more or less spoiled by long storage. In the Dutch Indies imported rice (from Saigon and Rangoon) had been mostly blamed. But my experiments on chickens showed the same results no matter what the variety or place of origin of the rice. The disease could be caused equally with polished foreign rice or polished Java rice. And the fact that the chicken disease was not caused by faulty preservation of the rice followed from the fact that the disease also appeared when the rice was fed immediately after polishing.

Vorderman's observations have led to very similar conclusions as to beriberi: "Imported rice has in itself no special influence on the origin of beriberi, nor has old rice."

To what extent some other hygienically important factors have an influence can be seen from the following data:

Age of Buildings

40–100 years	beriberi in 13 out of 26 prisons, i.e., in	50.0%
21– 40 "	" " 11 " " 32 " " "	34.4%
2– 20 "	" " 19 " " 42 " " "	45.2%

Floors

impermeable	beriberi	in	24	out	of	58	prisons, i.e.,	in	41.4%
partly permeable, partly impermeable	"	"	7	"	"	13	"	" "	53.9%
permeable	"	"	12	"	"	29	"	" "	41.4%

Ventilation

good	"	"	28	"	"	68	"	" "	41.2%
medium	"	"	8	"	"	11	"	" "	72.7%
faulty	"	"	7	"	"	21	"	" "	33.3%

Population density

sparsely populated	"	"	32	"	"	73	"	" "	44.6%
medium	"	"	1	"	"	1			
overcrowded	"	"	9	"	"	26	"	" "	34.6%

In no case are the differences so great and so marked as to warrant drawing even a somewhat positive conclusion.

On the Isolation of the Anti-beriberi Vitamin.

by B. C. P. JANSEN and W. F. DONATH

Reprinted from *Proc. Kon. Akad. Weten.*, Amsterdam, Vol. 29, pp. 1390–1400 (1926), by permission of the editors.

Vitamin B_1, commonly known as thiamin, was first successfully isolated by Jansen and Donath in Java during 1925. This represents an achievement of the highest magnitude in modern biochemistry and biology. Starting with 300 kilograms of rice polishings, these authors ultimately isolated some 100 milligrams of crystalline substance. Their paper, which is reprinted here, details the protocols of the involved, necessarily laborious procedures required for isolating any substance that is present in the original material only in the minute proportion of a few parts per million.

Although the authors, through their researches, assigned an incorrect formula for thiamin (the correct formulation being $C_{12}H_{18}N_4OS$), there can be no doubt that they actually isolated vitamin B_1.

In 1935 Williams improved the isolation methods and at the same time achieved a significant increase in the yields for such isolations. Also, he successfully established the chemical nature of the antineuritic vitamin. Cline and Williams further verified the accuracy of the chemical structure by achieving a total synthesis for this product. Nowa-

days, thanks to the exploratory studies by Jansen and Donath, the industrial synthesis of thiamin is a commonplace operation among manufacturers of pharmaceutical preparations.

The first attempts to isolate the substance that, according to Eykman's fundamental investigations, possesses a prophylactic property against beriberi, were made by G. Gryns, but they were ineffectual. Eykman found still a number of properties of this substance, among which the very remarkable one that it is easily soluble in water and in 80° alcohol, and readily dialysable. This is of vital importance, as it goes to show that this substance has a comparatively small molecule, and on that account cannot be classed under the proteins, nucleoproteids, and the like. In view of its considerable physiological activity it probably belongs to the group that Barger has included under the general name of the "simpler natural bases" and was termed by Guggenheim "die biogenen Amine."

In 1911 C. Funk published his first study on this substance which he designated by the name of "vitamin." In this publication he described a body, 20—40 mgrms. of which could cure a pigeon that had developed polyneuritis after a diet of polished rice. It appeared later on that this was not the "vitamin" sought for. Furthermore the symptoms that occurred on a diet of purified proteins + fats + carbohydrates + salts warranted the assumption of several of such "vitamins," which were differentiated by the designations A and B, afterwards also C, D and E, etc. vitamins. . . . After Funk a good many observers have tried to isolate the B-vitamin, and especially the anti-beriberi-vitamin, without any positive results, so far as we know. . . . To our great satisfaction we can say that we have succeeded in isolating the anti-beriberi-vitamin in the same laboratory where Eykman and Gryns have worked.

The material we started with were the fine rice-polishings (dedek) that can be procured in India at a very low price. An extract of it was fractionated in different ways. In order to determine the vitamin-content of the various fractions, we worked with small ricebirds called bondols (*Munia maja*). Groups of ten of these birds, caged together, were fed with polished rice, to which was added a known quantity of the fraction under examination. The polished rice had previously been washed in running water for 2×24 hours, while the deficiency of mineral salts and A-vitamin was compensated by addition of 2% of a salt-mixture, about equal to that used by Osborne and Mendel, and of ¼% cod-liver oil. These ricebirds are very fit reagents to testify the presence of the antineuritic vitamin, and to determine its content. With a rare exception (no more than 1 or 2% of the total number) all the ricebirds fed on washed, polished rice develop polyneuritis in from 9 to 13 days. If 5% of a definite sort of dedek is added to the rice, polyneuritis reveals itself only after from 15 to 23 days.

We now determined every time the quantity of the different [fractions] that had to be added to the washed, polished rice, so that the 10 rice-birds fed with this mixture contracted polyneuritis within from 15 to 23 days. As we found that a rice-bird ingests on an average 2 grms of rice a day, we could compute the quantity of a definite fraction per bird and per day that had to be added to the rice, to guard the animals from polyneuritis for 15—23 days.

For some kinds of dedek a quantity of 100 mgrms per ricebird and per day sufficed; however, with most commercial sorts this quantity amounted to 140 mgrs. Finely ground rice-polishings (dedek) were now extracted with tap-water. (The Batavian tapwater contains only about 130 mgrs of dissolved salts per Litre), to which 3½ cc of sulphuric acid had been added per Litre, to obtain the precise acidity (p_H ultimately $= \pm$ 4.5), and 200 cc of spiritus fortior to neutralize the action of micro-organisms. It seemed to us that formol was a less favorable disinfectant. The extraction was performed in a row of 4 wooden casks of $\pm$ 40 Litres each in accordance with the principle of the counter-current. The bottom and the lid of each cask was provided with an opening resp. for the affluence and the effluence of the liquid. A little above the bottom a second loose bottom had been applied for the greater part consisting of copper-gauze. On this gauze rests a layer of mineral grit, and on top of this the dedek (16 kg per cask). Every day one of the casks was refreshed, and the other three were moved up, so that the fresh dedek came in contact with the liquid that has already extracted the dedek in the other three casks, and the most extracted dedek was extracted with the fresh water-alcohol-sulphuric acid mixture. In this way almost 100 kg of dedek could be extracted every week. This extract contained $\pm$ 20 kg of solid matter and approximately all the vitamin contained in the dedek.

[Details of the fractionation procedure, given in the original paper, are here omitted.]

Of the original quantity of solid matter in 100 kg. of dedek only about 1.4 gramme is left. The vitamin-content of the dedek used, was such as to necessitate the addition of $\pm$ 7% dedek to the washed polished rice to protect the ricebirds against polyneuritis for from 15 to 30 days. It follows then that for 2 grms of rice, i.e. the quantity ingested daily by a rice-bird, 140 mgrms is required. So in 100 kg of dedek there is enough for about 700,000 ricebirds per day. . . .

By . . . fractionation . . . we have ultimately obtained from 300 kg of dedek $\pm$ 100 mgrm of a crystalline substance, which also after recrystallization had a melting point of 250° C. . . .

Now for the evidence that these crystals are, indeed, the anti-beriberi vitamin hydrochlorid.

Of some hundreds of groups of 10 ricebirds each, fed on a mixture of washed, polished rice and inactive fractions, there was not one group of which all the birds or even most of them kept healthy for more than 12 days, while only very few individuals could hold out longer than 14 days. We now conducted the following experiments with the vitamin-hydrochlorid, besides a number of preliminary tests (all of which gave the same result as the experiments proper) : Every time ten ricebirds were fed during $\pm$ 3 weeks with washed polished rice, to which different quantities of the vitamin-hydrochlorid had been added.

A. with vitamin purified through crystallization from absolute alcohol and acetone:

Cage I: 1 part vitamin-hydrochlorid to 1 million parts washed, polished rice; since the average daily diet of a ricebird is two grms of rice, this comes to 2 γ per bird and per day. One of the ricebirds contracts polyneuritis after 18 days, two after 23 days, the others are still in good health after 23 days.

Cage II: 1½ parts vitamin-hydrochlorid to 1 million parts washed, polished rice, i.e. 3 γ per bird and per day. After 3 weeks all the animals are healthy.

B. with vitamin-hydrochlorid purified via picrolonic acid:

Cage III: 1 part vitamin-hydrochlorid to 1 million parts washed polished rice: i.e. 2 γ per bird and per day: three ricebirds polyneuritis after resp. 13, 18 and 20 days. The others still healthy after 3 weeks.

Cage IV: 1½ parts vitamin-hydro-chlorid to one million parts washed, polished rice; i.e., 3 γ per ricebird and per day. After 3 weeks all are healthy.

C. with vitamin-hydrochlorid obtained through decomposition of the double salt with hydrogen-sulphid:

Cage V: 1 part vitamin-hydrochlorid to 1 million parts washed polished rice; i.e. 2 γ per ricebird and per day. This experiment has been in progress for 14 days now, but all the animals still keep in good health.

Cage VI: 2 parts vitamin-hydro-chlorid to 1 million parts washed, polished rice; i.e. 4 γ per ricebird and per day. After 3 weeks all the animals are quite well.

The foregoing justifies us in assuming 2 γ per ricebird and per day to be the critical limit: of the 30 ricebirds, fed with it, only one develops polyneuritis inside of 15 days; the majority keep in good health even for more than 3 weeks. Of the ricebirds that received 3 γ or 4 γ hydrochlorid daily not one developed polyneuritis. . . .

From these experiments, therefore, we may safely conclude that the hydro-chlorid, detected by us, with a melting point at 250° C., is in a high degree instrumental in warding off polyneuritis. But the question may be asked whether this salt is indeed the vitamin-hydro-chlorid, or whether perhaps the salt is contaminated with a small quantity of a still more active component that may be the vitamin that we endeavour to isolate. We believe that the latter supposition is altogether erroneous, if we consider that the salt has been purified through recrystallization, while the mother-lye appeared to be much less active. If the supposition were right, we should have to assume that the crystals had absorbed by selection the active component from the liquid, and had detained it after recrystallization, and transference to goldsalt and back again to hydrochlorid. To be sure this idea must really be precluded.

So a proportion of 1 or 2 parts vitamin to 1,000,000 parts rice would accordingly create in a man, who consumes ± 500 gms of rice a day, a want of ½ or 1 mgrm of vitamin. This is of the same order of magnitude as what we know of the consumption of other substances with great physiological activity, such as thyroxin, adrenalin, and the like.

Investigations upon Cocarboxylase. ✍

by M. LOHMANN and PH. SCHUSTER

Abridged from *Biochemische Zeitschrift*, Vol. 294, pp. 188–214 (1937), by permission of the authors. Translated by M. L. Gabriel for this volume.

Among the outstanding discoveries of recent years is the finding that certain vitamins function as action or prosthetic groups in enzyme systems regulating cellular respiration or intracellular metabolism. Our initial concept of vitamins as growth factors or anti-disease factors therefore requires extensive revision. The gross-pathological changes in avitaminosis must rather be viewed as lesions secondarily resulting from altered metabolic activity at the molecular level. Although we still lack complete data on the precise mechanisms in which many vitamins undoubtedly participate, the demonstrated relationship of some of them to respiratory enzymes has opened new pathways for further exploration.

A significant milestone in the genesis of this newly won and unifying concept is the classic investigation reported in 1937 by Lohmann and Schuster, reprinted in the following paper. The background to their momentous disclosures may be sketched briefly.

In 1930 investigators at Oxford noted that overdosing pigeons with insulin soon produced violent spasms. This finding led Kinnersley and Peters to investigate the relationship between brain carbohydrate metabolism in normal and vitamin deficient birds. They found that normal brain tissue catalyzed the in vitro *breakdown of glucose to lactic acid. However, brain tissue from deficient birds showed an abnormally high lactic acid concentration. They further noted that thiamin, added to vitamin-deficient tissue, produced an increase in respiration, but only as long as lactic acid was present. These data strongly suggested that another intermediate was involved. Some three years later, Peters and Sinclair finally identified the presumptive intermediate as pyruvic acid. Shortly thereafter, Lu and Platt observed that patients with beriberi consistently exhibited an elevated pyruvic acid blood level. It was not unlikely, therefore, to suppose that beriberi represented an enzymatic impairment of glucose metabolism at the pyruvic acid breakdown stage.*

An important step in explaining how thiamin might function was provided by Lohmann and Schuster's isolation of a coenzyme from yeast. Their coenzyme is identical with cocarboxylase, a doubly phosphorylated form of vitamin B_1, or thiamin. The carboxylase system is in turn responsible for splitting out carbon dioxide from many organic acids, including pyruvate, regularly generated during glucose metabolism. Cocarboxylase is also known to participate in at least five different enzymatic reactions coupled with cellular respiration. In principle at least, it is abundantly clear that thiamin deficiency prevents the production of a continuous energy flow necessary for the maintenance of any cell or group of cells. The clinical signs and neurological disturbances characteristically observed in thiamin deficient animals must therefore be considered as secondary effects following in the wake of enzymatic failure within the neurones innervating a given region.

I. INTRODUCTION

Through the investigations of Harden and Young in the year 1904 it was shown that a thermostable substance can be extracted with distilled water from dried yeast. This substance, which is indispensable for fermentation, was thoroughly investigated by von Euler and named cozymase. In 1931 it was found that another component of yeast essential for fermentation could be extracted with acid phosphate solution; this was identified as a magnesium salt.

In 1932 Auhagen, by washing dried yeast with weakly alkaline phosphate solution, demonstrated a third thermostable substance, "cocarboxylase," which is necessary for the decarboxylation of pyruvic acid. The isolation of cocarboxylase led to a preparation that could only have contained a small percentage of the active substance and the investigations were not continued since 1933.

We have now obtained cocarboxylase in pure crystallized form as the hydrochloride $C_{12}H_{21}O_8N_4P_2SCl$. It has turned out to be diphosphorylated aneurin (vitamin B_1). . . .

[Here the authors detail methods for isolating and assaying cocarboxylase and discuss some of its chemical properties; these sections have been omitted.— Editors.]

The activity of cocarboxylase as vitamin B_1.

On the basis of the chemical investigations of cocarboxylase, vitamin B_1 (aneurin according to the designation of Jansen) is a dephosphorylated cocarboxylase. In tests upon pigeons, our own experiments with single subcutaneous injections showed that the action of cocarboxylase sets in about as quickly as that of vitamin B_1, and that cocarboxylase is about twice as effective. As daily single doses, we have found the following values for single subcutaneous injections of 8 γ of cocarboxylase-HCl

TABLE XIV

	Subcutaneous		Peroral	
	B_1	cocarboxylase	B_1	cocarboxylase
Number of pigeons	6	6	8	8
Days until cured	3.2	5.7	3.4	6.1
Hours until onset of improvement	1¼-6	4-69	2-16	2-20
Individual dose in γ	3.1	1.8	2.9	1.6

dissolved in Ringer: 1.3, 1.2, 3.0, 1.7, 1.2, 1.4, 2.0 γ, an average of 1.7 γ of cocarboxylase-HCl. The results presented in Table XIV were provided by the Elberfelder Laboratory. All numbers are based on single administrations of 10 γ B_1-dihydrochloride or cocarboxylase hydrochloride. It is noteworthy that

in these experiments the onset of the cure with cocarboxylase given by subcutaneous injection was significantly later than with aneurin. 1.8 γ of cocarboxylase are equivalent to about 1.3 γ of aneurin dihydrochloride.

The monophosphate compound is also effective as a vitamin.

TABLE XV

Increase in respiration of brain slices of polyneuritic pigeons with B_1 and cocarboxylase

No.	Admixture, 5.0 mg. pyruvic acid as pyruvate	dry weight of brain slice in mg.		10 min.	20 min.	30 min.	40 min.	50 min.	60 min.
1	—	3.65	cmm O_2	2.6	5.5	7.0	10.4	12.6	15.8
			Q_{O_2}	4.3	4.5	3.8	4.3	4.1	4.3
2	+ aneurin 1.56 γ	5.51	cmm O_2	11.0	20.0	28.9	36.4	44.8	54.8
			Q_{O_2}	11.9	10.9	10.5	9.9	9.8	10.0
3	+ cocarboyxlase 1.61 γ	4.49	cmm CO_2	8.4	15.3	23.3	30.0	36.4	44.2
			Q_{O_2}	11.2	10.4	10.4	10.0	9.7	9.9

Assay of cocarboxylase by catatorulin [1] *test.*

According to Peters the respiration of pyruvate by mashed brain tissue of polyneuritic pigeons [suffering from beriberi] is strongly augmented by vitamin B_1. We have comparatively investigated the activity of B_1 and cocarboxylase in brain slices, using pyruvate as substrate in phosphate solution as described by Peters. One experiment is presented in Table XV, in which B_1 and cocarboxylase display the same effect. . . .

DISCUSSION

Through the investigations of Warburg and Christian, Theorell, Kuhn, and Rudy it was shown that vitamin B_2 displays its full activity only as the phosphoric acid ester. In the case of cocarboxylase we have found something somewhat similar, that, in general, an organic P-free compound acts as a vitamin; the specific enzymatic action, however, is exerted only in the phosphorylated form together with the appertaining protein, and the effect can be unequivocally demonstrated in the vitamin component itself. The "vitamin" is necessary for the metabolism of the constituent cell itself and its abundant presence in yeast is therefore not the result of any special altruism for animal metabolism.

It is worthy of note that in brewers' yeast, according to calculations, the vitamin B_1 is present almost exclusively in the diphosphorylated form and that it can be present only in small part in the P-free form in which it was isolated from brewers' yeast by Windaus and co-workers. Our yield of the twice as effective cocarboxylase is about eight times larger than of the P-free aneurin.

On the other hand, in a rice bran kindly put at our disposal by Professor Jansen, only a moderately small cocarboxylative effect could be demonstrated. Although the vitamin content of this rice bran preparation was not determined, it must be assumed that in rice bran, in contrast to brewers' yeast, the vitamin B activity essentially resides in the aneurin, for the first time obtained in crystalline form by Jansen and Donath from this material. In this connection it must be kept in mind that, by contrast to living brewers' yeast, the rice bran represents long-dead cell material, in which doubtless a great number of autolytic processes have taken place. Only special experiments can inform us as to what compounds are originally present.

The experiments on brain slices of polyneuritic pigeons have shown that cocarboxylase, like aneurin, accelerates the oxidation of pyruvate, and experiments on brain suspensions have shown that aneurin becomes transformed into a substance having cocarboxylase activity. Thus it is evidently diphosphorylated. Although the enzymatic synthesis appears slight in the experiments hitherto performed, the true extent of synthesis is concealed by the simultaneously occurring decomposition. These experiments do not necessarily imply that the breakdown of pyruvic acid in animal tissues must be accomplished by the same carboxylase as in yeast. Probably another reaction takes place, since animal tissues are able to decarboxylate pyruvic acid anaerobically only to a very slight extent, and acetaldehyde does not augment the respiration of brain slices in normal or polyneuritic pigeons. The experiments of Lipmann which have appeared in the meantime, are noteworthy; he found that the respiration of alkaline-washed *B. delbrückii* with pyruvate as substrate is enhanced by cocarboxylase and even more by cocarboxylase plus phosphoflavin, with the formation of acetic acid and CO_2. Aneurin itself was ineffective.

[1] Catatorulin was the provisional name coined by Passmore, Peters, and Sinclair for a substance which augmented the respiration of polyneuritic pigeons' brain tissue. It is presumably identical with thiamine.—*Editors.*

The assumption suggests itself that the aneurin molecule can react quite generally with pyruvic acid if it is made capable of forming an enzyme with a protein (in the sense of Kuhn) by esterification with phosphoric acid. This protein is different in different cells: In connection with the diphosphoaneurin it acts in brewers' yeast predominantly as pure carboxylase, in *B. delbrückii* as a dehydrase of pyruvic acid with simultaneous splitting off of CO_2. Concerning the way in which vitamin B_1 acts in the animal body, at present it can only be said that its action is most probably upon pyruvic acid. . . .

METABOLISM

CHRONOLOGY

ca. 1500   Leonardo da Vinci (1452–1510) compared animal nutrition to the burning of a candle, and pointed out that animals could not survive in an atmosphere that would not support combustion.

1614   Sanctorius of Padua published *De medicina statica aphorismi.* He made quantitative measurements of body weight, total intake, and total excrement; he attributed losses to "insensible perspiration."

1648   Van Helmont published *Ortus Medicinae.* He coined the word "gas" and described the properties of carbon dioxide.

1660   Lefevre in "Traité de Chimie" held that the function of air in respiration was to purify the blood.

1660–1678   Robert Boyle's experiments upon gases and effects of combustion and respiration on the atmosphere.

1668   Mayow's *Treatise on Respiration,* containing accounts of experiments on alterations produced in air by respiration and combustion.

ca. 1700   Stahl's phlogiston theory.

1754   Black discovered "fixed air" (carbon dioxide).

1766   Cavendish discovered "inflammable air" (hydrogen) :

ca. 1771   Scheele produced oxygen from silver carbonate.

1772   Rutherford described "residual air" (nitrogen).

1774   Priestley produced oxygen by heating mercuric oxide.

1777   Crawford published the first experiments on animal calorimetry, comparing heat production in a guinea pig with combustion.

1780   Lavoisier and Laplace published their memoir on heat, in which they reached the conclusion that respiration is a form of combustion.

1789   Seguin and Lavoisier made the first measurements of human metabolic rate.

1823   Prévost and Dumas showed that urea is transported by the blood.

1828   Wöhler prepared urea [1] by reacting lead cyanate with ammonia.

1836   Magendie demonstrated the need for dietetic nitrogen.

1839   Boussingault quantitatively studied the balance between the elementary constitution of the maintenance ration of a cow and that of the excretions and the milk.

1840   Publication of Justus von Liebig's *Thierchemie* which united the fields of chemistry and physiology.

1845   Kolbe synthesized acetic acid, previously obtainable only as the result of vital activity.

1849   Regnault and Reiset published extensive comparative studies of respiration and calorimetry.

1850–1855   Bernard discovered the glycogenic function of the liver and isolated glycogen.

1862   Pettenkofer devised an apparatus for analyzing respiratory gas exchange, thus making possible *indirect calorimetry* by the determination of respiratory quotients.

1872   Pflüger showed that oxidation occurs in the tissues rather than in the blood.

1883   Rubner discovered that metabolic rate is proportional to the surface area of the body.

1887–1904   Zuntz, Geppert, Atwater, and others perfected instruments and techniques for indirect calorimetry.

Memoir on Heat. ✍

by ANTOINE LAVOISIER and PIERRE LAPLACE

Selected from Mémoire sur la Chaleur, *Mémoires de l'Académie des Sciences*, Paris, 1780. Translated by M. L. Gabriel for this volume.

Even a confirmed vitalist, who rejects the notion that living organisms are "nothing but" machines, will admit that progress in biological science has always depended on hypotheses formulated "as if" organisms were indeed machines. As long as animal heat was ascribed to "vital forces" an understanding of its nature was impossible, for unless a working hypothesis is couched in terms of chemical and physical events, it cannot

---

[1] Since cyanates at the time were prepared from animal sources, this was not truly a synthesis of an organic substance from in- organic constituents. (See McKie, D., Nature, May 20, 1944, No. 3890, pp. 608–610.)

be tested experimentally. Lavoisier's and Laplace's attack on this problem was made possible by their decision to study the production of animal heat by the same quantitative methods that they had applied to non-living chemical reactions. Their devastatingly simple conclusion that respiration is a form of combustion made it clear that the riddles of metabolism could be attacked with the instruments of the chemist and the physicist. The way was thus opened for the numerous triumphs of nineteenth and twentieth century physiologists in laying bare many of the biochemical reactions that govern the utilization of energy by the living organism.

THIS MEMOIR IS the result of experiments upon heat which M. de Laplace and I made together during the last winter; the mildness of the season did not permit us to perform a greater number. . . .

We have devised the following apparatus [for making measurements of the heat which is developed by combustion, the respiration of animals, combinations of oil of vitriol with water, and the like], all of which have been impossible by the means hitherto known.

The plate represents a vertical section showing the interior of the device. Its volume is divided into three chambers; we shall distinguish them by the terms *inner chamber, middle chamber,* and *outer chamber.* The inner chamber *f* is constructed of a meshwork of iron wire reinforced by strips of the same metal; the experimental object is placed in this chamber; the top of the chamber is fitted with a cover which is entirely open above; its bottom consists of an iron-wire netting.

The middle chamber is intended to contain ice which entirely surrounds the inner chamber and which is melted by the heat of the experimental object; this ice is supported and retained by a grill under which is a sieve. In proportion as the ice is melted by the heat of the object in the innermost vessel, the water runs down through the grill and the sieve; it then runs down the cone and the tube and is collected in the vessel placed under the apparatus; the stopcock permits one to stop the outflow of the water at will. Finally, the outer chamber is designed to be filled with ice, the purpose of which is to prevent the entrance of heat from the external air or surrounding objects; the water produced by the melting of this ice runs down pipe S T, which can be opened or closed by means of stopcock *r*. The entire apparatus is covered by a lid entirely open above and closed beneath; it is constructed of tin painted with oil to prevent rust.

In performing an experiment, one fills the middle chamber and the inner cover with crushed ice, as well as the outer chamber and the outside lid. One must be careful to crush the ice fine and to pack it down well into the apparatus. The inside ice (as we shall call the ice enclosed in the middle chamber and inner lid) is allowed to drain; when it has drained sufficiently, the device is opened, the desired object is placed inside, and the lid is replaced immediately. One waits until the object is completely cooled and the apparatus sufficiently drained; then one weighs the water which has collected in the vessel. Its weight exactly measures the heat emitted by the object; for clearly all its heat has been absorbed by the inner ice which has been protected from the effects of any other heat by the ice contained in the lid and in the outer container.

It is essential that there be no communication between the middle chamber and the outer chamber, which can be easily tested by filling the outer chamber with water. If there were communication between these two chambers, the ice melted by the atmosphere, the heat of which affects the wall of the outer chamber, might pass into the middle chamber, and then the water flowing out from the latter would no longer be a measure of the heat lost by the experimental object.

When the atmospheric temperature is above zero, heat enters the middle cavity only with difficulty because it is stopped by the ice in the lid and the outer chamber; but if the external temperature is below zero, the atmosphere may cool the inner ice; it is therefore essential to work at temperatures above zero; in cold weather the apparatus must be kept in a heated room; furthermore, the ice used must not be colder than zero degrees; if it is, it must be crushed and spread out in thin layers for a time in a place where the temperature is above zero.

The inner ice always retains a small amount of water which adheres to its surface, and one might think that this water would affect the experimental results; but it must be pointed out that at the beginning of each experiment the ice is already saturated with all the water it can thus retain, so that though a small part of the melted ice remains adhering to the inner mass of ice, a very nearly equal quantity of water, originally adhering to the surface of the ice, must run down into the collecting vessel, since the surface of the inner ice changes very little during the course of the experiment. . . .

We have had two machines constructed as described; one of them is intended for experiments in which it is not necessary to change the air within the chamber; the other apparatus is designed for experiments in which the air must be renewed, such as those involving combustion and respiration; the latter apparatus differs from the former only in that the two covers are pierced by two holes through which pass two thin pipes which serve for the passage of air between the outside and the inside; by this means it is possible to blow atmospheric air upon combustible objects. . . .

EXPERIMENTS ON HEAT, CARRIED OUT BY THIS METHOD

We took a small earthen vessel which had been dried; after having placed it on a balance and tared it very exactly, we placed glowing coals in it, blowing upon them to keep them at red heat; at the instant when their weight was one ounce [30.59 gms] we transferred them quickly to one of our machines; their combustion, in the interior of the apparatus, was maintained by means of a bellows; they were consumed in 32 minutes. At the beginning of the experiment the outside thermometer stood at $1\frac{1}{2}°$ and it rose to $2\frac{1}{2}°$ during the experiment; the apparatus when well-drained yielded 6 pounds, 2 ounces [2,998 gms] of melted ice; this was produced by the combustion of one ounce of carbon.

The outside thermometer being at 1½°, we placed a guinea pig into one of our machines; its internal body temperature was about 32° [40° C.], i.e., not very different from that of the human body. To prevent its suffering during the experiment, we placed the animal in a little basket lined with cotton, the temperature of which was zero; the animal remained for 5 hours and 36 minutes in the apparatus; during this period we gave it four or five changes of air by means of a bellows. After removing the animal, we left the basket in the apparatus and waited until it had cooled off; the well-drained machine yielded about 7 ounces [214 gms] of melted ice.

In a second experiment, the outside thermometer was still at 1½°; the same guinea pig remained in the apparatus for 10 hours and 36 minutes, the air being renewed only three times; the machine yielded 14 ounces, 5 gros [447.38 gms]. The animal did not appear to suffer at all during these experiments.

According to the first experiment, the amount of ice which the animal could melt in 10 hours would be 12 ounces, 4 gros [382.38 gms]; according to the second experiment this quantity, for the same interval, would be 13 ounces, 6 gros, 27 grains [422.05 gms]; the average of these two results is 13 ounces, 1 gros, 13½ grains [402.21 gms].

COMBUSTION AND RESPIRATION

Until recently, only vague and imperfect ideas were current regarding the phenomena of the heat liberated in combustion and respiration. Experience had shown that bodies could not burn, nor could animals respire, in the absence of atmospheric air; but nothing was known of the manner in which it influences these two important natural processes and the resulting changes which the air undergoes. The most widespread opinion attributed to the air only the functions of cooling the blood as it passed through the lungs, and of holding the fire against a combustible object by its pressure. The important discoveries which have been made during the last few years on the nature of aerial fluids have greatly extended our knowledge of this subject; it is established that a single kind of air, known as *dephlogisticated air, pure air,* or *vital air,* is concerned in combustion, respiration, and the calcination of metals; this type of air comprises only about a quarter of the atmospheric air, and it is either absorbed, or altered, or converted into fixed air by the addition of a principle which we shall name the *base of fixed air,* in order to avoid any discussion as to its nature; thus, the air does not act simply as a mechanical force, but as an agency of new combinations. M. Lavoisier, having observed these phenomena, suspected that the heat and light liberated in combustion are due, at least to a great extent, to changes which the pure air undergoes. The facts pertaining to combustion and respiration are explained in such a natural and simple manner on this hypothesis, that he did not hesitate to propose it, if not as a demonstrated truth, at least as a very reasonable conjecture, worthy of the attention of natural philosophers. . . .

We have confined ourselves here to a comparison of the quantities of heat which are liberated in combustion and in respiration with the corresponding alterations of the pure air, without going into the question whether this heat comes from the air, or from the combustible substances and respiring animals. With the object of studying these alterations, we have performed the following experiments:

Upon a large trough filled with mercury we set a bell-jar full of dephlogisticated air [oxygen]; this air was not perfectly pure; it contained 16 parts of pure air [oxygen] per 19 parts and it included about 1/57 of its volume of fixed air [carbon dioxide]. We introduced under the bell-jar a small earthen jar, filled with coal which had previously been freed of its inflammable air by strong heat; upon the coal we placed a little tinder upon which was a small fragment of phosphorus, weighing at most a tenth of a grain [5 milligrams]. The earthen jar and all its contents had been weighed very exactly; we then raised the mercury within the bell-jar up to a marked level (E) by suction applied to the interior, in order that the expansion of the air produced by the burning of the carbon would not lower the level of the mercury too much below that of the outside mercury, which would have permitted the escape of air from within the bell-jar. Next, by means of a red-hot iron, passed very quickly through the mercury, we ignited the phosphorus, which set fire to the tinder and thus to the coal. Combustion lasted for 20 or 25 minutes, and when the ember was extinguished, and the inside air had cooled to room temperature, we marked a second line at the level (E′) where the mercury had risen by diminution of the volume of the enclosed air. We then introduced some caustic alkali under the bell-jar; all the fixed air was absorbed, and having allowed sufficient time for this to occur, when the mercury had ceased to rise in the bell-jar, we marked a third line (E″) at the level of the surface of the caustic alkali; we took care to observe, at the three positions E, E′, and E″, the heights of the mercury in the bell-jar above its level in the trough. Atmospheric air introduced into the bell-jar by means of a glass tube had the effect of lowering the mercury level to that of the outside. We then removed the earthen vessel, which we dried and weighed very exactly; the loss of weight gave us the quantity of carbon consumed. The external temperature varied very little during the course of the experiment, and the barometric pressure was about 28 inches.

In order to determine the volumes of air contained [at levels E, E′, and E″], we filled them with plain water, the respective weights of which gave the volumes of these spaces in cubic inches.

But, since the enclosed air had been unequally compressed as a result of the different heights of the mercury in the bell-jar, we reduced the volumes, by computation from the observed heights of the mercury, to that which the air would have occupied if it had been compressed by a 28-inch column of mercury. Finally, we reduced all our experimental results to the values which would have been obtained had the external temperature been 10°, utilizing the fact that, at a temperature of 10°, air expands $\frac{1}{215}$ for each degree of temperature increase; therefore, the volumes of air which we shall report must be taken as the values for a temperature of 10° and a pressure of 28 inches of mercury.

In the preceding experiment, the bell-jar had contained 202.35 inches [4,026.8 cm³] of dephlogisticated air; its volume, by the sole combustion of carbon, was reduced to 170.59 inches [3,394.7 cm³]. After absorption of the fixed air by the caustic alkali, the volume of the remaining air was only 73.93 inches [1471.2 cm³]; the weight of the carbon consumed, apart from its ash, was 17.2 grains [1] [0.912 gms]; the weights of the tinder and the phosphorus together might have been half a grain [26 mg]; moreover, we have found, through many experiments, that the weight of ash formed by the coal is approximately 10 grains per ounce [17.4%]; it might therefore be estimated very nearly that 18 grains [0.954 gms] of carbon were consumed in the experiment, taking into account its ash.

The dephlogisticated air which we used contained about $\frac{1}{57}$ of its volume of fixed air which had not been absorbed by the water over which it had been stored for several months; this intimate adhesion of fixed air to the pure air has led us to believe that, even after the

---

[1] For the critical reader who may wonder at the number of significant figures reported by the authors, it may be noted that Lavoisier used a balance with a sensitivity of $\frac{1}{10}$ milligram, the equal of a fine modern analytical balance.—*Editors.*

fixed air was absorbed by caustic alkali in our experiments, the remaining air still contained a little fixed air, which we may without appreciable error estimate at $\frac{1}{57}$ of its total volume. According to this hypothesis, in order to obtain the volume of all the pure air consumed by the carbon, one must take the difference between the volume of the air before combustion and the volume of the air remaining after absorption with caustic alkali, and then subtract $\frac{1}{57}$. Making a similar correction for the volume of air absorbed by the alkali, one may obtain the volume of fixed air formed in combustion; it will thus be found that one ounce of carbon, in burning, consumes 4037.5 inches of pure air and forms 3021.1 inches of fixed air. If one designates the volume of pure air consumed as unity, its volume, after combustion, would be reduced by 0.74828.

In order to estimate the weight of these volumes of pure air and fixed air, the weight of a cubic inch of each of these airs must be known; now, it has been observed that pure air is a little heavier than atmospheric air, approximately by a ratio of 187 to 185. The weight of atmospheric air has been determined very exactly by M. de Luc. Utilizing these determinations, it is found that at a temperature of 10° and a barometric pressure of 28 inches, a cubic inch of dephlogisticated air weighs 0.47317 grains. M. Lavoisier has observed that at the same temperature and pressure, a cubic inch of fixed air weighs very nearly 0.7 of a grain. According to these results, an ounce of carbon, in burning, consumes 3.3167 ounces of pure air and forms 3.6715 ounces of fixed air. Thus, in ten parts by volume of fixed air, there are about nine parts of pure air and one part of a principle supplied by the carbon, which is the base of fixed air; but a determination of such delicacy requires a greater number of experiments.

We have previously seen that an ounce of carbon, in burning, melts 6 pounds, 2 ounces of ice, from which it may be readily concluded that, in the combustion of carbon, the alteration of an ounce of pure air is capable of melting 29.547 ounces of ice, and that the production of one ounce of fixed air is capable of melting 26.692 ounces.

It is with the greatest circumspection that we present these results on the quantities of heat liberated by the alteration of an ounce of pure air by the combustion of carbon. We have performed only one experiment on the heat liberated by this combustion, and although it was carried out under quite favorable conditions, nevertheless we shall not be quite confident of its exactness until we have repeated it a number of times. As we have said before, and we cannot stress this too much, it is not so much the result of our experiments, as the method we have employed that we present to the natural philosophers, inviting them, if the method appears to offer advantages, to confirm these experiments, which we intend to repeat ourselves with the greatest care. . . .

In order to determine the alterations which the respiration of animals brings about in pure air, we filled the bell-jar of the apparatus previously described with this gas, and we introduced into it various guinea-pigs of nearly the same weight as the one used in our experiment on animal heat. In one of these experiments, the bell-jar contained 248.01 inches of pure air before the guinea pig was put in; the animal was kept there for an hour and a quarter. In order to introduce it into the bell-jar, we passed it through the mercury; it was removed in the same manner. After the inside air had been allowed to cool to room temperature, its volume was slightly diminished to 240.25 inches; finally after the fixed air had been absorbed by caustic alkali, 200.56 inches of air remained. In this experiment, 46.62 inches of pure air had been altered, and 37.96 inches of fixed air produced, correcting for the small amount of fixed air contained by the dephlogisticated air in the bell-jar. If the volume of altered pure air be designated as unity, the reduction in volume due to respiration would be 0.814; in the combustion of carbon the volume of air was diminished by a ratio of 1 to 0.74828; this difference may be ascribed in part to errors of measurement, but it also results from a cause which we had not at first suspected and which those who wish to repeat these experiments might well be warned against.

In order to keep the bell-jar stable in the trough, we raised the level of the mercury inside slightly above the outside level; now, in introducing the animal and in removing it from the bell-jar, we observed that a small amount of air was carried in along the body of the animal, although it was partly immersed in the mercury; the mercury does not adhere closely enough to the hair and skin to prevent all communication between the outside air and the air under the bell-jar; thus the air appears to be less reduced by respiration than is actually the case.

The weight of the fixed air produced in the previous experiment is 26.572 grains; from which it follows that in an interval of ten hours the animal would have produced 212.576 grains of fixed air.

At the beginning of the experiment, the animal, breathing an air much purer than atmospheric air, might in a given time produce a larger quantity of fixed air; but at the end it breathes with difficulty, because the fixed air, accumulating by its weight at the bottom of the bell-jar where the animal is located, displaces the pure air which rises to the top of the bell-jar, and probably also because the fixed air is itself noxious to animals. It may therefore be assumed, with no appreciable error, that the amount of fixed air produced is the same as if the animal had been breathing atmospheric air, the quality of which is about the average between that of the air in the bottom of

the bell-jar at the beginning and at the end of the experiment.

We then determined directly the amount of fixed air produced by a guinea-pig breathing air the same as the atmosphere. For this purpose, we placed one in a jar through which we had set up a current of atmospheric air; the air, compressed in a suitable apparatus, entered the vessel through a glass tube, and emerged through a second curved tube, the concave part of which was immersed in mercury, and the lower end of which terminated in a second flask filled with caustic alkali. The air was then led by a third tube into a second flask full of caustic alkali, and thence out into the atmosphere. The fixed air formed by the animal in the jar was in large part retained by the caustic alkali of the first flask; whatever escaped was absorbed by the alkali of the second flask; the increase in weight of the flasks gave us the weight of the fixed air there combined. During a three-hour interval, the weight of the first flask increased 63 grains; that of the second increased 8 grains; thus the total weight of the two flasks increased by 71 grains. Assuming that this quantity of fixed air is due solely to the respiration of the animal, it would, in ten hours, have formed 236.667 grains of fixed air, which differs by about one-ninth from the results obtained in the previous experiment. This difference could be attributed to the difference in size and strength of the two animals and to their momentary state during the experiment.

If the vapors [expired water] of respiration, carried by the air current, had been deposited in the flasks, the increase in weight of the caustic alkali would not have given the amount of fixed air produced by the animal; it was to avoid this inconvenience that we used a curved tube with its concave part immersed in mercury; the vapors of respiration condensed against the walls of this part of the tube and collected in its concavity, with the result that the air entering the first flask contained no appreciable amount of moisture, as shown by the fact that the part of the tube entering the flask remained transparent; it may therefore be assumed that though the weight of the flasks might have been augmented by these vapors, this increase would have been compensated for by the evaporation of water from the alkali. It might still be feared that a part of the fixed air combined came from the atmospheric air itself. To reassure ourselves in this regard we repeated the same experiment, but without placing a guinea-pig in the vessel; no increase then occurred in the weight of the flasks; that of the second flask diminished by 4 or 5 grains, no doubt owing to evaporation of water from its alkali.

A third experiment performed on a guinea-pig in dephlogisticated air gave 226 grains as the amount of fixed air produced in ten hours.

Taking an average of these experiments and several similar ones performed with a number of guinea-pigs, both in dephlogisticated air and in atmospheric air, we have obtained an estimate of 224 grains as the amount of fixed air produced in ten hours by the guinea-pig on which we had experimented in our apparatus to determine its animal heat.

Inasmuch as these experiments were carried out at a temperature of 14°–15°, it is possible that the amount of fixed air produced by respiration is a little less than at a temperature of zero degrees, which is that of the interior of our apparatus; for greater precision it would therefore be necessary to determine the production of fixed air at the latter temperature; we shall take up this question in further experiments which we intend to carry out.

The foregoing experiments are contrary to those which MM. Scheele and Priestley have reported on the alterations of pure air by the respiration of animals. Respiration, according to these two excellent naturalists, produces very little fixed air and a large amount of vitiated air, which the latter has designated as *phlogisticated;* but, upon investigating the effect of respiration of birds and guinea-pigs on pure air with the greatest possible care, by a great number of experiments, we have constantly observed that the transformation of this air into fixed air is the main alteration produced by the respiration of animals. By having guinea-pigs breathe a large amount of pure air and observing by means of caustic alkali the amount of fixed air produced by their respiration, and by subsequently causing the residual air to be breathed by birds, and absorbing the newly-formed fixed air once more by caustic alkali, we have been able to convert into fixed air a large part of the pure air which we have been using; the remaining air had nearly the same quality which it would have had assuming that the transformation of pure air into fixed air is the only effect of respiration upon the air. It therefore seems certain to us that if respiration produces other alterations in pure air, they are inconsiderable, and we have no doubt that any naturalist performing the same experiments with a large mercury apparatus will be led to the same conclusion.

It was previously seen that in the combustion of carbon, the formation of an ounce of fixed air can melt 26.692 ounces of ice; on the basis of this result, it is found that the formation of 224 grains of fixed air must melt 10.38 ounces. This amount of melted ice consequently represents the heat produced by the respiration of a guinea-pig during ten hours.

In the experiment on animal heat of a guinea-pig, this animal emerged from our apparatus with nearly the same heat with which it entered, for it is known that the internal heat of animals is always nearly constant. Without the constant renewal of its heat, all the heat which it had at first would have been gradually dissipated, and we should have found it cold upon taking it out of the apparatus, like all the inanimate objects which we have used in our experiments. But the animal's vital functions continually restore to it the heat which it gives off to its environment, and which in our experiment is diffused into the inner ice, of which it melted 13 ounces in ten hours. This amount of melted ice thus represents approximately the amount of heat renewed during this time interval by the vital functions of the guinea-pig. Perhaps an ounce or two should be subtracted, or maybe more, on account of the fact that the extremities of the body of the animal were chilled in the apparatus, although the interior of the body retained nearly the same temperature; furthermore, the moisture which its internal heat had evaporated melted a small amount of ice as it cooled, adding to the water draining out of the apparatus.

On subtracting about 2½ ounces from this quantity of ice, one obtains the amount melted by the effect of the respiration of the animal upon the air. Now, if one considers the inevitable errors in these experiments and in the factors which were the starting point for our calculations, it will be seen that it is not possible to hope for a more perfect agreement between these results. Thus the heat which is liberated in the transformation of pure to fixed air by respiration may be regarded as the principal cause of the conservation of animal heat, and if other causes are involved, they are of lesser significance.

Respiration is therefore a combustion, very slow to be sure, but perfectly similar to that of carbon. It occurs in the interior of the lungs, without the liberation of any perceptible light because the fire, as fast as it is freed, is absorbed by the humidity of these organs. The heat developed by this combustion is transferred to the blood which passes through the lungs, and thence is transmitted throughout the animal system. Thus the air which we breathe serves two purposes equally necessary for our preservation: it removes from the blood the base of fixed air, an excess of which would be most injurious; and the heat which this combination releases in the lungs replaces the constant loss of heat into the atmosphere and surrounding bodies to which we are subject.

On the Mechanism of Formation of Sugar in the Liver.

by CLAUDE BERNARD

From *Comptes-Rendus de l'Académie des Sciences*, Vol. 41, pp. 461–469 (1855). Translated by Fannie Dancyger and M. L. Gabriel for this volume.

More than any other man of his generation, Claude Bernard was responsible for the introduction of experimental methods into physiology. Working in the tradition of Lavoisier and Wöhler to elucidate the chemical and physical activities underlying living phenomena, he made many fundamental discoveries which are part of the fabric of biological science today. To Bernard we owe the concept (and the term) of internal secretion, discovery of the functions of the pancreatic juice, the demonstration of the sympathetic vaso-motor mechanism, and the mechanism of carbon monoxide poisoning, to mention only a few of his contributions. One of his most illuminating insights was the conception of the constancy of the "internal environment." His aphorism, "La fixité du milieu intérieur est la condition de la vie libre," has become virtually axiomatic in comparative physiology. Basic to the evolution of this viewpoint was Bernard's experimental demonstration that the liver—"un véritable laboratoire vital," he called it—takes up and releases sugar and hence that the body does not merely break down foodstuffs, but is capable of synthesizing metabolic intermediates as well. The following important paper, in which Bernard reports the isolation of glycogen and deduces its synthesis by the liver, is one of a series which may be compared in their impact on biological thought with Wöhler's synthesis of urea or Kolbe's synthesis of acetic acid, which heralded the birth of organic chemistry by destroying the distinction between organic and inorganic substances. Reading Bernard's experimental writings, one must be struck by his superb talent for thinking physiologically, a genius which moved a contemporary to say of him, "Ce n'est pas un grand physiologiste, c'est la physiologie même."

THE GLYCOGENIC FUNCTION of the liver has attracted the close attention of physiologists, chemists, and physicians because of the importance of the ideas it raises in general physiology.

Having established the widespread occurrence of this function through many experiments on man and animals, having studied it under physiological conditions and localized it in the liver, I felt obliged to investigate the nature of this phenomenon more closely and to attempt to discover the intimate mechanism of the production of sugar in animals.

The new experiments which I shall report to the Academy today will, I believe, throw a clear light on this interesting aspect of the problem.

It is unnecessary for me to repeat here all the indisputable facts upon which I have established the reality of the glycogenic function. For six years, these facts have taken their place in science, and I may congratulate myself on having seen them confirmed in all countries by the most competent physiologists and chemists.

Nevertheless, since recently some authors have introduced inexact experiments on the question of the production of sugar in the animal organism, I

thought it necessary, before embarking on the subject, to dispose of these inexactitudes by reestablishing in order and very succinctly some of the fundamental facts which form the basis for the glycogenic theory.

First, I have said in my memoir that animals possess a physiological function by virtue of which sugar is produced in the organism, because sugar always persists in the liver and the blood of carnivorous animals whose food contains no sugar. This is a fundamental fact; for until recently it was generally supposed that the sugar found in the organism was always introduced in nature through the diet. Today no one argues this question any more, and it is perfectly established, since my experiments, that sugar (glucose) is produced in the animal organism without the intervention of sugary or amylaceous substances.

Second, I have also said that this glycogenic function must be localized in the liver. Indeed, in a carnivorous animal the liver is in reality the central point from which the sugar is distributed throughout the body, and, as I have especially stressed, the blood which enters the liver by the portal vein contains no sugar, whereas the same blood which leaves by the hepatic veins always contains appreciable amounts. Consequently, it was impossible to avoid the conclusion that the sugar originates in the liver, whose tissue is moreover constantly impregnated with sugar in the physiological state. . . .

MECHANISM OF THE GLYCOGENIC FUNCTION OF THE LIVER

All secretions necessarily require two things, namely (1) blood, and (2) glandular tissue. We shall have to estimate the respective role of each of these elements in the production of sugar. . . .

The hypotheses . . . prevalent today as to the mechanism of secretion state that the glandular organ itself supplies nothing to the secretion, but that its tissue is restricted to acting by a sort of contact or catalytic action upon the elements of the blood that pass through the glandular organ at the very moment when the secretion takes place. In the particular case of the secretion of sugar in the liver . . . all the authors assume that the sugar is formed *directly* in the blood.

The facts which I shall now reveal are calculated to prove, it seems to me, that the glycogenic function of the liver must be understood quite otherwise, and that instead of searching *in the blood* for the immediate precursor of sugar, it must be sought *in the hepatic tissue itself*.

The following experiment illuminates this fact; I shall describe it in some detail so that it may be easily repeated. The results are, in my opinion, very important and worthy of the attention of both physiologists and chemists.

I chose an adult dog, vigorous and in good health, which had been fed for several days exclusively on meat, and I sacrificed it by severing the medulla seven hours after an ample meal of tripe. The abdomen was immediately opened; the liver was removed avoiding injury to its tissue, and the organ, while still warm and before the blood had had time to coagulate in its vessels, was washed with cold water through the portal vein. For this purpose I took a tube of gutta percha about one meter long bearing copper nozzles at both ends. The tube having previously been filled with water, one of its ends was securely fastened to the portal venous trunk at its point of entry to the liver, and the other end was coupled to the water tap of the medical laboratory of the Collège de France. When the faucet was opened, water streamed through the liver very rapidly, as the force of the water current was great enough, as far as measurable, to raise a column of mercury to a height of 127 centimeters. Under the influence of this energetic washing, the liver swelled, the color of its tissue became pale, and the blood was expelled with the water which escaped in a strong continuous jet through the hepatic veins. At the end of a quarter of an hour the tissue of the liver was already nearly bloodless, and the water which emerged from the hepatic veins was entirely colorless. I subjected the liver to this continuous washing for 40 minutes without interruption. I had determined at the beginning of the experiment that the red-colored water which flowed out of the hepatic veins was sweet and gave an abundant precipitate on heating, and I verified at the end of the treatment that the perfectly colorless water which emerged from the hepatic veins did not contain any traces of albuminous matter or sugar.

The liver was then removed from the action of the water current; and I made sure, by boiling a piece of the liver with a little water, that its tissue was well-washed, since it no longer contained sugar. The decoction did not reduce cupro-potassium liquid and did not exhibit any trace of fermentation with yeast. From the cut hepatic tissue and from the cut ends of the vessels there escaped a small quantity of a turbid liquid which did not contain any trace of sugar. I then left this liver in a jar at room temperature. After twenty-four hours I found that this organ, washed entirely bloodless, which I had left the night before completely free of sugar, now contained sugar in abundance. I was sufficiently convinced of this when I examined a little of the liquid which had flowed out around the liver and which was very sweet; then, by injecting cold water into the portal vein with a small syringe and collecting this water as it escaped through the hepatic veins, I found that this liquid fermented very abundantly and very actively with yeast.

This simple experiment, in which one can see before his eyes the abundant reappearance of sugar in a liver which had been completely deprived of it and of its blood by means of the washing, is most instructive for the solution of the problem of glycogen function. This experiment clearly proves, as we have already said, that in a fresh liver in the physiological, i.e., functional, state there are two substances: (1) sugar, which is very soluble in water and is carried away by the blood during washing; and (2) another substance, so little soluble in water that it remains bound to the hepatic tissue after the latter has been freed of its sugar and its blood by forty minutes' washing. It is the latter substance which, in the undisturbed liver, gradually changed to sugar by a kind of fermentation, as we shall show.

In fact, this new formation of sugar in the washed liver is completely prevented by boiling. For example, if one boils half of a liver right after the washing, one can verify that the decoction, which is generally opaline, contains no sugar, nor does it contain any the next day, proof that none has developed. One observes, on the contrary, in the other half of the liver which was not cooked, that sugar has been produced after a few hours, and its quantity increases gradually until it sometimes attains, after 24 hours, proportions of sugar equal to those originally found in the liver.

This formation of sugar generally stops after 24 hours, and if after this the liver is subjected again to washing, in order to remove the new sugar formation, one can see that in general it no longer produces any, because the matter which formed it is no doubt exhausted. Then only an albuminous substance is dissolved, which always accompanies the production of sugar, though it seems to be completely independent of it, as I shall point out later. Finally, this glycogenic activity generally seemed to me to be more rapid when contact with the air was increased by cutting the liver in pieces and sprinkling it with water.

We have said above that the hepatic substance which is able to change into sugar must be scarcely soluble in water. This same substance is equally insoluble in alcohol, as the following experiment shows:

I took the liver of an animal during digestion. I crushed the warm tissue after washing it a little by injecting ordinary alcohol into the portal vein with a small syringe in order to rid the hepatic tissue of part of its blood. I then separated the vessels and nerves of the liver by pressing its tissue through a fine strainer, in order to collect only the pulp of the organ which passed through the sieve. The resulting paste was then agitated, soaked, and washed with cold alcohol several times in order to exhaust it completely of any sugar it might contain, and to keep only substances insoluble in alcohol. The liver pulp was then collected on a filter and placed on filter paper in a drying stove, the temperature of which did not exceed 40° C. and in which a draft accelerated the drying. I took the precaution of spreading the material to ensure even drying. In this way I obtained a powdery substance formed from the glandular part of the liver itself which was well dried and freed of sugar, but which still retained the hepatic substance in question, able to form sugar when placed in water. In fact, when I added some ordinary water to this hepatic powder and then left it at room temperature, I observed after a few hours that the water contained a considerable amount of sugar. It could not be objected that the sugar which appeared had been retained in the liver tissue because alcohol is not as good a solvent as water; for if I added some hepatic powder to water which was kept boiling for several minutes, I did not notice any appearance of sugar, which accords perfectly with what we have already said of this substance, whose glycogenic reaction in liver washed with water is equally prevented by boiling.

Nor does ether seem to alter the novel substance with which we are concerned, because for several days I soaked hepatic pulp, previously treated with alcohol and dried, and I observed that this pulp still retained its capacity to form sugar.

I shall limit myself to these experiments today. The substance, of which I have done no more than indicate the existence thus far, will have to be isolated and studied carefully later on from a chemical and physiological point of view. I will only add, in this report, that I have found that this substance only exists in the liver in its normal or functional state, and that it disappears completely from the tissue of this organ in all circumstances when the glycogenic function is stopped, circumstances which, by the way, I have determined long ago in my memoir. This substance is characteristic exclusively of the tissue of the liver in which it originates, because I have observed very often that there are no traces of it in the portal vein or in the blood of other parts of the body.

Finally, I want to call attention to the fact that during life, this substance, renewing itself incessantly in the hepatic tissue under the influence of nutrition, is there constantly transformed into sugar, which in the liver replaces the sugar continually being carried away by the blood stream through the hepatic veins. After death, in a liver removed from the body, this substance, under the influence of humidity, can continue to be transformed into sugar until it is exhausted. But since no sugar leaves the liver through the circulatory system, it constantly accumulates and its proportion increases in the hepatic tissue after death. Thus the tissue of the liver always contains more sugar on the following day than at the moment when an animal is sacrificed, and sometimes this difference is considerable. All estimates of the amount of sugar in the liver must be verified therefore in the light of these new facts.

In conclusion, the only object of my work for the time being is to prove that the sugar which is formed in the liver is not produced there and then in the blood, if I may express myself thus, but that its presence is always preceded by a special substance deposited in the tissue of the liver which is its immediate precursor. If I have decided to publish this unfinished work, it is because it seemed to me desirable, in order to solve the problem of glycogenesis which concerns us, to attract the attention of chemists to phenomena which are unknown to them and which to me seem likely to change the views currently adopted to understand the chemical production of sugar in the liver. In fact, it is not necessary to make hypotheses on the origin of the sugar of the liver or on the possibility of the direct and immediate breakdown of this or that component of the blood in order to produce this sugar. It is necessary to isolate this singular hepatic substance which is the forerunner of sugar, to discover how it is secreted in the liver, and how it then undergoes the successive transformations which change it into sugar. Between these two extremes, the insoluble material as it is secreted by the vital action of the liver, and the produced sugar which leaves the organ with the blood of the hepatic veins, there probably exists a series of intermediate transformations which I have not seen, but which chemists will no doubt discover.

Deuterium as an Indicator in the Study of Intermediary Metabolism. ❧

by RUDOLF SCHOENHEIMER and D. RITTENBERG

Reprinted from *The Journal of Biological Chemistry*, Vol. 111, pp. 163–168 and 175–181 (1935), by permission of Dr. Rittenberg.

A new conception of the metabolic activities of the organism was introduced into physiology by the work of Rudolf Schoenheimer and his associates, summarized aptly in the title of Schoenheimer's classic book The Dynamic State of Body Constituents *(1942). Schoenheimer and his colleagues "tagged" molecules or portions of molecules by incorporating into them isotopic nitrogen ($_7N^{15}$) or deuterium($_1H^2$); they were thus able to trace their pathways and eventual fate. From their brilliantly conceived experiments a new picture of the organism emerged: It turned out that the permanent structural elements of the body, previously considered stable, were actually in unending flux, constantly exchanging molecules. Even the apparently dormant fat depots, far from being inert, were found to be incessantly turning over their contents in exchange with other tissues. The supposedly unitary amino acids themselves were discovered to be rapidly broken down and rebuilt in new combinations.*

It is important to realize that this revolutionary understanding of intermediary metabolism was achieved through application of a novel tool, the isotopic tracer, and hence could not have come about until research on atomic structure had provided an understanding of isotopes and made possible their isolation. Deuterium, for example, was first isolated by Urey in 1932. Physiology and atomic physics, running their separate courses through the nineteenth and early twentieth centuries, thus ultimately converged in tracer biology. The versatility of this method, in its infancy when the following papers were written, soon led to its widespread application in biology and medicine. One of the happiest byproducts of the atomic energy program has been the availability of several hundred compounds involving dozens of isotopes suitable for labeling experiments. From the pioneering work of the thirties, tracer research has grown into a vast field already abundantly productive and promising even greater successes to come.

THE STUDY OF the metabolism of substances which occur in nature in large amounts and are continually synthesized and destroyed in the animal body presents almost insuperable difficulties. If substances such as natural fatty acids, amino acids, etc., are administered to an animal, we lose track of them the moment they enter the body, since they are mixed with the same substances already present. Furthermore, if a substance A is given to an animal and an excess of a substance B is afterwards discovered in the body or in the excretions, we can never be sure that the substance A has been converted into B, for a stimulation of the formation of B from some other source may equally well have occurred. The difficulty in following physiological substances in the course of their transportation in the body, and their conversion into other substances, accounts for our ignorance with respect to many of the most fundamental questions concerning intermediate metabolism. The solution of these problems will be possible only when direct methods for tracing such substances are available.

In order to follow directly the metabolism of physiological substances many attempts have been made to introduce easily detectable chemical groups into the molecule. Interesting results have been obtained by the use of synthetic derivatives containing halogens or phenyl groups, but all such substances differ so greatly from the corresponding natural substances in chemical and physical character that they are treated differently by the body. Problems of *normal* transport and metabolism cannot be studied with such material.

In order successfully to label a physiological substance, it is essential that the chemical and physical properties of the labeled substance be so similar to the unlabeled one that the animal organism will not be able to differentiate between them. The chemist, on the other hand, must be able to distinguish and to estimate them in small quantities and at high dilutions.

A possibility for such a label is the use of an isotope. As the chemical properties of the various isotopes of an element are almost identical, it is to be expected that the properties of an organic molecule will remain unaltered if one or even several of its atoms are replaced by their isotopes. At present the only available isotope of elements which occur in organic molecules is the heavy isotope of hydrogen (deuterium). It occurs in nature in the ratio of 1 atom of deuterium to 5000 atoms of ordinary hydrogen (protium). Water obtained from all sources investigated showed almost the same concentration of deuterium. The variations in density are of the order of 3 parts per million. Stewart and Holcomb and Breusch and Hofer have analyzed the water obtained from animal organs and found the density to be the same as that of tap water. The fact that the hydrogen in physiological material contains the same amount of deuterium as ordinary water is in itself a proof that the organism cannot distinguish between molecules which contain only protium and those few organic molecules which contain deuterium atoms. If they were treated in a different way, a dilution or concentration of one or the other isotope would have been observed in biological material.

We have already prepared several physiological substances (fatty acids and sterol derivatives) with 1 or more atom per cent of deuterium. In spite of the large deuterium content we could not detect any differences in their properties within the limits of our physical methods. The melting points and the optical rotations of the optically active substances were unaltered. We describe in this paper only the preparation of deuterium-containing stearic acid from linoleic acid. Other substances will be described in detail in later publications dealing with their use in animal experiments.

Despite their resemblance to the natural products these substances can easily be distinguished for on combustion the resulting water contains an amount of heavy water equivalent to the deuterium content of the organic material. If natural stearic acid is burned, the water obtained contains 0.02 atom per cent of heavy water, whereas stearic acid 6-7-9-10d_4 yields water with 11.11 atoms per cent of heavy water.

With the help of highly sensitive methods already worked out by physicists we are able to determine deuterium or heavy water with a precision of 0.001 per cent. The fate of such substances, after administration to animals, can therefore always be traced in minute amounts with the aid of these methods.

In order to label a substance, the deuterium must be put into the molecule in such a position that the hydrogen (or in our case, the deuterium) is not interchangeable with the hydrogen of water. . . .

The procedure discussed can be used only for such substances as contain *stable* hydrogen. A substance such as oxalic acid, for example, cannot be investigated as both hydrogens in it are labile.

In dealing with the intermediary metabolism of organic substances the physiologist is primarily interested in the fate of the carbon atoms rather than that of the hydrogen. By definition the conversion of sugars into fats, for example, means the utilization of the carbon of the sugar for the fat synthesis, even if all the hydrogen atoms of the sugar were removed from the carbon during the process.* By using our method for the study of the conversion of one substance into another, we can probably follow only processes in which the hydrogen (or deuterium) remains fixed at the carbon atom during conversion.

For theoretical reasons the use of

---

* The use of a carbon isotope C^{13} instead of deuterium would open some fields which cannot be attacked with deuterium. But even if such an isotope were available, the preparation and analysis of compounds would offer greater difficulties than the use of the hydrogen isotope. Nitrogen isotopes could undoubtedly open a wide field for the investigation of the nitrogen metabolism.

deuterium seems to us unlimited for tracing the *transportation* of organic molecules containing stably bound hydrogen atoms. Analysis for deuterium will always indicate the route taken by such substances after their administration. On the other hand, if the *conversion* of one substance into another is to be investigated, the deuterium, even if at a stable position initially, may be lost in the metabolic process when (a) chemical reactions occur at the carbon atom at which the deuterium atom is bound, or (b) a ketone group is formed at one of the neighboring carbon atoms. We are not able as yet to state to what extent such conditions would limit our work. A partial loss, which has to be expected, would certainly not invalidate such experiments. An investigation of this question is in progress.

If deuterium is taken away from the carbon atom of the organic molecule, either by such interchange reactions with the body fluids, or by combustion of the whole molecule, the resulting heavy water will mix with the body fluids. As the kidney and other secretory organs are not able to concentrate heavy water the deuterium will be equally distributed in all fluids. Therefore a determination of the deuterium in the body fluids during or at the end of such experiments will indicate how much of the substance administered is burned, or how much of the deuterium has become labile. The determination of deuterium in the body fluids, which we have carried out in almost all animal experiments, can therefore give very valuable clues.

Other reactions between the body fluids and organic body material can be followed with the help of deuterium. Substances synthesized in the organism will use some of the hydrogen from the water of the body fluids. Reitz and Bonhoeffer have shown that green algæ grown in water mixed with heavy water contain deuterium atoms which are not exchangeable with water.

Therefore, by administering heavy water to animals over a certain period, the analysis of stable deuterium in its different organic constituents will indicate which of these substances used hydrogen of the body fluids for their synthesis. Deuterium in such cases will be a general indicator for following the synthesis of organic material. . . .

THE ROLE OF THE FAT TISSUES

In this communication we report on some exploratory experiments connected with the metabolism of fat in which we have tested our methods and their application to biological problems. We have fed mice for several days on a diet comprising a deuterium-containing fat, and followed it after absorption. The animals were kept on a diet which was insufficient in quantity for them to maintain their weight. We expected that under these conditions almost all of the ingested fat would be burned and that relatively little would be deposited. Much to our surprise we found that, in spite of the fact that the animals had lost weight, a large proportion of the absorbed fat was deposited in the depots, indicating that the fat which was burned was not oxidized directly after absorption but had been taken from the fat depots. We have direct proof that a part of the deuterium-rich fat was burned in our animals, as the body fluids which we distilled off from our animals contained appreciable amounts of heavy water.

It is well known that the properties of the storage fat in animals are somewhat dependent upon the properties of the food fat. It has been found possible to change the properties of the body fat somewhat by feeding either excessive amounts for a short period, or smaller amounts over a long period, of fats which differed markedly from the body fat. The changes observed in the properties of the storage fat are usually small since there exists a tendency in the animal to alter the deposited fat to that typical for its species.

Our methods enabled us to follow the fate of small amounts of fats, which could not be traced by any other method. We analyzed mice after feeding them for 4 days on a diet with as little as 1 per cent fat, and were able to determine how much of the fat was deposited in the fat tissues and how much was burned.

EXPERIMENTAL

The fat which we fed was a partially hydrogenated linseed oil. It had properties similar to that of olive oil. . . .

The water obtained by combustion of 0.609 gm. of the oil was purified by the methods described in Paper II of this series. The atom per cent of deuterium in this oil was 5.74. . . .

Feeding Experiments—Male mice were used in these experiments. Each animal was kept in a 600 cc. beaker containing 10 gm. of ether-extracted wool for bedding. The food was placed in a small glass cup suspended by a glass rod from a wire screen covering the beaker. Food was placed in the cup every day. Very little was spilled.

At the end of the feeding period, the mice were killed with ether, and weighed again. The whole intestinal tract from the esophagus to the anus was taken out and put back into the beaker which contained the food cup, the wool, some spilled food, and the feces. The organs (liver, spleen, kidneys, adrenals, heart, and testes) were removed and analyzed separately. The amount of consumed fat was calculated from the amount of fatty acids given and the amount of fatty acids remaining in the beaker after the mouse was taken out.

ANALYTICAL METHODS

The carcasses of the mice, either individually or in groups, were placed in a 300 cc. round bottom flask with a short neck.

Distillation of Body Water—The flask was connected with a carbon dioxide-alcohol-cooled trap and the system evacuated with an oil pump. The carcasses soon froze and ice sublimed into the trap. Several gm. were collected in this manner. The water collected in the trap was purified for the deuterium analysis in the manner described in Paper II.

Isolation of Fatty Acids and Unsaponifiable Material from Carcasses and Organs—The method used for separating the total unsaponifiable material was similar to that described by Schoenheimer and Breusch. With some modifications it could also be used for the quantitative separation of the total fatty acids of the animals and the residues in the beakers.

It is based on the observation that all the organic matter of animals dissolves easily in hot alkaline alcohol, which simultaneously saponifies the esters. The method was simplified and is now applicable to the determination of unsaponifiable material and fatty acids in organic material. We describe only the analysis of the mouse carcass. The procedure used in working up the organs and the material in the beakers was similar.

After a part of the body water had been distilled off, 70 cc. of 95 per cent ethyl alcohol, 10 cc. of water, and 7 gm. of solid KOH were added. The liquid was refluxed on a steam bath for 2 hours. All except the bones dissolved. The solution was filtered through glass wool, and the residue washed with hot alcohol. The filtrate and washings were combined and the alcohol distilled off. The remaining liquid was washed into a separatory funnel with ether and water. The aqueous layer was extracted three times with ether. The ether was washed with small amounts of water which were combined with the aqueous layer. The ether contained the unsaponifiable matter and was used to isolate the sterols.

In order to separate the fatty acids, the alkaline aqueous layer was acidified with hydrochloric acid and twice extracted with ether. On acidifying, a generally small but sometimes voluminous precipitate occurs; this is not soluble in ether, and collects at the water-ether interface. It packs together on stirring with a glass rod and the water can easily be drawn off. The ether is washed with water until it is neutral. Before the last separation of ether and water the liquid is allowed to stand for 24 hours so that the ether-insoluble precipitate packs together. The water is drawn off and the precipitate and ether layer are transferred to an Erlenmeyer flask, dried with Na_2SO_4, and treated with a small amount of norit which absorbs a brown-colored material but no fatty acids. The ether solution is filtered and the ether evaporated in an atmosphere of CO_2. The residue was weighed and the deuterium content was determined according to the procedure described in Paper II.

To estimate the amount of fat consumed, the fatty acids of the beaker were analyzed in a similar manner. The beaker contained the wool, small amounts of spilled food, the feces, and the intestines of the animals. A 500 cc. round bottom flask fitted with a rubber stopper and water inlet and outlet was placed over the beaker as a reflux condenser, and the contents were boiled with alkaline alcohol as described above. The bread particles did not dissolve and were filtered off through glass wool. The quantitative isolation was effected as described above.

Mice Kept on Diet Containing 20 Per Cent Fat—The diet consisted of 80 per cent whole wheat bread and 20 per cent of deuterium-containing linseed oil prepared as described above. Each mouse and each beaker was analyzed separately. The amount of food given was such that the animals consumed almost all of it except a few particles which they spilled.

TABLE I

Results of Experiments on Mice Fed a Diet Containing 20 Per Cent Fat

The diet fat contains 5.74 atoms per cent of D.

Experiment No.	Feeding period	Weight of animals	Loss of weight	Amount of fat consumed	Amount of total fat in depots	D_2 in		Diet fat in		Heavy water in body fluids
						Depot fat	Organ fat	Depot fat	Organ fat	
	days	gm.	gm.	gm.	gm.	atom per cent	atom per cent	per cent	per cent	per cent
1	2	22.5	1.8	0.54	2.06	0.27		4.7		
2	2	13.8	0.1	0.58	0.42	2.17		37.8		
3	4	20.9	1.3	1.12	2.00	0.71		12.3		
4	4	15.1	0.4	1.28	0.39	2.61		37.6		
5	8	17.1	1.1	2.61	0.97	2.71		47.4		0.33
6	8	15.9		2.72	0.94	2.36	3.33	41.3	58.0	0.47
7	8	19.2	0.6	2.53	0.64	2.78		48.6		

TABLE II

Results of Experiments on Mice Fed Different Amounts of Fat

Experiment No.	Fat in diet	Feeding period	Weight of animals together	Loss of weight	Amount of fat consumed	Amount of total fat in depots	D_2 in		Diet fat in		Heavy water in body fluid
							Depot fat	Organ fat	Depot fat	Organ fat	
	per cent	days	gm.	gm.	gm.	gm.	atom per cent	atom per cent	per cent	per cent	per cent
8	4	10	58.9	2.2		5.4	0.715	0.85	12.5	14.8	0.036
9	1	4	51.1	2.8	0.251	3.9	0.091	0.17	1.6	2.96	0.008

Despite their noticeable hunger, they did not eat this spilled food as it was contaminated with urine. All the mice lost some weight during the feeding periods, which varied from 2 to 8 days. The body water was analyzed only from the mice of Experiments 5 and 6, as this method was developed during the experiment. The results are given in Table I. ,

Mice on 4 Per Cent Fat Diet—The mice were kept in separate beakers, but the analyses were carried out on the combined mice and the combined beaker contents. The values therefore give the average for all the mice (Table II).

Mice on 1 Per Cent Fat Diet—In order to obtain a homogeneous mixture the fat was dissolved in ether and mixed with the finely ground bread, and the ether evaporated. The procedure was the same as in the experiment with the 4 per cent fat diet (Table II).

DISCUSSION

The partially hydrogenated linseed oil which we fed may, as a food component, be considered as equivalent to a natural fat. Its iodine number and physical properties correspond to those of olive oil. On theoretical grounds we cannot expect that molecules containing more deuterium than usual will be treated in a manner different from those in which the hydrogen is present in its ordinary isotopic ratio. We are confident that these results show us the route that the analogous natural compounds take in the organism.

We realize that our initial experiments have not given us all the information which our method could supply. Some of the analytical methods were developed during the course of the research so that our data are not complete. We have shown, however, that this method has a wide field of use so that, even on so small an animal as a mouse, we could follow the fat from a diet containing it to the extent of only 1 per cent.

The diet on which the mice were kept consisted principally of carbohydrate in order to avoid any disturbance of the fat metabolism. The small loss of body weight which all the animals showed resulted from insufficiency of food. The animals appeared healthy and ate almost all of the diet except the small amount which was scattered in the beaker and had become contaminated with urine or feces.

We worked up the animals in such fashion that no fat was lost. Since it is almost impossible to obtain quantitatively the fat of the depots alone, we have analyzed the total fat of the animal after the internal organs had been removed. The error involved in this procedure is small as the quantity of fat in the skin, muscles, and other organs is small in proportion to that in the depots. In this paper by depot fat is understood the total fat of the animal less that of the internal organs. The fact that in all our experiments a large part of the fat that we fed was found in the fat depots raises the problem as to whether all the fat, after absorption, is deposited in the depots before it is oxidized. From our experiments we can certainly say that the greater part takes this route.

The fat in the internal organs had a higher deuterium content than the fat in the depots. This means that a small part of the absorbed fat goes directly to the organs. The absolute amount is not large since the total amount of fat in the organs is very small. We can as yet draw no conclusions as to the content of the liver since this organ was not worked up alone, but in conjunction with the other organs. When we began this work, we did not expect that we should be able to analyze for the deuterium content of the liver fat of a mouse which had been fed for only a few days on a low fat diet. We are at present investigating this problem.

The analysis of the body fluids shows that a part of the ingested fat is burned. We did not attempt to determine the water balance of the animals in our experiments and cannot therefore directly estimate how much of the ingested fat was oxidized during the course of the experiment. Our analyses show that the mice which were fed a diet containing 1 per cent fat, for 4 days, consumed 251 mg. of fat. Of this we found 119 mg. (47 per cent) in the fat depots. The body fluids of the mice had a concentration of 0.008 per cent D_2O. This amount of heavy water would be formed by the combustion of 50 mg. of our fat (20 per cent). The remainder of the deuterium must have been lost in the water excreted (urine, respiration, feces, etc.).

After 8 days on a diet containing 20 per cent fat, about 50 per cent was found in the depots. As it is known that the properties of the fat depots are but slightly influenced by the fat of the diet, we must conclude that the absorbed fat is rapidly converted to the special fat of the animal. We must also expect that the deuterium-containing fatty acids have been converted to other fatty acids.

Part Three

∿

MICROBIOLOGY

CHRONOLOGY

1676	Leeuwenhoek discovered "animalcules" or infusoria.
1683	Leeuwenhoek discovered bacteria.
1762	Plenciz formulated the view that infectious diseases were caused by a living agent (a theory that goes back to the Italian physician Fracastoro (1483–1533).
1773–1786	Müller taxonomically separated bacteria from protozoa.
1780's	Controversy between Needham and Spallanzani over spontaneous generation.
1778	Von Gleichen stained bacteria with indigo and carmine.
1810	Appert, a French chef, demonstrated a procedure for preservation of foods by canning.
1836	Cagniard de Latour and Schwann announced that yeast was the cause of fermentation.
1836–1837	Schultze's and Schwann's experiments opposing spontaneous generation.
1838	Ehrenberg separated bacteria from other micro-organisms.
1840	Liebig proposed that fermentation is chemical and not dependent upon living microbes.
1845	Siebold characterized Protozoa correctly as "animals whose organization is reducible to one cell."
1854	Schroeder and Dusch showed that bacteria could be removed from air by filtering it through cotton-wool.
1854	Pasteur discovered microbial fermentation of beet sugar.
1863	Fresenius first used a solid culture medium (potato) for micro-organisms.
1864	Pasteur's demolition of the doctrine of spontaneous generation.
1864	Lister instituted the practice of antisepsis.
1864	Controversy between von Nägeli and Koch regarding pleomorphism versus genetic distinctness of bacteria.
1867	Lister reported his method of antiseptic surgery.
1876	Cohn discovered spores in *B. subtilis*.
1876	Koch showed that anthrax was caused by a specific organism.

1882   Koch announced his method for isolating bacteria in pure culture by plating them on solid media (first gelatin, later agar).

1885   Pasteur treated Joseph Meister for rabies.

1885   Hansen instituted pure culture starters in the fermentation of beer.

1897   Buchner resolved the Liebig-Pasteur controversy by producing fermentation in cell-free extracts.

The twentieth century has seen the assimilation of microbiology into the mainstream of biology in general. With an increasing understanding of the life processes of micro-organisms, their study soon became unified with the study of these processes among other living things. The modern microbiologist, unless he be interested primarily in the applied aspects of his science, is an enzymologist, say, or a geneticist, or a cytologist, whose researches lie within these respective disciplines, but who happens to be using micro-organisms as material for his investigations. To continue a chronology of microbiology into the modern period, therefore, would obscure this important illustration of the way in which the unity of life leads inevitably to a convergence and ultimate synthesis of all branches of biology.

Observations . . . Concerning Little Animals, etc. ～

by ANTONY VAN LEEUWENHOEK

Abridged from *Philosophical Transactions*, London, Vol. 11, p. 821 (1677).

We who have been brought up in the twentieth century are so accustomed to television, electronic computers, and other technological marvels that our sense of wonder has become jaded, and the newest and most astounding results of scientific achievement meet with easy acceptance. It requires a distinct effort of the imagination, therefore, to picture the sensational impact upon seventeenth century civilization of Leeuwenhoek's discovery that man's physical environment, indeed his very body, is populated by omnipresent and incredibly minute hordes of sub-visible living creatures "a thousand times smaller than the eye of a big Louse." These words of Leeuwenhoek, in fact, serve as a reminder that in his day there was not even—there could not be—a unit of measurement appropriate to the size scale of this new world.

OBSERVATIONS, COMMUNICATED to the Publisher by Mr. Antony van Leewenhoeck, in a Dutch Letter of the 9th of Octob. 1676. here English'd: Concerning little Animals by him observed in Rain-Well-Sea-and Snow water; as also in water wherein Pepper had lain infused.

In the year 1675 I discover'd living creatures in Rain water, which had stood but few days in a new earthen pot, glased blew within. This invited me to view this water with great attention, especially those little animals appearing to me ten thousand times less than those represented by Mons. *Swamerdam,* and by him called *Water-fleas* or *Water-lice,* which may be perceived in the water with the naked eye.

The *first* sort by me discover'd in the said water, I divers times observed to consist of 5, 6, 7, or 8 clear globuls, without being able to discern any film that held them together, or contained them. When these *animalcula* or living Atoms did move, they put forth two little horns, continually moving themselves: The place between these two horns was flat, though the rest of the body was roundish, sharpning a little towards the end, where they had a tayl, near four time the length of the whole body, of the thickness (by my Microscope) of a Spiders-web; at the end of which appear'd a globul, of the bigness of one of those which made up the body; which tayl I could not perceive, even in very clear water, to be mov'd by them. These little creatures, if they chanced to light upon the least filament or string, or other such particle, of which there are many in water, especially after it hath stood some days, they stook intangled therein, extending their body in a long round, and striving to dis-intangle their tayl; whereby it came to pass, that their whole body lept back towards the globul of the tayl, which then rolled together Serpent-like, and after the

manner of Copper- or Iron-wire that having been wound about a stick, and unwound again, retains those windings and turnings. This motion of extension and contraction continued a while; and I have seen several hundreds of these poor little creatures, within the space of a grain of gross sand, lye fast cluster'd together in a few filaments.

I also discover'd a *second* sort, the figure of which was oval; and I imagined their head to stand on the sharp end. These were a little bigger than the former. The inferior part of their body is flat, furnished with divers incredibly thin feet, which moved very nimbly, and which I was not able to discern till after several Observations. The upper part of the body was round, and had within, 8, 10, or 12 globuls, where they were very clear. These little animals did sometimes change their figure into a perfect round, especially when they came to lye on any dry place. Their body was also very flexible; for as soon as they hit against any the smallest fibre or string, their body was bent in, which bending presently also yerked out again. When I put any of them on a dry place, I observ'd, that changing themselves into a round, their body was raised pyramidal-wise with an extant point in the middle, and having lain thus a little while with a motion of their feet, they burst asunder, and the globuls were presently diffus'd and dissipated, so that I could not discern the least thing of any film, in which the globuls had doubtless been inclosed: And at this time of their bursting asunder I was able to discover more globuls than when they were alive.

But then I observ'd a third sort of little Animals, that were twice as long as broad, and to my eye yet eight times smaller than the first. Yet for all this, I thought I discerned little feet, whereby they moved very briskly, both in a round and streight line.

There was, further, a fourth sort, which were so small, that I was not able to give them any figure at all. These were a thousand times smaller than the eye of a big Louse: For I judge, the *axis* of the eye of such a Louse to be more than ten times as long as the axis of any of the said little creatures. These exceeded all the former in celerity. I have often observ'd them to stand still as 'twere upon a point, and then turn themselves about with that swiftness, as we see a Top turn round, the circumference they made being no bigger than that of a small grain of Sand; and then extending themselves streight forward, and by and by lying in a bending posture.

I discover'd also several other sorts of Animals, but these were very big respectively; of which I intend not to speak here; only this, that they were generally made up of such soft parts, as the former, they bursting asunder as soon as they came to want water. . . .

Observations of water, wherein whole Pepper has layn infused several dayes.

1. Having several times endeavoured to discover the cause of the pungency of *Pepper* upon our tongue, and that the rather, because it hath been found, that though Pepper had lain a whole year in vinegar, yet it retained still its pungency; I did put about ⅓ of an ounce of whole pepper in water, placing it in my Study, with this design, that the pepper being thereby rendred soft, I might be enabled the better to observe what I proposed to myself. This pepper having lain about 3 weeks in the water, to which I had twice added some Snow-water, the other water being in great part exhaled; I looked upon it the 24 of *April,* 1676. and discerned in it, to my great wonder, an incredible number of little animals of divers kinds; and among the rest, some that were 3 or 4 times as long as broad; but their whole thickness did, in my estimation, not much exceed that of the hair of a Louse. They had a very pretty motion, often tumbling about and sideways; and when I let the water run

off from them, they turned as round as a Top, and at first their body changed into an oval, and afterwards, when the circular motion ceased, they returned to their former length.

The 2*d* sort of creatures, discover'd in this water, were of a perfect oval figure, and they had no less pleasing or nimble a motion than the former; and these were in far greater numbers. And there was a 3*d* sort, which exceeded the two former in number; and these had tayls also, like those I had formerly observed in Rain-water.

The 4*th* sort of creatures, which moved through the 3 former sorts, were incredibly small, and so small in my eye, that I judged, that if 100 of them lay one by another, they would not equal the *length* of a grain of course Sand; and according to this estimate, ten hundred thousand of them could not equal the dimensions of a *grain* of such course Sand.

There was discover'd by me a fifth sort, which had near the thickness of the former, but they were almost twice as long.

2. The 26*th* of *April,* I took 2½ ounces of Snow-water, which was about three years old, and which had stood either in my Cellar or Study in a Glass-bottle well stopped. In it I could discover no living creatures: And having poured some of it into a Porcelain Thea-cup, I put there in half an ounce of whole pepper, and so placed it in my Study. Observing it daily until the 3*d* of *May,* I could never discover any living thing in it; and by this time the water was so far evaporated, and imbibed by the pepper, that some of the pepper-corns began to lye dry. This water was now very thick of odd particles; and then I poured more Snow-water to the pepper, until the pepper-corns were covered with water half an inch high. Whereupon viewing it again the fourth and fifth of *May,* I found no living creatures in it; but the sixth, I did very

many, and those exceeding small ones, whose body seem'd to me twice as long as broad, but they moved very slowly and often round ways.

The 7th, I saw them yet in far greater numbers.

The 10th, I put more Snow-water to the pepper, because the former was again so exhaled, that the pepper corns began to be dry again.

The 13th and 14th, I saw the little creatures as before; but the 18th, the water was again so dryed away, that it made me pour on more of it. And the 23th, I discover'd, besides the aforesaid little animals, another sort, that were perfectly oval, and in figure like Cuckow-eggs. Me thought, the head of them stood on the sharp end: Their body did consist, within of 10, 12 or 14 globuls, which lay separate from one another. When I put these *animalcula* in a dry place, they then changed their body into a perfect round, and often burst asunder, & the globuls, together with some aqueous particles, spred themselves every where about, without my being able to discern any other remains. These globuls, which in the bursting of these creatures did flow asunder here and there, were about the bigness of the first very small creatures. And though as yet I could not discern any feet in them, yet me thought they must needs be furnished with very many, seeing that the smallest creatures, which I said before to be very plentiful in this water, and lay sometimes more than an 100 of

them on one of the oval creatures, were by the motion, made in the water by the great ones (though to my eye they seem'd to lye still) driven away by them, in the manner as we blow away a feather from our mouth. Of the same oval creatures I never could discover any very little ones, how attentive soever I was to observe them.

The 24th of *May* observing this water again, I found in it the oval little animals in much greater abundance. And in the evening of the same day, I perceived so great a plenty of the same oval ones, that 'tis not only one thousand which I saw in one drop; and of the small ones, several thousands in one drop.*

The 25th, I saw yet more oval creatures: And the 26th, I found so vast a plenty of those oval creatures, that I believe, there were more than 6 or 8000 in one drop; besides the abundance of those very little animals, whose number was yet far greater. This water I took from the very surface; but when I took up any from beneath, I found that not so full of them by far. Observing that these creatures did augment into vast numbers, but not being able to see them increase in bigness, I began to think whether they might not in a moment, as 'twere, be composed or put together: But this speculation I leave to others.

---

* This phaenomenon and some of the following ones seeming to be very extraordinary, the Author hath been desired to aquaint us with his method of observing, that others may confirm such Observations as these.

Memoir on the Organized Corpuscles Which Exist in the Atmosphere. Examination of the Doctrine of Spontaneous Generation. ⌇

by LOUIS PASTEUR

Abridged from *Annales de Chimie et de Physique*, Vol. 64, pp. 1–110 (1862). Translated by M. L. Gabriel for this volume.

To the biologist of today, educated to appreciate the staggering physico-chemical complexity of protoplasm, the spontaneous generation of such an ordered and homeostatic system seems remotely unlikely. But a century ago cytology was in its infancy, biochemistry was yet scarcely born, and the inherent improbability of spontaneous generation was by no means apparent. True, the cruder forms of the doctrine had been overthrown by Redi and others and it was no longer possible to believe in the origin of maggots from carrion or worms from slime. But the microscope had revealed a world of organisms of apparently primeval simplicity. Might not such elemental microscopic forms of life be capable of forming themselves de novo? To answer this question in the middle nineteenth century was no simple matter, since sterile techniques had yet to be discovered. In fact, it was out of the very attempts to solve the problem of spontaneous generation that these techniques emerged; without them microbiology as a science could not have developed. Pasteur's masterful monograph on spontaneous generation, portions of which are reprinted in the following pages, holds a central place in the history of microbiology as the definitive disproof of the doctrine of spontaneous generation. Less familiar are the sections of this monograph on the culturing of microorganisms in defined media (p. 116), the fullest implications of which were not exploited until recently. The use of chemically defined media is now basic for studies on vitamins, antibiotics, and biochemical genetics.

DURING THE PAST twenty years chemists have discovered a group of truly extraordinary phenomena designated by the generic name *fermentations*. All require the presence of two substances: one *fermentable*, such as sugar; the other *nitrogenous*, which is always an albuminoid substance. According to the commonly accepted theory, albuminous substances, when they have been exposed to contact with the air, undergo an alteration, a particular oxidation of an unknown nature, which gives them the characteristic of a *ferment*, i.e., the property of then acting by contact upon fermentable substances.

The oldest ferment and the most remarkable of all was known to be an organized being—the yeast of beer. But since in all fermentations discovered since yeast was found to be an organism (1836), the existence of organized beings could not be recognized even after careful search, physiologists had regretfully given up little by little the hypothesis of M. Cagniard de Latour as to the probable relationship between the organization of the ferment and its property of being a ferment.

My studies have led me to entirely different conclusions. I have found that all the fermentations—slimy, lactic, butyric, the fermentation of tartaric acid, of malic acid, of urine—were always related to the presence and the multiplication of organized beings. And the fact of the organization of yeast, far from being a troublesome thing for the theory of fermentation, on the contrary placed it within the common rule and made it typical of all ferments. In my view, the albuminoid substances were never a ferment, but the nutriment of the ferments. The true ferments were organized beings.[1]

This granted, the ferments originate, it was known, by virtue of contact of albuminoid material with oxygen. If so, two alternatives are possible, I said to myself: "Since the ferments are organized, either oxygen alone, by its contact with nitrogenous material, gives them origin, and these ferments are spontaneously generated; or, if the ferments are not spontaneously generated, the oxygen must act, not by intervening

in their formation, but by stimulating a germ simultaneously introduced with the oxygen, or existing in the nitrogenous or fermentable material." At the point which I had reached in my studies on fermentations, I was obliged, therefore, to form an opinion on the question of spontaneous generation. The researches to be reported here were consequently only a digression made necessary by my studies on fermentations.

My first concern was to find a method which would allow the collection in any season of solid particles that float in the air and to study them under the microscope. It was necessary to eliminate, if possible, the objections which the partisans of spontaneous generation oppose to the ancient hypothesis of the aerial dissemination of germs.

When the organic substances of infusions have been heated, they become populated by infusoria or molds. These organized productions are neither as numerous nor as varied as when the liquid has previously not been brought to a boil, but they always appear. Now their germs, under these conditions, can only come from the air, because the boiling destroys those which the vessels or the substances of the infusion have introduced into the liquid. The first experimental questions to be resolved are therefore the following: Are there germs in the air? Are they present in sufficiently great numbers to explain the appearance of organized productions in infusions which have previously been heated? Is it possible to obtain an approximate idea of the relationship between a given volume of ordinary air and the number of germs which this volume contains?

The procedure which I followed in order to collect the dust in suspension in the air and to examine it with the microscope is very simple; it consists of filtering a measured volume of air through gun cotton, which is soluble in a mixture of alcohol and ether. The fibers of the

---

[1] It was later demonstrated, as papers in the section on enzymes show, that Pasteur was incorrect in his view that all ferments were organized. The experiments of the Buchner brothers in which fermentation of sugar was observed under the influence of cell-free extracts of yeast mark the end of the controversy over the organized or unorganized nature of ferments.—*Editors.*

cotton stop the solid particles. The cotton is then dissolved. After standing for a sufficient length of time, all the solid particles fall to the bottom of the liquid; they are then washed several times and placed on the stage of the microscope where they are readily studied. . . .

The dust may be allowed to react with different reagents, using ordinary methods—iodine solution, potash, sulfuric acid, stains.

By means of these simple manipulations, it can be recognized that there are constantly in the ordinary air a variable number of corpuscles the form and structure of which indicate that they are organized. Their dimensions range from the smallest diameters up to .01—.015 mm and more. Some are perfectly spherical, others ovoid. Their contours are more or less sharply outlined. Many are entirely translucent, but some are opaque with granules inside. Those which are translucent with sharp contours so closely resemble the spores of the most common molds that the most skilful microscopist could not see the difference. Some resemble round or encysted infusoria and some the eggs of these little creatures. But as for affirming that this is a spore, moreover the spore of a particular species, and that that is an egg, and the egg of such and such a microorganism, I believe that this is not possible. I confine myself to the assertion that these corpuscles are evidently organized, resembling in every respect the germs of lowest organisms, so diverse in volume and in structure, that they doubtlessly belong to a great number of species. Are there really fecund germs among them? This is a very interesting question; I believe that I have been able to demonstrate this in a definite way. But before presenting the experiments which pertain more particularly to this part of the subject, it is indispensable to ascertain first whether the facts announced by Dr. Schwann on the in-

activity of air which has been heated are correct. MM. Pouchet, Mantegazza, Joly, and Musset dispute this. Let us try to see on which side the truth lies; at the same time this will furnish the base of our future researches.

Into a flask of 250 to 300 cc, I introduce 100–150 cc of water containing sugar and albumin, made up in the following proportions:

water	100
sugar	10
albuminous material and minerals obtained from brewers' yeast	.2–.7

The constricted neck of the flask communicates with a platinum tube heated red hot. The liquid is boiled for 2–3 minutes, then it is allowed to become completely cool. The flask is filled with ordinary air at atmospheric pressure but all parts of the air have been brought to the temperature of red hot platinum; then the neck of the flask is sealed in a flame.

The flask thus prepared is placed in an incubator at a constant temperature neighboring 30°; it can remain there indefinitely without the liquid which it contains undergoing the slightest alteration. Its clarity, its odor, its very slight acid reaction, hardly detectable with blue litmus paper, persist without appreciable change. Its color slightly deepens with time, doubtlessly under the influence of a direct oxidation of the albuminous matter or of the sugar.

I affirm with the utmost sincerity that never have I had a single such experiment performed which has given me a doubtful result. Sugared yeast water brought to the boil for two to three minutes and then exposed to air which has been heated does not alter in any degree,* even after being kept eighteen

---

* I have had occasion to repeat the experiment more than fifty times, and in every case this liquid, so alterable, has not exhibited a trace of organized productions in the presence of heated air.

months at a temperature of 25–30°, while if one leaves it in ordinary air, after a day or two it is in the course of a manifest alteration and is found to be full of bacteria, vibrios, or covered with mucors.

The experiment of Dr. Schwann applied to sugared yeast water is consequently of an irreproachable exactitude.

How does it come about nevertheless that many observers, MM. Pouchet, Mantegazza, and Schwann himself have arrived at contradictory results?

I myself, in unpublished experiments, had found that experiments done with heated air only succeeded exceptionally. I shall report some of them.

On the ninth of August 1857, I prepared several flasks of one-quarter liter capacity as follows. In every one I placed 80 cc of very clear sugared brewers' yeast water, including 100 grams of sugar per liter and three grams of nitrogenous and mineral substances obtained from the soluble portions of the yeast. The necks of the flasks were drawn out in a flame, then I brought the liquid to a boil; after 2–4 minutes I closed the constricted point by a flame during the boiling. I next successively inverted each flask in a mercury bath at the bottom of which I broke its point; I then introduced into the first flask approximately 70 cc of oxygen prepared with potassium chlorate, and conducted to the flask in a porcelain tube heated red hot. Into the second flask I introduced 50 cc of oxygen of very recent production obtained from the decomposition of water by an electric pile. Into the third and fourth flasks I introduced 50 to 60 cc of ordinary air coming out of a porcelain tube heated red hot. Finally into a fifth flask I introduced 50 cc of ordinary unheated air. I then placed the five flasks, inverted over mercury in glass vessels, in an incubator at a constant temperature of 25–30° C.

On the thirteenth of August there were organized productions *in all the*

flasks. The liquid in the first was turbid and milky because of the presence of a torula having the form of very fine granules united in chains. The second flask burst during the night of the fifteenth to the sixteenth of August because it had filled with gas by fermentation. A microscopic study of the portions of the liquid remaining in the glass showed globules of brewers' yeast. Flasks three, four, and five showed tufts of mold floating in a clear liquid.

In summary, I obtained results directly contrary to those of Dr. Schwann. Molds and torulas could be born in the presence of heated air in liquids which had been subjected to boiling.

I did not publish these experiments; the conclusions which it was necessary to deduce from them were too serious for me not to have the fear that there existed some hidden cause of error in spite of the care which I had taken to make them irreproachable.

I succeeded later on in recognizing this cause of error. . . . In all these experiments, it was the mercury which introduced the germs into the liquids. I shall later give convincing proofs of this. But we may remark now that the mercury in a laboratory vessel is constantly exposed to the dust of the air and that the liquid must consequently conceal a multitude of these organized corpuscles. Their lightness will cause them to rise to the surface only if they have an appreciable volume. Besides, even if these corpuscles were present only at the surface of the mercury it would not be possible to avoid them in the manipulations. If one deposits dust on the surface of the mercury and one then immerses in it a tube of glass, a test tube, or any kind of a vessel, one will see the surface dust being drawn little by little into the interface between the solid body and the mercury. If the object is pushed down a decimeter or more, the dust will follow to this depth, and the last particles to arrive will be drawn from a great distance from the point where the object was immersed.

We can summarize the experiments of this chapter in the following manner: Sugared yeast water, a liquid which is exceedingly alterable on contact with ordinary air, may be preserved intact for years if exposed to the action of heated air after having been subjected to boiling for two or three minutes. But the experiment must be properly carried out. If it is performed with a mercury bath with all the precautions imaginable, it only succeeds exceptionally, if it succeeds at all. The liquid becomes altered almost as easily as in ordinary air, because it is impossible that the manipulation, in whatever manner it may be carried out, can avoid introducing germs from the interior or the surface of the mercury or the wall of the vessel.

The results of the experiments of the two preceding chapters have shown us:

1. That there are always in suspension in the ordinary air organized corpuscles entirely resembling the germs of the lower organisms.

2. That sugared water of brewer's yeast, a liquid which is readily alterable in ordinary air, remains intact, clear, without ever giving birth to infusoria or to molds, when it is left in contact with air which has been previously heated.

Granted this, let us try to discover what will happen upon contact with this same air, on inoculation into this sugared albuminous water of dust which we have collected by the method described, without introducing anything else except this dust.

Whatever be the method of experimentation it is necessary that it eliminate the mercury bath entirely, because this would confuse all the results. I have adopted the following arrangements in order to introduce the dust of the air into the putrescible or fermentable liquids in the presence of heated air.

Let us return to our flask enclosing sugared water of yeast and heated air. I shall suppose that the flask has been in the incubator at 25° to 30° for one or two months, without having undergone any detectable alteration, a manifest proof of the inactivity of heated air with which it has been filled under ordinary atmospheric pressure.

The point of the flask being always closed, I fit it, by means of a rubber tube, to a tube of strong glass of 10–12 mm of interior diameter, in which I have placed a piece of tube of small diameter, open at its ends, free to slide inside the large tube, and enclosing a small pledget of cotton laden with dust. To it is attached a brass tube in the form of a T, furnished with stopcocks, one of these stopcocks communicating with an air-pump, another with a platinum tube heated red hot, the third with the tube.

When all parts of the apparatus have been arranged and the platinum tube has been brought to red heat by a gas burner one makes a vacuum, after having closed the stopcock which leads to the platinum tube. This stopcock is then opened in such a way as to allow the heated air to enter the apparatus little by little. The vacuum and the entrance of heated air are repeated alternately ten to twelve times. The small tube containing the cotton is thus filled with heated air which penetrates right into the smallest interstices of the cotton, but it has kept its dust. This done, I break the point of the flask through the rubber tube without untying the strings, then I make the little tube with the dust drop into the flask. Finally, I reseal the neck of the flask in a flame and the flask is again placed in the incubator. Now, it always happens that the colonies of microorganisms begin to appear in the flask after 24, 36, or 48 hours at most.

This is exactly the time necessary for the same formations to appear in sugared yeast water when it is exposed to contact with the common air. . . .

Another very simple method for demonstrating that all the organized productions in infusions (previously heated) originate from corpuscles which exist in suspension in the atmospheric air.

I believe that I have rigorously demonstrated in the preceding chapters that all the organized productions of infusions, previously heated, have no origin other than the solid particles which the air always transports and which is constantly deposited on all objects. If there could still remain the least doubt in this respect in the mind of the reader, it would be dispelled by the experiments which I shall now describe.

I place into a glass flask one of the following liquids, all extremely alterable upon contact with ordinary air; water of brewers' yeast, water of brewers' yeast with sugar added, urine, sugar beet juice, pepper water; I then draw out the neck of the flask in such a way as to give it various curvatures. I then bring the liquid to a boil for several minutes until steam issues freely through the open narrow end of the neck, without any other precautions. I then allow the flask to cool. It is a remarkable thing, likely to astonish everybody used to the delicacy of experiments relating to so-called "spontaneous" generation, that the liquid in such a flask will remain indefinitely unchanged. It may be handled without fear, it may be transported from one place to another, it may be submitted to all the temperature variations of the seasons, and the liquid does not undergo the least alteration. It retains its odor and flavor; it is as well preserved as though by the method of Appert.[2] The only change it will undergo is that which might be produced, in certain cases, by a direct oxidation, purely chemical. . . .

[2] Appert originated the method of preserving food now known as canning.—*Editors.*

It would seem that the ordinary air, entering with force during the first moments, ought to enter the flask in an entirely crude state. This is true, but it meets a liquid still at a temperature approaching the boiling point. The entrance of air then occurs more slowly, and when the liquid is sufficiently cooled so as not to rob the germs of their vitality, the entrance of the air is sufficiently slow so that it leaves in the humid curves of the neck all the dust capable of acting on the infusions and there bringing about organized formations. At least, I do not see any other possible explanation for these curious results. For, if after one or several months in the incubator, the neck of the flask is removed by a stroke of the file, without otherwise touching the flask, after 24, 36, or 48 hours, the molds and the infusoria will begin to show themselves exactly as in the open, or as if the flask had been inoculated with dust from the air.

The same experiments can be repeated upon milk, provided that one takes the precaution to produce the boiling under pressure at a temperature above 100°, and to allow the flask to cool while heated air is entering. One can then leave the open flask alone. The milk is preserved without alteration. I have been able to leave milk prepared in this fashion in the incubator at 25–30° for several months without its altering. One notices only a slight thickening of the cream due to a direct chemical oxidation.

I do not know anything more convincing than these experiments, so easy to repeat, and which one can vary in a thousand different ways. . . .

I have at this moment in my laboratory a number of very alterable liquids which have been preserved for 18 months in open vessels with curved and inclined necks, particularly several of those which had been deposited at the office of the Academy of Sciences during its session of 6th of February, 1860, when I had the honor of presenting these new results.

The great interest of this method is that it finally proves unequivocally that the origin of life in infusions which have been brought to a boil is solely due to solid particles in suspension in the air. Gas, various fluids, electricity, magnetism, ozone, things known or things occult—there is absolutely nothing in the ordinary atmospheric air which, in the absence of its solid particles, conditions the putrefaction or fermentation of the liquids which we have studied. . . .

The experiments which I have communicated in the previous chapters may be summarized in the following double proposition:

(1) There are constantly in the air organized corpuscles which cannot be distinguished from the true germs of the organisms of infusions;

(2) When one inoculates the corpuscles and the amorphous debris with which they are associated into liquids which have been subjected to boiling and which would have remained unchanged in previously heated air if this inoculation had not been performed, one observes the appearance in these liquids of exactly the same organisms which they develop in the open air.

This granted, will a partisan of the theory of spontaneous generation wish to continue to maintain his principles even in the face of the above evidence? He can still do so; but in that case his reasoning must necessarily be the following, and I shall let the reader be the judge of it:

"There are present in the air," he will say, "solid particles, such as carbonate of lime, silica, soot, fibers of wool, of cotton, dirt, etc., and also organized corpuscles with a perfect resemblance to the spores of molds or the eggs of infusoria. Well, I prefer to ascribe the origin of the molds and the infusoria to the first amorphous corpuscles rather than to the second."

In my opinion, the inconsistency of such reasoning is self-evident. The entire progress of my researches consists in having driven partisans of the doctrine of spontaneous generation into this corner.

CHAPTER 9.

On the mode of nutrition of ferments, properly speaking, of molds, and of vibrios.

It is essential to remark that up to the present all experiments on spontaneous generation have been carried out on infusions of vegetable or animal matter, in other words, on liquids containing substances which had previously belonged to an organism. Whatever may be the previous conditions of temperature and of boiling which they have been made to undergo, these substances have a constitution and properties acquired under the influence of life.

This fact has served as a theme for all the theories of spontaneous generation. Now, I am going to demonstrate in this chapter that the appearance of lower organisms does not necessarily presuppose the presence of plastic organic matter, of these albuminoid substances which the chemist has never been able to produce, and which in their formation require the participation of vital forces.

The new experiments which I am going to publish will show how little basis there is for all the theories on the spontaneous formation of lower organisms, in which imagination has played so great a part and in which the true principles of experimental method have played so little. In all theories of spontaneous generation which have had the most adherence, an essential role has been assigned to the organic matter of infusions. By itself it was thought to enjoy special properties acquired in its previous formation under the influence of life.

Albuminoid substances, on this view, would preserve in some manner a remnant of vitality, which would permit them to organize themselves upon contact with oxygen, when the conditions of temperature and humidity are favorable.

We shall see that these opinions are entirely erroneous, and that the albuminous substances are only nutrients for the germs of infusoria and molds; that they have no other role in the infusions, for they can be replaced by crystallizable substances, such as salts of ammonia and phosphates.

In this way all the theories relating to the spontaneous formation of the lowest organisms are deprived of one of their essential foundations.

Experience has shown me, in fact, that in the experiments I have reported one could replace the sugared water of brewers' yeast, urine, milk, etc., by an infusion composed as follows:

Pure water	100	
Rock sugar	10	
Ammonium tartrate	0.2–0.5	
Dissolved ashes of brewers' yeast	0.1	grams

If one inoculates into this liquid, in the presence of heated air, dust which exists in suspension in the air, one observes the formation of bacteria, vibrios, molds, etc. The nitrogenous albuminous matter, fatty substance, essential oils, the pigment substances characteristic of these organisms, are formed entirely with the aid of the elements of ammonia, of phosphates, and of sugar.

If we compose the liquid in the same manner with the addition of chalk:

Pure water	100	
Rock sugar	10	
Ammonium tartrate	0.2–0.5	
Dissolved ashes of brewers' yeast	0.1	
Pure carbonate of lime	3.5	grams

the same phenomena are produced, but with a more marked tendency toward the fermentations called lactic, slimy, butyric, and all the vegetable or animal ferments characteristic of these fermentations will appear simultaneously or successively.

I shall later publish a detailed report on the results which I have obtained in these studies, which have always seemed to me to offer great interest for the question of so-called spontaneous generation.

It is thus that I have been led to undertake the following experiments, the success of which has exceeded my expectations.

In pure distilled water I dissolve crystallized salts of ammonia, rock sugar, and phosphates obtained by calcining brewers' yeast; then I inoculate into the liquid some spores of *Penicillium* or of any mold.* These spores germinate easily, and soon, in only two or three days, the liquid is full of tufts of mycelium, of which a great number soon spread out at the surface of the liquid where they fructify. There is nothing stunted about the vegetation. By taking the precaution to use an acid salt of ammonia, one prevents the development of infusoria, which by their presence would soon stop the progress of the little plants by absorbing the atmospheric oxygen, which the mold cannot do without. All the carbon of the plant is

---

* Following is the composition of some of these liquids which I have employed:

20 grams rock sugar ⎫
2   "   bitartrate of ammonia ⎬
0.5 "   ashes of brewers' yeast ⎭
1   liter of pure water.

20 grams rock sugar ⎫
1   "   tartaric acid ⎪
1   "   potassium nitrate ⎬
0.5 "   ashes of yeast ⎭
1   liter of pure water.

I inoculated the spores of the molds on the surface of these liquids or of other similar ones.

The salt of ammonia may be replaced by a salt of ethylamine. But I have not obtained development of little plants upon substituting arsenates for phosphates. I have exhibited various examples of these results to the Academy in its session of November 12th, 1860.

obtained from the sugar, which gradually disappears completely; the nitrogen comes from the ammonia, and its mineral matter from the phosphates. With respect to the assimilation of nitrogen and phosphates, there is therefore a complete analogy between the ferments, the molds, and the plants of a complex organism. The following facts will prove this in a definitive manner.

If in the experiment which I have just reported, I omit any one of the substances in solution, the vegetation is prevented. For example, the mineral substance appears to be least indispensable for beings of this nature. Now, if the liquid is deprived of phosphate, no more vegetation is possible, no matter what the proportion of sugar and the ammoniacal salts. . . . If one similarly omits the salt of ammonia, the plant does not undergo any development. There is only a very feeble commencement of germination because of the effect of the presence of the albuminoid matter of the inoculated spores, in spite of the fact that there is a superabundance of nitrogen in the surrounding air or in solution in the liquid. Finally, it is still the same if one omits the sugar, the carbon-containing nutriment, even though there may be in the air or in the liquid any proportion of carbonic acid. This indicates that with respect to the origin of the carbon, the molds differ essentially from the phanerogamic plants. The

molds do not decompose carbonic acid; they do not give off oxygen. The absorption of oxygen and the emission of carbonic acid are, on the contrary, necessary and permanent processes of their life.

These facts give us precise ideas as to the mode of nutrition of the molds, with respect to which science does not yet possess coherent observations.

In another regard, this method affords a means by which plant physiology will be able without difficulty to approach the most delicate questions concerning the life of these little plants, in such a way as to prepare the way on a sound basis for the study of the same problems in the higher plants.

Although it may be feared that one may not be able to apply to the larger plants the results furnished by these organisms of such lowly appearance, there would nonetheless be great interest in resolving the difficulties which are raised by the study of the life of plants, by beginning with those where the least degree of complication of organization makes conclusions easiest and most sure; the plant is reduced here in a way to a cellular state, and the progress of science shows more and more that the study of processes carried on under the influence of vegetal or animal life, in their most complicated manifestations, leads back in the last analysis to the discovery of phenomena pertaining to the cell itself.

Investigations upon the Etiology of the Traumatic Infective Diseases (1878). ~

by ROBERT KOCH

Excerpted from the English translation (1880) of *Untersuchungen über die Aetiologie der Wundinfektionskrankheiten*, Leipzig, F. C. Vogel, 1878.

Among many contributions, both theoretical and practical, which earned Robert Koch a central place in the history of microbiology, the most fundamental, perhaps, were his recognition of the biological individuality of bacteria and his perfection of the technical means of demonstrating this. Although the mycologist Brefeld had already pointed out the precautions necessary for growing fungi in pure culture from single spores, the difficulties of performing such isolations in bacteria seemed insuperable. Koch's technique of plating—growing bacteria on a culture medium solidified with gelatin or agar—made it possible for the first time to isolate and study the progeny of single micro-organisms. Koch also perfected methods for fixing bacteria and staining them with aniline dyes. Using these techniques, he was able to demonstrate that bacteria maintain their specific infective qualities and characteristic morphology after being grown in pure culture for many generations. His criteria for proving the implication of specific micro-organisms in the causation of disease, famous as "Koch's postulates," which grew out of these studies, are now axiomatic in microbiological research.

IN THIS SUMMARY I shall confine myself to the most obvious conclusions. It has indeed of late become too common to draw the most sweeping conclusions as to infective diseases in general from the most unimportant observations on bacteria. I shall not follow this custom, although the material at my command would furnish rich food for meditation. For the longer I study infective diseases the more am I convinced that generalisations of new facts are here a mistake, and that every individual infective disease or group of closely allied diseases must be investigated for itself.

As regards the artificial traumatic infective diseases observed by me, the conditions which must be established before their parasitic nature can be proved, we completely fulfilled in the case of the first five, but only partially in that of the sixth. For the infection was produced by such small quantities of fluid (blood, serum, pus, etc.) that the result cannot be attributed to a merely chemical poison.

In the materials used for inoculation bacteria were without exception present, and in each disease a different and well marked form of organism could be demonstrated.

At the same time, the bodies of those animals which died of the artificial traumatic infective diseases contained bacteria in such numbers that the symptoms and the death of the animals were sufficiently explained. Further, the bacteria found were identical with those which were present in the fluid used for inoculation, and a definite form of organisms corresponded in every instance to a distinct disease.[1]

These artificial traumatic infective diseases bear the greatest resemblance to human traumatic infective diseases, both as regards their origin from putrid substances, their course, and the result of post-mortem examination. Further, in the first case, just as in the last, the parasitic organisms could be only imperfectly demonstrated by the earlier methods of investigation; not till an improved method of procedure was introduced was it possible to obtain complete proof that they were parasitic diseases. We are therefore justified in assuming that human traumatic infective diseases will in all probability be proved to be parasitic when investigated by these improved methods.

On the other hand, it follows from the fact that a definite pathogenic bacterium, e. g., the septicæmic bacillus, cannot be inoculated on every variety of animal (a similar fact is also true with regard to the bacillus anthracis); that the septicæmia of mice, rabbits, and man are not under all circumstances produced by the same bacterial form. It is of course possible that one or other of the bacteric forms found in animals also play a part in such diseases in the human subject. That, however, must be especially

demonstrated for each case; *a priori* one need only expect that bacteria are present; as regards form, size and conditions of growth, they may be similar, but not always the same, even in what appear to be similar diseases in different animals.

Besides the pathogenic bacteria already found in animals there are no doubt many others. My experiments refer only to those diseases which ended fatally. Even these are in all probability not exhausted in the six forms mentioned. Further experiments on many different species of animals, with the most putrid substances and with every possible modification in the method of application, will doubtless bring to light a number of other infective diseases, which will lead to further conclusions regarding infective diseases and pathogenic bacteria.

But even in the small series of experiments which I was able to carry out, one fact was so prominent that I must regard it as constant, and, as it helps to remove most of the obstacles to the admission of the existence of a contagium vivum for traumatic infective diseases, I look on it as the most important result of my work. I refer to the differences which exist between pathogenic bacteria and to the constancy of their characters. A distinct bacteric form corresponds, as we have seen, to each disease, and this form always remains the same, however often the disease is transmitted from one animal to another. Further, when we succeed in reproducing the same disease *de novo* by the injection of putrid substances, only the same bacteric form occurs which was before found to be specific for that disease.

Further, the differences between these bacteria are as great as could be expected between particles which border on the invisible. With regard to these differences, I refer not only to the size and form of the bacteria, but also to the conditions of their growth, which can be best recognized by observing their situa-

---

[1] These conditions, since known as Koch's postulates, have become the ground rules for medical microbiology.—*Editors.*

tion and grouping. I therefore study not only the individual alone, but the whole group of bacteria, and would, for example, consider a micrococcus which in one species of animal occurred only in masses (i. e., in a zooglæa form), as different from another which in the same variety of animal, under the same conditions of life, was only met with as isolated individuals. Attention must also be paid to the physiological effect, of which I scarcely know a more striking example than the case of the bacillus and the chain-like micrococcus growing together in the cellular tissue of the ear; the one passing into the blood and penetrating into the white blood corpuscles, the other spreading out slowly into the tissues in its vicinity and destroying everything around about; or again, the case of the septicæmic and pyæmic micrococci of the rabbit in their different relations to the blood; or lastly, the bacilli only extending over the surface of the aural cartilage in the erysipetalous disease, as contrasted with the bacillus anthracis, likewise inoculated on the rabbit's ear, but quickly passing into the blood.

As, however, there corresponds to each of the diseases investigated a form of bacterium distinctly characterized by its physiological action, by its conditions of growth, size, and form, which, however often the disease be transmitted from one animal to another, always remains the same and never passes over into another form, e.g., from the spherical to the rod shaped, we must in the meantime regard these different forms of pathogenic bacteria as distinct and constant species.

This is, however, an assertion that will be much disputed by botanists, to whose special province this subject really belongs.

Amongst those botanists who have written against the subdivision of bacteria into species, is Nägeli, who says, "I have for ten years examined thousands of different forms of bacteria, and I

have not yet seen any absolute necessity for dividing them even into two distinct species."

Brefeld also states that he can only admit the existence of specific forms justifying the formation of distinct species when the whole history of development has been traced by cultivation from spore to spore in the most nutritive fluids.

Although Brefeld's demand is undoubtedly theoretically correct it cannot be made a *sine qua non* in every investigation on pathogenic bacteria. We should otherwise be compelled to cease our investigations into the etiology of infective diseases till botanists have succeeded in finding out the different species of bacteria by cultivation and development from spore to spore. It might then very easily happen that the endless trouble of pure cultivation would be expended on some form of bacterium which would finally turn out to be scarcely worthy of attention. In practice only the opposite method can work. In the first place certain peculiarities of a particular form of bacterium different from those of other forms, and in the second place its constancy, compel us to separate it from other less known and less interesting, and provisionally to regard it as a species. And now, to verify this provisional supposition, the cultivation from spore to spore may be undertaken. If this succeeds under conditions which cut out all sources of fallacy, and if it furnishes a result corresponding to that obtained by the previous observations, then the conclusions which were drawn from these observations and which led to its being ranked as a distinct species must be regarded as valid.

On this, which as it seems to me is the only correct practical method, I take my stand, and, till the cultivation of bacteria from spore to spore shows that I am wrong, I shall look on pathogenic bacteria as consisting of different species.

In order, however, to show that I do not stand alone in this view, I shall here mention the opinion of some botanists who have already come to a similar conclusion.

Cohn states that, in spite of the fact that many dispute the necessity of separating bacteria into genera or species, he must nevertheless adhere to the method as yet followed by him, and separate bacteria of a different form and fermenting power from each other, so long as complete proof of their identity is not given.

From his investigations on the effects of different temperatures and of desiccation on the development of bacterium termo, Eidam came to the conclusion that different forms of bacteria require different conditions of nutriment, and that they behave differently towards physical and chemical influences. He regards these facts as a further proof of the necessity of dividing organisms into distinct species.

I shall bring forward another reason to show the necessity of looking on the pathogenic bacteria which I have described as distinct species. The greatest stress, in investigations on bacteria, is justly laid on the so-called pure cultivations, in which only one definite form of bacterium is present. This evidently arises from the view that if, in a series of cultivations, the same form of bacterium is always obtained, a special significance must attach to this form: it must indeed be accepted as a constant form, or in a word as a species. Can, then, a series of pure cultivations be carried out without admixture of other bacteria? It can in truth be done, but only under very limited conditions. Only such bacteria can be cultivated pure, with the aids at present at command, which can always be known to be pure, either by their size and easily recognizable form, as the bacillus anthracis, or by the production of a characteristic coloring matter as the pigment bacteria.

When, during a series of cultivations, a strange species of bacteria has by chance got in, as may occasionally happen under any circumstances, it will in these cases be at once observed, and the unsuccessful experiment will be thrown out of the series without the progress of investigation being thereby necessarily interfered with.

But the case is quite different when attempts are made to carry out cultivations of very small bacteria, which, perhaps, cannot be distinguished at all without staining; how are we then to discover the occurrence of contamination? It is impossible to do so, and therefore all attempts at pure cultivation in apparatus, however skilfully planned and executed, must, as soon as small bacteria with but little characteristic appearances are dealt with, be considered as subject to unavoidable sources of fallacy, and in themselves inconclusive.

But nevertheless a pure cultivation is possible, even in the case of the bacteria which are smallest and most difficult to recognise. This, however, is not conducted in cultivation apparatus, but in the animal body. My experiments demonstrate this. In all the cases of a distinct disease, e. g., of septicæmia of mice, only the small bacilli were present, and no other form of bacterium was ever found with it, unless in the case where that causing the tissue gangrene was intentionally inoculated at the same time. In fact, there exists no better cultivation apparatus for pathogenic bacteria than the animal body itself. Only a very limited number of bacteria can grow in the body, and the penetration of organisms into it is so difficult that the uninjured living body may be regarded as completely isolated with respect to other forms of bacteria than those intentionally introduced. It is quite evident, from a careful consideration of the two diseases produced in mice— septicæmia and gangrene of the tissue— that I have succeeded in my experiments in obtaining a pure cultivation. In the putrefying blood, which was the cause of these two diseases, the most different forms of bacteria were present, and yet only two of these found in the living mouse the conditions necessary for their existence. All the others died, and these two alone, a small bacillus and a chain-like micrococcus, remained and grew. These could be transferred from one animal to another as often as was desired, without suffering any alteration in their characteristic form, in their specific physiological action and without any other variety of bacteria at any time appearing. And further, as I have demonstrated, it is quite in the power of the experimenter to separate these two forms of bacteria from each other. When the blood in which only the bacilli are present is used, these alone are transmitted, and thenceforth are obtained quite pure; while on the other hand, when a field mouse is inoculated with both forms of bacteria, the bacilli disappear, and the micrococcus can be then cultivated pure. Doubtless an attempt to unite these two forms again in the same animal by inoculation would have been successful. In short, one has it completely in one's power to cultivate several varieties of bacteria together, to separate them from each other, and eventually to combine them again. Greater demands can hardly be made on a pure cultivation, and I must therefore regard the successive transmission of artificial infec-tive diseases as the best and surest method of pure cultivation. And it can further claim the same power of demon-strating the existence of specific forms of bacteria, as must be conceded to any faultless cultivation experiments.

From the fact that the animal body is such an excellent apparatus for pure cultivation, and that, as we have seen, when the experiments are properly arranged and sufficient optical aids used, only one specific form of bacterium can be found in each distinct case of artificial traumatic infective disease, we may now further conclude that when, in examining a traumatic infective disease, several different varieties of bacteria are found, as e. g., chains of small granules, rods, and long, oscillating threads—such as were seen together by Coze and Feltz in the artificial septicæmia of rabbits—we have to do either with a combined infective disease,—that is, not a pure one, —or, what in the case cited is more probable, an inexact and inaccurate observation. When, therefore, several species of bacteria occur together in any morbid process, before definite conclusions are drawn as to the relations of the disease in question to the organisms, either proof must be furnished that they are all concerned in the morbid process, or an attempt must be made to isolate them and to obtain a true pure cultivation. Otherwise we cannot avoid the objection that the cultivation was not pure, and therefore not conclusive. . . .

On the Mosaic Disease of the Tobacco Plant. ∾

by DM. IWANOWSKY

From *Bulletine de l'Académie Impériale des Sciences*, St. Petersburg, Vol. 35, p. 67 (1892). Translated by M. L. Gabriel for this volume.

Iwanowsky's discovery of a disease-producing agent capable of passing through the pores of a bacteria-trapping porcelain filter inadvertently ushered in a new branch of microbiology—the science of virology. The nature of the causative entity of the tobacco mosaic disease was obscure at first, as might be expected. Iwanowsky initially thought it was a bacterial product, but later, 'mindful of its reproductive capacity, came to regard it as a minute bacterium. The word "virus" was introduced in 1898 by Beijerinck who discarded the bacterial theory of the causation of tobacco mosaic disease and proposed the notion of a "living fluid contagion." It was not until 1936 that Eriksson-Quensel and Svedberg showed, on the basis of studies with the ultra-centrifuge and electro-phoresis apparatus, that the causative agent of tobacco mosaic disease could not be bacterial, but was of molecular dimensions. This discovery confirmed Stanley's announcement of the previous year that purified protein preparations retained infective properties with a high degree of activity.

TWO YEARS AGO I described, jointly with Mr. W. Polowzow, a very widespread disease of tobacco which we named pox disease and the cause of which we then set forth. On that occasion we expressed the view that the mosaic disease of tobacco described by Ad. Mayer in Holland is actually separable into two distinct diseases, of which one (according to Mayer, the second phase of the mosaic disease) is the pox disease studied by us. During an investigation of the diseases of tobacco in Crimea in the summer of 1890 I was able to convince myself of the complete correctness of the opinion expressed by us at that time, since I also encountered there the disease form which Mayer had described as the first phase of the mosaic disease and I was able to ascertain that this form is an entirely independent, and in many respects a very interesting disease.* Among the tobacco growers of that region (Tatars) it is known merely by the name "Bosuch" (i.e., sickness) ; by some it is also called marble-disease. The outward appearance of the diseased plant, the developmental course of the disease, and its distribution on the plantation fully agree with the descriptions of Mayer,

---

* I shall designate it as mosaic disease, although it represents only one developmental stage of the disease described by Mayer under this name.

so that it is not necessary for me to discuss this question further. The difference in appearance first begins at the point where Mayer asserts that "if the disease develops further in typical fashion, some of the lighter and thinner parts of the leaf die prematurely, not unlike but much more extensively than a similar dotted necrosis which often occurs in fully ripe leaves, without detriment to the quality of the product." In the accompanying plate, Mayer depicts a leaf thickly covered with brown spots; these spots are here and there run together and some of them have fallen out of the leaf, so that as a consequence the leaf appears to have broad openings. In my opinion, the pictured leaf has been attacked by two quite different diseases: the mosaic disease (in the sense adopted by me) and the pox disease. Both diseases, although they are of quite different origins can naturally occur on one and the same plant.* The brown spots are, however, for the most part not connected with the yellow parts of leaves attacked by mosaic disease as should be the case according to Mayer's view; not infrequently one can find them in the middle of the dark green healthy part. On the contrary, the independence of the two diseases cannot any longer be subject to doubt. In support of this may I adduce the following facts:

(1.) Neither in Little Russia nor in Bessarabia have I encountered the mosaic disease, although the pox disease is very prevalent there.

(2.) In Crimea, where both diseases occur, one can find, on inspection of the tobacco plants, examples affected only by mosaic disease, and others only by pox disease. These plants can most readily be distinguished according to the very

young leaves. In plants attacked by the mosaic disease (as Mayer also has observed) all further new growths (new leaflets and shoots) display the characteristic changes of this disease, namely mosaic patterns consisting of dark green and yellow patches. Hence, when we encounter examples of brown-spotted tobacco plants in which the young leaves show no trace of mosaic pattern, we can say definitely that these plants are suffering from pox disease.

(3.) The mosaic disease is contagious while the pox disease, on the contrary, does not possess this property.

(4.) The cause of the pox disease lies in the conditions of transpiration of water from the leaves; the spots appear in completely healthy leaves upon occurrence of a quick and sudden increase in the plant's transpiration. The causes of the mosaic disease are, on the contrary, quite different; it is, as previously mentioned, infectious.

(5.) The pox disease is found in *Datura Stramonium, Hyoscyamus niger* and many other plants; the mosaic disease, on the other hand, according to Mayer's experience, is not transmitted to other representatives of the family Solanaceae.

In favor of the view that both diseases represent different developmental stages of one and the same disease, Mayer cites only the similar range of distribution and their succession in time: "To be sure, some workers," writes Mayer, "wish to recognize in both forms, or better, stages, of the disease, two independent diseases, but only for the reason that the first stage frequently escapes superficial observation. The similar range of distribution and the succession in time of the two forms argue completely against this."

My investigations on the mosaic disease are not yet completed, since I have encountered great difficulties which must first be overcome (as, for example, the inability of the tobacco mosaic

---

* It is even possible that plants attacked by the mosaic disease succumb more easily to the pox disease than healthy plants because sick plants fall prey more readily than healthy plants especially to new diseases.

microbes to develop on the usual artificial media). Yet I am already in a position to confirm the following statements of Mayer:

(1.) *that the juice of plants affected with tobacco mosaic disease is infectious;* when introduced into healthy plants after a certain time it evokes in them the tobacco mosaic disease;

(2.) *that upon being heated to a temperature near the boiling point, the juice loses its infectious properties;*

(3.) *that the infectiousness of the disease, in consideration of the absence of fungi and other parasites, must be attributed to Bacteria.*

On the other hand, I must most definitely contradict the assertion of this author that the juice of leaves affected by mosaic loses its infective characteristics after filtration through a double layer of filter paper. In my experience the filtered extract of diseased leaves when transferred to healthy leaves produces the disease symptoms as effectively as the unfiltered juice. On the other hand, this statement of the author does not accord with the view that the mosaic disease is caused by bacteria, since a double layer of filter paper, as is known, cannot hold back bacteria. If this observation of Mayer were correct, one would then have to reach the conclusion that the mosaic disease is caused, not by bacteria, but by fungi, the spores of which cannot pass through filter paper. I have, however, found *that the juice*

of leaves affected by mosaic disease retains its contagious properties even after filtration through Chamberland filter candles. According to the currently prevailing views, the latter observation is most simply explained, it seems to me, by the assumption of a toxin, secreted by the bacteria present in the tobacco plants, which is dissolved in the filtered juice. Besides this, however, another likewise tenable explanation is possible: namely that the bacteria in the tobacco plant penetrate through the pores of the Chamberland filter candle, although before every experiment I tested the filter which I was using in the usual manner and I made certain of the absence of fine cracks and openings.* As a further positive proof of the effectiveness of the filter candle I used, I regard the fact that liquids most favorable for the development of bacteria remained completely unchanged for several months after filtration through these candles. In any case, further investigation will, I hope, clarify this question; the foregoing short note has only the purpose of establishing the independence of the two diseases—the mosaic and the pox disease—and showing that they do not represent, as Ad. Mayer believes, different stages of development of the same disease.

---

* Through a filter candle immersed in a cylinder of water no air could be forced by means of a rubber bulb.

On the Antibacterial Action of Cultures of a Penicillium, with Special Reference to Their Use in the Isolation of B. Influenzae. ～

by ALEXANDER FLEMING

Abridged from the *British Journal of Experimental Pathology*, Vol. 10, pp. 226–236 (1929), by permission of the author.

The element of chance has played a part in scientific discovery more than once. An example that has become familiar to most readers is the story of how penicillin was "accidentally" discovered through Sir Alexander Fleming's observation of a clear area of bacterial destruction in a culture plate which had become contaminated with mold. But, though the story is true, its isolated recital conveys a totally erroneous conception of the manner in which chance discoveries become incorporated into the historical stream of scientific knowledge. As Pasteur remarked, "Chance favors the prepared mind." But even keenness of observation and acumen on the part of a single observer are not fruitful unless the time has been made ripe by the general advance of knowledge. To place Fleming's discovery in its proper perspective, one must appreciate that similar observations of inhibition of one micro-organism by another had been made repeatedly for more than half a century. Tyndall in 1876 had described the antagonistic action of a species of Penicillium *on bacterial growth. In 1896 Gosio recorded the first isolation of an antibiotic in crystalline form. During the early part of the twentieth century crude antibiotic preparations even enjoyed a short-lived flurry of attention as therapeutic agents, though they were soon abandoned because of the erratic results obtained. Why, then, was it only after Fleming's discovery of penicillin that antibiotics became a practicality? Florey has pointed out that the crucial difference between the pioneer observations on antibiotics and the recent successful attack on the problem lay in the failure of earlier microbiologists to pursue the chemical investigations necessary to separate and purify the active agents in their extracts. In the 1930's, on the other hand, microbiology had become acutely chemistry-minded, and it was this approach which culminated in the preparation of solid penicillin by Chain, Florey, and others in 1940, and which has given us today's rapidly growing battery of antibiotic weapons against infection.*

WHILE WORKING WITH staphylococcus variants a number of culture-plates were set aside on the laboratory bench and examined from time to time. In the examinations these plates were necessarily exposed to the air and they became contaminated with various micro-organisms. It was noticed that around a large colony of a contaminating mould the staphylococcus colonies became transparent and were obviously undergoing lysis.

Subcultures of this mould were made and experiments conducted with a view to ascertaining something of the properties of the bacteriolytic substance which had evidently been formed in the mould culture and which had diffused into the surrounding medium. It was found that broth in which the mould had been grown at room temperature for one or two weeks had acquired marked inhibitory, bactericidal and bacteriolytic properties to many of the more common pathogenic bacteria.

CHARACTERS OF THE MOULD

The colony appears as a white fluffy mass which rapidly increases in size and after a few days sporulates, the centre becoming dark green and later in old cultures darkens to almost black. In four or five days a bright yellow colour is produced which diffuses into the medium. In certain conditions a reddish colour can be observed in the growth.

In broth the mould grows on the surface as a white fluffy growth changing in a few days to a dark green felted mass. The broth becomes bright yellow and this yellow pigment is not extracted by $CHCl_3$. The reaction of the broth becomes markedly alkaline, the pH varying from 8.5 to 9. Acid is produced in three or four days in glucose and saccharose broth. There is no acid production in 7 days in lactose, mannite or dulcite broth.

Growth is slow at 37°C. and is most rapid about 20°C. No growth is observed under anaerobic conditions.

In its morphology this organism is a penicillium and in all its characters it most closely resembles *P. rubrum.* Biourge (1923) states that he has never found *P. rubrum* in nature and that it is an "animal de laboratoire." This penicillium is not uncommon in the air of the laboratory.

IS THE ANTIBACTERIAL BODY ELABORATED IN CULTURE BY ALL MOULDS?

A number of other moulds were grown in broth at room temperature and the culture fluids were tested for antibacterial substances at various intervals up to one month. The species examined were: *Eidamia viridiscens, Botrytis cineria, Aspergillus fumigatus, Sporotrichum, Cladosporium, Penicillium,* 8 strains. Of these it was found that only one strain of penicillium produced any inhibitory substance, and that one had exactly the same cultural characters as the original one from the contaminated plate.

It is clear, therefore, that the production of this antibacterial substance is not common to all moulds or to all types of penicillium.

In the rest of this article allusion will constantly be made to experiments with filtrates of a broth culture of this mould, so for convenience and to avoid the repetition of the rather cumbersome phrase "Mould broth filtrate," the name "penicillin" will be used. This will denote the filtrate of a broth culture of the particular penicillium with which we are concerned.

METHODS OF EXAMINING CULTURES FOR ANTIBACTERIAL SUBSTANCE

The simplest method of examining for inhibitory power is to cut a furrow in an agar plate (or a plate of other suitable culture material), and fill this in with a mixture of equal parts of agar and the broth in which the mould has grown. When this has solidified, cultures of various microbes can be streaked at right angles from the furrow to the edge of the plate. The inhibitory substance diffuses very rapidly in the agar, so that in the few hours before the microbes show visible growth it has spread out for a centimetre or more in sufficient concentration to inhibit growth of a sensitive microbe. On further incubation it will be seen that the proximal portion of the culture for perhaps one centimetre becomes transparent, and on examination of this portion of the culture it is found that practically all the microbes are dissolved, indicating that the anti-bacterial substance has continued to diffuse into the agar in sufficient concentration to induce dissolution of the bacteria. This simple method therefore suffices to demonstrate the bacterio-inhibitory and bacteriolytic properties of the mould culture, and also by the extent of the area of inhibition gives some measure of the sensitiveness of the particular microbe tested. . . .

PROPERTIES OF THE ANTIBACTERIAL SUBSTANCE

Effect of heat.—Heating for 1 hour at 56° or 80° C. has no effect on the anti-

bacterial power of penicillin. Boiling for a few minutes hardly affects it. . . . Boiling for 1 hour reduces it to less than one quarter its previous strength if the fluid is alkaline, but if it is neutral or very slightly acid then the reduction is much less. Autoclaving for 20 minutes at 115° C. practically destroys it.

Effect of filtration.—Passage through a Seitz filter does not diminish the antibacterial power. This is the best method of obtaining sterile active mould broth.

Solubility.—It is freely soluble in water and weak saline solutions. My colleague, Mr. Ridley, has found that if penicillin is evaporated at a low temperature to a sticky mass the active principle can be completely extracted by absolute alcohol. It is insoluble in ether or chloroform.

Rate of development of inhibitory substance in culture.—A 500 c.c. Erlenmeyer flask containing 200 c.c. of broth was planted with mould spores and incubated at room temperature (10° to 20° C.). The inhibitory power of the broth to staphylococcus was tested at intervals.

After 5 days complete inhibition in 1 in 20   dilution.
"   6   "   "   "   "   1 in 40   "
"   7   "   "   "   "   1 in 200   "
"   8   "   "   "   "   1 in 500   "

Grown at 20° C. the development of the active principle is more rapid and a good sample will completely inhibit staphylococci in a 1 in 500 or 1 in 800 dilution in 6 or 7 days. As the culture ages the antibacterial power falls and may in

14 days at 20° C. have almost disappeared.

The antibacterial power of penicillin falls when it is kept at room temperature. The rate of this fall can be seen from Table I.

TABLE I.—*Effect of Keeping at Room Temperature on the Anti-Staphylococcal Power of Penicillin.*

Growth of staphylococcus in dilutions of penicillin as under.

	1/20.	1/40.	1/60.	1/80.	1/100.	1/200.	1/300.	1/400.	1/600.	1/800.	1/1000.	Control.
At time of filtration .	−	−	−	−	−	−	−	−	−	±	++	++
After 4 days . .	−	−	−	−	−	−	−	−	−	±	++	++
" 7 " . .	−	−	−	−	−	−	−	±	+	+	++	++
" 9 " . .	−	−	−	−	−	−	−	±	+	+	++	++
" 13 " . .	−	−	−	−	−	+	+	+	+	+	++	++
" 15 " . .	−	±	+	+	+	+	+	+	+	+	++	++

If the reaction of penicillin is altered from its original pH of 9 to a pH of 6.8 it is much more stable.

The small drops of bright yellow fluid which collect on the surface of the mould may have a high antibacterial titre. One specimen of such fluid completely inhibited the growth of staphylococci in a dilution of 1 in 20,000 while the broth in which the mould was growing, tested at the same time, inhibited staphylococcal growth in 1 in 800.

If the mould is grown on solid medium and the felted mass picked off and extracted in normal salt solution for 24 hours it is found that the extract has bacteriolytic properties.

If this extract is mixed with a thick suspension of staphylococcus suspension and incubated for 2 hours at 45° C. it will be found that the opacity of the suspension has markedly diminished and after 24 hours the previously opaque suspension will have become almost clear.

Influence of the medium on the antibacterial titre of the mould culture.—So far as has been ascertained nutrient broth is the most suitable medium for the production of penicillin. The addition of glucose or saccharose, which are fermented by the mould with the production of acid, delays or prevents the appearance of the antibacterial substance. Dilution of the broth with water delays the formation of the antibacterial substance and diminishes the concentration which is ultimately reached. . . .

THE RATE OF KILLING OF STAPHYLOCOCCI BY PENICILLIN

Some bactericidal agents like the hypochlorites are extremely rapid in their action, others like flavine or novarsenobillon are slow. Experiments were made to find into which category penicillin fell.

To 1 c.c. volumes of dilutions in broth of penicillin were added 10 c.mm. volumes of a 1 in 1000 dilution of a staphylococcus broth culture. The tubes were then incubated at 37° C. and at intervals 10 c.mm. volumes were removed and plated with the following result:

Number of colonies developing after sojourn in penicillin in concentrations as under:

	Control.	$\frac{1}{80}$.	$\frac{1}{40}$.	$\frac{1}{20}$.	$\frac{1}{10}$.
Before	27	27	27	27	27
After 2 hours	116	73	51	48	23
" 4½ "	∞	13	1	2	5
" 8 "	∞	0	0	0	0
" 12 "	∞	0	0	0	0

It appears, therefore, that penicillin belongs to the group of slow acting antiseptics, and the staphylococci are only completely killed after an interval of over 4½ hours even in a concentration 30 or 40 times stronger than is necessary to inhibit completely the culture in broth. In the weaker concentrations it will be seen that at first there is growth of the staphylococci and only after some hours are the cocci killed off. The same thing can be seen if a series of dilutions of penicillin in broth are heavily infected with staphylococcus and incubated. If the cultures are examined after four hours it may be seen that growth has taken place apparently equally in all the tubes but when examined after being incubated overnight, the tubes containing penicillin in concentrations greater than 1 in 300 or 1 in 400 are perfectly clear while the control tube shows a heavy growth. This is a clear illustration of the bacteriolytic action of penicillin.

TOXICITY OF PENICILLIN

The toxicity to animals of powerfully antibacterial mould broth filtrates appears to be very low. Twenty c.c. injected intravenously into a rabbit were not more toxic than the same quantity of broth. Half a c.c. injected intraperitoneally into a mouse weighing about 20 gm. induced no toxic symptoms. Constant irrigation of large infected surfaces in man was not accompanied by any toxic symptoms, while irrigation of the human conjunctiva every hour for a day had no irritant effect.

In vitro penicillin which completely inhibits the growth of staphylococci in a dilution of 1 in 600 does not interfere with leucocytic function to a greater extent than does ordinary broth. . . .

DISCUSSION

It has been demonstrated that a species of penicillium produces in culture a very powerful antibacterial substance which affects different bacteria in different degrees. Speaking generally it may be said that the least sensitive bacteria are the Gram-negative bacilli, and the most susceptible are the pyogenic cocci. Inhibitory substances have been described in old cultures of many organisms; generally the inhibition is more or less specific to the microbe which has been used for the culture, and the inhibitory substances are seldom strong enough to withstand even slight dilution with fresh nutrient material. Penicillin is not inhibitory to the original penicillium used in its preparation.

Emmerich and other workers have shown that old cultures of *B. pyocyaneus* acquire a marked bacteriolytic power. The bacteriolytic agent, pyocyanase, possesses properties similar to penicillin in that its heat resistance is the same and it exists in the filtrate of a fluid culture. It resembles penicillin also in that it acts only on certain microbes. It differs however in being relatively extremely weak in its action and in acting on quite different types of bacteria. The bacilli of anthrax, diphtheria, cholera and typhoid are those most sensitive to pyocyanase, while the pyogenic cocci are unaffected, but the percentages of pyocyaneus filtrate necessary for the inhibition of these organisms were 40, 33, 40 and 60 respectively (Bocchia, 1909). This degree of inhibition is hardly comparable with 0.2% or less of penicillin which is necessary to completely inhibit the pyogenic cocci or the 1% necessary for *B. diphtheriæ*.

Penicillin, in regard to infections with sensitive microbes, appears to have some advantages over the well-known chemical antiseptics. A good sample will completely inhibit staphylococci, *Streptococcus pyogenes* and pneumococcus in a dilution of 1 in 800. It is therefore a more powerful inhibitory agent than is carbolic acid and it can be applied to an infected surface undiluted as it is non-irritant and non-toxic. If applied, therefore, on a dressing, it will still be effective even when diluted 800 times which is more than can be said of the chemical antiseptics in use. Experiments in connection with its value in the treatment of pyogenic infections are in progress.

In addition to its possible use in the treatment of bacterial infections penicillin is certainly useful to the bacteriologist for its power of inhibiting unwanted microbes in bacterial cultures so that penicillin insensitive bacteria can readily be isolated. A notable instance of this is the very easy isolation of Pfeiffers bacillus of influenza when penicillin is used.

Isolation of a Crystalline Protein Possessing the Properties of Tobacco-Mosaic Virus. ❦

by W. M. STANLEY

Reprinted from *Science*, Vol. 81, pp. 644–645 (1935) by permission of the editor and author.

Following Iwanowsky's discovery of the tobacco mosaic virus in 1892, inevitable divergences of viewpoint as to the nature of viruses developed, owing to the puzzling necessity of reconciling their resemblances to living entities with a minuteness of size unprecedented even among bacteria. In 1898 Beijerinck had discarded the bacterial theory of tobacco mosaic disease and proposed the theory of a "living fluid contagion." Other suggestions were those of Baur (1906) that the responsible agent was a non-living organized chemical product of metabolism, and, somewhat closer to the mark, the idea advanced by Duggar and Karrer in 1923 that there might be a relationship between viruses and genes or chromatin particles. Stanley's achievement in crystallizing the tobacco mosaic virus was therefore more than a technical tour de force; *it inaugurated a new kind of thinking in biology. Certain biological properties, formerly regarded as pertaining exclusively to the cellular level of organization, were now seen to be characteristic of a purified protein—a large and complex molecule, to be sure, but a single molecular species, nonetheless. Two years later, Bawden and Pirie reported that viruses were in fact nucleoprotein. The implications of this new awareness have already had far-reaching results in investigations into the nature of reproduction, the chemistry of the gene, the mechanism of immunity, and many other frontiers of biological research.*

A CRYSTALLINE MATERIAL, which has the properties of tobacco-mosaic virus, has been isolated from the juice of Turkish tobacco plants infected with this virus. The crystalline material contains 20 per cent. nitrogen and 1 per cent. ash, and a solution containing 1 milligram per cubic centimeter gives a positive test with Millon's biuret, xanthoproteic, glyoxylic acid and Folin's tyrosine reagents. The Molisch and Fehlings tests are negative, even with concentrated solutions. The material is precipitated by 0.4 saturated ammonium sulfate, by saturated magnesium sulfate, or by safranine, ethyl alcohol, acetone, trichloracetic acid, tannic acid, phosphotungstic acid and lead acetate. The crystalline protein is practically insoluble in water and is soluble in dilute acid, alkali or salt solutions. Solutions containing from 0.1 per cent. to 2 per cent. of the protein are opalescent. They are fairly clear between pH 6 and 11 and between pH 1 and 4, and take on a dense whitish appearance between pH 4 and 6.

The infectivity, chemical composition and optical rotation of the crystalline protein were unchanged after 10 successive crystallizations. In a fractional crystallization experiment the activity of the first small portion of crystals to come out of solution was the same as the activity of the mother liquor. When solutions are made more alkaline than about pH 11.8 the opalescence disappears and they become clear. Such solutions are devoid of activity and it was shown by solubility tests that the protein had been denatured. The material is also denatured and its activity lost when solutions are made more acid than about pH 1. It is completely coagulated and the activity lost on heating to 94° C. Preliminary experiments, in which the amorphous form of the protein was partially digested with pepsin, or partially coagulated by heat, indicate that the loss in activity is about proportional to the loss of native protein. The molecular weight of the protein, as determined by two preliminary experiments on osmotic pressure and diffusion, is of the order of a few millions. That the molecule is quite large is also indicated by the fact that the protein is held back by collodion filters through which proteins such as egg albumin readily pass. Collodion filters which fail to allow the protein to pass also fail to allow the active agent to pass. The material readily passes a Berkefeld "W" filter.

The crystals are over 100 times more active than the suspension made by grinding up diseased Turkish tobacco leaves, and about 1,000 times more active than the twice-frozen juice from diseased plants. One cubic centimeter of a 1 to 1,000,000,000 dilution of the crystals has usually proved infectious. The disease produced by this, as well as more concentrated solutions, has proved to be typical tobacco mosaic. Activity measurements were made by comparing the number of lesions produced on one half of the leaves of plants of Early Golden Cluster bean, *Nicotiana glutinosa* L., or *N. langsdorffii* Schrank after inoculation with dilutions of a solution of the crystals, with the number of lesions produced on the other halves of the same leaves after inoculation with dilutions of a virus preparation used for comparison.

The sera of animals injected with tobacco-mosaic virus give a precipitate when mixed with a solution of the crystals diluted as high as 1 part in 100,-000. The sera of animals injected with juice from healthy tobacco plants give no precipitate when mixed with a solution of the crystals. Injection of solutions of the crystals into animals causes the production of a precipitin that is active for solutions of the crystals and juice of plants containing tobacco-mosaic virus but that is inactive for juice of normal plants.

The material herein described is quite different from the active crystalline material mentioned by Vinson and Petre and by Barton-Wright and McBain, which consisted, as Caldwell has demonstrated, largely of inorganic matter having no connection with the activity. These preparations were less active than ordinary juice from diseased plants, and the activity they possessed diminished on further crystallizations.

The crystalline protein described in this paper was prepared from the juice of Turkish tobacco plants infected with tobacco-mosaic virus. The juice was brought to 0.4 saturation with ammonium sulfate and the precipitated globulin fraction thus obtained was removed by filtration. The dark brown globulin portion was repeatedly fractionated with ammonium sulfate and then most of the remaining color was removed by precipitation with a small amount of lead subacetate at pH 8.7. An inactive protein fraction was removed from the light yellow colored filtrate by adjusting to pH 4.5 and adding 2 per cent. by weight of standard celite. The celite was removed, suspended in water at pH 8, and the suspension filtered. The active protein was found in the colorless filtrate. This procedure was repeated twice in order to remove completely the inactive protein. Crystallization was accomplished by adding slowly, with stirring, a solution containing 1 cubic centimeter of glacial acetic acid in 20 cubic centimeters of 0.5 saturated ammonium sulfate to a solution of the protein containing sufficient ammonium sulfate to cause a faint turbidity. Small needles about 0.03 millimeters long appeared immediately and crystallization was completed in an hour. Crystallization may also be caused by the addition of a little saturated ammonium or magnesium sulfate to a solution of the protein in 0.001 N acid. Several attempts to obtain crystals by dialyzing solutions of the protein gave only amorphous material. To date a little more than 10 grams of the active crystalline protein have been obtained.

Although it is difficult, if not impossible, to obtain conclusive positive proof of the purity of a protein, there is strong evidence that the crystalline protein herein described is either pure or is a solid solution of proteins. As yet no evidence for the existence of a mixture of active and inactive material in the crystals has been obtained. Tobaccomosaic virus is regarded as an autocatalytic protein which, for the present, may be assumed to require the presence of living cells for multiplication.

Studies on the Chemical Nature of the Substance Inducing Transformation of Pneumococcal Types. ❧

by OSWALD T. AVERY, COLIN M. MACLEOD, and MACLYN McCARTY

Reprinted from the *Journal of Experimental Medicine,* Vol. 79, pp. 137–158 (1944), by permission of the editor and authors.

The article which follows lies in the common meeting ground of genetics, chemistry, and microbiology. It could, with equal justification, have been placed in the chapters on genetics or evolution. Its scientific roots go back to Koch's insistence on the hereditary continuity of bacterial species, to Miescher's perception that nucleic acids are associated with cellular reproduction, and to the work of the pioneers of genetics who placed the site of the gene in the chromatin substance of the nucleus. The non-specific induction of mutations had been accomplished by the use of X-rays by Muller in 1927, and later with various chemical agents by Auerbach and others. In 1928, Griffith had successfully brought about the transformation of one bacterial type into another within the body of an inoculated animal. The significance of the work of Avery and his collaborators lies in the fact that for the first time transformation in an organism amounting to the induction of a specific mutation was brought about in vitro by a highly refined substance, consisting principally of nucleic acid. The corollary of this, that nucleic acid in some way specifically controls the synthesis by the cell of specific products, has important and widely ramifying implications. Should it prove practicable in the future for man to direct the course of mutation into desired channels, the historian of that accomplishment will surely trace its early beginnings to the investigations reported in the following pages.

BIOLOGISTS HAVE LONG attempted by chemical means to induce in higher organisms predictable and specific changes which thereafter could be transmitted in series as hereditary characters. Among microörganisms the most striking example of inheritable and specific alterations in cell structure and function that can be experimentally induced and are reproducible under well defined and adequately controlled conditions is the transformation of specific types of Pneumococcus. This phenomenon was first described by Griffith who succeeded in transforming an attenuated and non-encapsulated (R) variant derived from one specific type into fully encapsulated and virulent (S) cells of a heterologous specific type. A typical instance will suffice to illustrate the techniques originally used and serve to indicate the wide variety of transformations that are possible within the limits of this bacterial species.

Griffith found that mice injected subcutaneously with a small amount of a living R culture derived from Pneumococcus Type II together with a large inoculum of heat-killed Type III (S) cells frequently succumbed to infection, and that the heart's blood of these animals yielded Type III pneumococci in pure culture. The fact that the R strain was a virulent and incapable by itself of causing fatal bacteremia and the additional fact that the heated suspension of Type III cells contained no viable organisms brought convincing evi-

dence that the R forms growing under these conditions had newly acquired the capsular structure and biological specificity of Type III pneumococci.

The original observations of Griffith were later confirmed by Neufeld and Levinthal, and by Baurhenn abroad, and by Dawson in this laboratory. Subsequently Dawson and Sia succeeded in inducing transformation *in vitro*. This they accomplished by growing R cells in a fluid medium containing anti-R serum and heat-killed encapsulated S cells. They showed that in the test tube as in the animal body transformation can be selectively induced, depending on the type specificity of the S cells used in the reaction system. Later, Alloway was able to cause specific transformation *in vitro* using sterile extracts of S cells from which all formed elements and cellular debris had been removed by Berkefeld filtration. He thus showed that crude extracts containing active transforming material in soluble form are as effective in inducing specific transformation as are the intact cells from which the extracts were prepared.

Another example of transformation which is analogous to the interconvertibility of pneumococcal types lies in the field of viruses. Berry and Dedrick succeeded in changing the virus of rabbit fibroma (Shope) into that of infectious myxoma (Sanarelli). These investigators inoculated rabbits with a mixture of active fibroma virus together with a suspension of heat-inactivated myxoma virus and produced in the animals the symptoms and pathological lesions characteristic of infectious myxomatosis. On subsequent animal passage the transformed virus was transmissible and induced myxomatous infection typical of the naturally occurring disease. Later Berry was successful in inducing the same transformation using a heat-inactivated suspension of washed elementary bodies of myxoma virus. In the case of these viruses the methods employed were similar in principle to those used by Griffith in the transformation of pneumococcal types. These observations have subsequently been confirmed by other investigators.

The present paper is concerned with a more detailed analysis of the phenomenon of transformation of specific types of Pneumococcus. The major interest has centered in attempts to isolate the active principle from crude bacterial extracts and to identify if possible its chemical nature or at least to characterize it sufficiently to place it in a general group of known chemical substances. For purposes of study, the typical example of transformation chosen as a working model was the one with which we have had most experience and which consequently seemed best suited for analysis. This particular example represents the transformation of a non-encapsulated R variant of Pneumococcus Type II to Pneumococcus Type III.

EXPERIMENTAL

Transformation of pneumococcal types *in vitro* requires that certain cultural conditions be fulfilled before it is possible to demonstrate the reaction even in the presence of a potent extract. Not only must the broth medium be optimal for growth but it must be supplemented by the addition of serum or serous fluid known to possess certain special properties. Moreover, the R variant, as will be shown later, must be in the reactive phase in which it has the capacity to

respond to the transforming stimulus. For purposes of convenience these several components as combined in the transforming test will be referred to as the *reaction system*. Each constituent of this system presented problems which required clarification before it was possible to obtain consistent and reproducible results. . . .

[The experimental procedures, described by the authors in great detail, will here be indicated by a much abbreviated summary.—*Editors*.]

Preparation of the transforming substance involves collection of cells by centrifuging mass cultures of Pneumococcus Type III, extraction with saline solution containing sodium desoxycholate, and precipitation with absolute ethyl alcohol. The solution is then deproteinized, reprecipitated with alcohol, dissolved and digested with a bacterial enzyme capable of digesting polysaccharide. The active material is separated by fractionation in ethyl alcohol.

Elementary chemical analysis showed agreement with the theoretical proportions of sodium desoxyribonucleate. Treatment with various enzymes showed no loss of activity with trypsin and chymotrypsin, nor with ribonuclease. The activity was destroyed only by enzyme preparations containing the depolymerase for desoxyribose nucleic acid. The transforming substance in purified state exhibited little or no serological activity, in contrast to its biological specificity in inducing pneumococcal transformation.

Examination in the analytical ultracentrifuge indicated that the substance was homogeneous and that the molecules were uniform in size and very asymmetric. Examination by electrophoresis in the Tiselius apparatus revealed only a single electrophoretic component of relatively high mobility comparable to that of a nucleic acid. Transforming activity was associated with the fast moving component giving the optically visible boundary. Thus in both the electrical and centrifugal fields, the behavior of the purified substance is consistent with the concept that biological activity is a property of the highly polymerized nucleic acid.

Ultraviolet absorption curves showed maxima in the region of 2600 Å and minima in the region of 2350 Å. These findings are characteristic of nucleic acids.

In its highly purified state the material as isolated is capable of inducing transformation in amounts ranging from 0.02 to 0.003 μg. The latter represents a final concentration of the purified substance of 1 part in 600,000,000.

DISCUSSION

The present study deals with the results of an attempt to determine the chemical nature of the substance inducing specific transformation of pneumococcal types. A desoxyribonucleic acid fraction has been isolated from Type III pneumococci which is capable of transforming unencapsulated R variants derived from Pneumococcus Type II into fully encapsulated Type III cells. Thompson and Dubos have isolated from pneumococci a nucleic acid of the ribose type. So far as the writers are aware, however, a nucleic acid of the desoxyribose type has not heretofore been recovered from pneumococci nor has specific transformation been experimentally induced *in vitro* by a chemically defined substance.

Although the observations are limited to a single example, they acquire broader significance from the work of earlier investigators who demonstrated the interconvertibility of various pneumococcal types and showed that the specificity of the changes induced is in each instance determined by the particular type of encapsulated cells used to evoke the reaction. From the point of view of the phenomenon in general, therefore,

it is of special interest that in the example studied, highly purified and protein-free material consisting largely, if not exclusively, of desoxyribonucleic acid is capable of stimulating unencapsulated R variants of Pneumococcus Type II to produce a capsular polysaccharide identical in type specificity with that of the cells from which the inducing substance was isolated. Equally striking is the fact that the substance evoking the reaction and the capsular substance produced in response to it are chemically distinct, each belonging to a wholly different class of chemical compounds.

The inducing substance, on the basis of its chemical and physical properties, appears to be a highly polymerized and viscous form of sodium desoxyribonucleate. On the other hand, the Type III capsular substance, the synthesis of which is evoked by this transforming agent, consists chiefly of a non-nitrogenous polysaccharide constituted of glucose-glucuronic acid units linked in glycosidic union. The presence of the newly formed capsule containing this type-specific polysaccharide confers on the transformed cells all the distinguishing characteristics of Pneumococcus Type III. Thus, it is evident that the inducing substance and the substance produced in turn are chemically distinct and biologically specific in their action and that both are requisite in determining the type specificity of the cell of which they form a part.

The experimental data presented in this paper strongly suggest that nucleic acids, at least those of the desoxyribose type, possess different specificities as evidenced by the selective action of the transforming principle. Indeed, the possibility of the existence of specific differences in biological behavior of nucleic acids has previously been suggested but has never been experimentally demonstrated owing in part at least to the lack of suitable biological methods. The techniques used in the study of transformation appear to afford a sensitive means of testing the validity of this hypothesis, and the results thus far obtained add supporting evidence in favor of this point of view.

If it is ultimately proved beyond reasonable doubt that the transforming activity of the material described is actually an inherent property of the nucleic acid, one must still account on a chemical basis for the biological specificity of its action. At first glance, immunological methods would appear to offer the ideal means of determining the differential specificity of this group of biologically important substances. Although the constituent units and general pattern of the nucleic acid molecule have been defined, there is as yet relatively little known of the possible effect that subtle differences in molecular configuration may exert on the biological specificity of these substances. However, since nucleic acids free or combined with histones or protamines are not known to function antigenically, one would not anticipate that such differences would be revealed by immunological techniques. Consequently, it is perhaps not surprising that highly purified and protein-free preparations of desoxyribonucleic acid, although extremely active in inducing transformation, showed only faint trace reactions in precipitin tests with potent Type III antipneumococcus rabbit sera.

From these limited observations it would be unwise to draw any conclusion concerning the immunological significance of the nucleic acids until further knowledge on this phase of the problem is available. Recent observations by Lackman and his collaborators have shown that nucleic acids of both the yeast and thymus type derived from hemolytic streptococci and from animal and plant sources precipitate with certain antipneumococcal sera. The reactions varied with different lots of immune serum and occurred more fre-

quently in antipneumococcal horse serum than in corresponding sera of immune rabbits. The irregularity and broad cross reactions encountered led these investigators to express some doubt as to the immunological significance of the results. Unless special immunochemical methods can be devised similar to those so successfully used in demonstrating the serological specificity of simple non-antigenic substances, it appears that the techniques employed in the study of transformation are the only ones available at present for testing possible differences in the biological behavior of nucleic acids.

Admittedly there are many phases of the problem of transformation that require further study and many questions that remain unanswered largely because of technical difficulties. For example, it would be of interest to know the relation between rate of reaction and concentration of the transforming substance; the proportion of cells transformed to those that remain unaffected in the reaction system. However, from a bacteriological point of view, numerical estimations based on colony counts might prove more misleading than enlightening because of the aggregation and sedimentation of the R cells agglutinated by the antiserum in the medium. Attempts to induce transformation in suspensions of resting cells held under conditions inhibiting growth and multiplication have thus far proved unsuccessful, and it seems probable that transformation occurs only during active reproduction of the cells. Important in this connection is the fact that the R cells, as well as those that have undergone transformation, presumably also all other variants and types of pneumococci, contain an intracellular enzyme which is released during autolysis and in the free state is capable of rapidly and completely destroying the activity of the transforming agent. It would appear, therefore, that during the logarithmic phase of growth when cell division is most active and autolysis least apparent, the cultural conditions are optimal for the maintenance of the balance between maximal reactivity of the R cell and minimal destruction of the transforming agent through the release of autolytic ferments.

In the present state of knowledge any interpretation of the mechanism involved in transformation must of necessity be purely theoretical. The biochemical events underlying the phenomenon suggest that the transforming principle interacts with the R cell giving rise to a coordinated series of enzymatic reactions that culminate in the synthesis of the Type III capsular antigen. The experimental findings have clearly demonstrated that the induced alterations are not random changes but are predictable, always corresponding in type specificity to that of the encapsulated cells from which the transforming substance was isolated. Once transformation has occurred, the newly acquired characteristics are thereafter transmitted in series through innumerable transfers in artificial media without any further addition of the transforming agent. Moreover, from the transformed cells themselves, a substance of identical activity can again be recovered in amounts far in excess of that originally added to induce the change. It is evident, therefore, that not only is the capsular material reproduced in successive generations but that the primary factor, which controls the occurrence and specificity of capsular development, is also reduplicated in the daughter cells. The induced changes are not temporary modifications but are permanent alterations which persist provided the cultural conditions are favorable for the maintenance of capsule formation. The transformed cells can be readily distinguished from the parent R forms not alone by serological reactions but by the presence of a newly formed and visible capsule which is the immunological unit of type specificity and the accessory structure essential in determining the infective capacity of the microorganism in the animal body.

It is particularly significant in the case of pneumococci that the experimentally induced alterations are definitely correlated with the development of a new morphological structure and the consequent acquisition of new antigenic and invasive properties. Equally if not more significant is the fact that these changes are predictable, type-specific, and heritable.

Various hypotheses have been advanced in explanation of the nature of the changes induced. In his original description of the phenomenon Griffith suggested that the dead bacteria in the inoculum might furnish some specific protein that serves as a "pabulum" and enables the R form to manufacture a capsular carbohydrate.

More recently the phenomenon has been interpreted from a genetic point of view. The inducing substance has been likened to a gene, and the capsular antigen which is produced in response to it has been regarded as a gene product. In discussing the phenomenon of transformation Dobzhansky has stated that "If this transformation is described as a genetic mutation—and it is difficult to avoid so describing it—we are dealing with authentic cases of induction of specific mutations by specific treatments. . . ."

Another interpretation of the phenomenon has been suggested by Stanley who has drawn the analogy between the activity of the transforming agent and that of a virus. On the other hand, Murphy has compared the causative agents of fowl tumors with the transforming principle of Pneumococcus. He has suggested that both these groups of agents be termed "transmissible mutagens" in order to differentiate them from the virus group. Whatever may prove to be the correct interpretation, these differences in viewpoint indicate the implications of the phenomenon of transformation in relation to similar problems in the fields of genetics, virology, and cancer research.

It is, of course, possible that the biological activity of the substance described is not an inherent property of the nucleic acid but is due to minute amounts of some other substance adsorbed to it or so intimately associated with it as to escape detection. If, however, the biologically active substance isolated in highly purified form as the sodium salt of desoxyribonucleic acid actually proves to be the transforming principle, as the available evidence strongly suggests, then nucleic acids of this type must be regarded not merely as structurally important but as functionally active in determining the biochemical activities and specific characteristics of pneumococcal cells. Assuming that the sodium desoxyribonucleate and the active principle are one and the same substance, then the transformation described represents a change that is chemically induced and specifically directed by a known chemical compound. If the results of the present study on the chemical nature of the transforming principle are confirmed, then nucleic acids must be regarded as possessing biological specificity the chemical basis of which is as yet undetermined.

Part Four

~❧

PLANT PHYSIOLOGY

AUXINS

1880   Charles and Francis Darwin showed that a phototropic "influence" is transmitted from the tip of a unilaterally illuminated plant to the basal regions.

1910   Boysen-Jensen demonstrated that the influence is material, since it can cross an incision but cannot pass through a mica barrier.

1919   Paál showed that when the tip is cut off and replaced to one side, growth of the base is greater on this side.

1926–1928   Went demonstrated that the responsible material could diffuse into agar blocks and thus be collected. He developed quantitative assay methods for the growth substance.

1933   Kögl, Haagen-Smit, and Erxleben isolated auxins and characterized them chemically.

1935   Zimmerman and Wilcoxon discovered several synthetic substances with hormone activity.

1937   Avery, Burkholder, and others pursued quantitative studies on effects of auxins in plant metabolism.

1937   Thimann suggested that a given concentration of auxin might produce inhibitory effects in one tissue and stimulation in another, different tissues being characterized by a series of overlapping optimal concentration curves.

1938   Van Overbeek reported that certain non-geotropic mutants in maize did not show the usual inequality of auxin distribution.

1939   Borgström found that shoots exposed to ethylene exhibited positive geotropism associated with the predicted auxin distribution. Ethylene must in some way influence the transverse movement of auxin.

1941   Commoner and Thimann found that concentrations of $10^{-5}M$ of iodoacetate can halt coleoptile growth but produce no effect on cellular respiration. They assumed that only a small fraction of respiration might be involved in growth.

1942   Reinders found that auxin present in concentrations as low as 1 mg/liter stimulated water uptake in potato discs along with an increase in respiration and loss in dry weight.

1943   Commoner, Fogel, and Muller demonstrated that auxin will promote water absorption against an osmotic gradient. The effect is inhibited by iodoacetate.

A recent article reviewing the published literature pertaining to auxins and covering the years 1947–1951 lists nearly five hundred reference articles. It is obvious that it would be impossible to review or compress the findings within the limitations of this section. Instead we have chosen to outline the current status of the auxin concept as we now understand it.

Auxin produces a wide variety of effects depending on the concentration, the tissue affected, the ease with which it is transported, and its stability in different tissues. It is not unlikely that some single feature of cellular activity is involved in all the different effects.

The study of synthetic auxins suggests that a certain spatial array is requisite to physiological activity. This would in turn indicate that the auxin must conform to the molecular configuration of some cell component, presumably an enzyme protein. Abundant evidence actually exists for the view that catalytically active auxins combine with a variety of proteins to affect the basic processes of protoplasmic streaming and cell respiration. It is tempting to speculate that auxin serves as a co-enzyme for a number of enzymes respectively concerned with water and solute uptake, cell division, cellulose deposition, organic acid metabolism, and other reactions overtly manifested as growth.

Sensitiveness of Plants to Light: Its Transmitted Effects.

by CHARLES DARWIN and FRANCIS DARWIN

Selected from *The Power of Movement in Plants*, London, 1880.

There is perhaps no single figure who has influenced the direction of modern biological thought more than the distinguished Charles Darwin. Darwin, almost universally known for his creative views on natural selection and evolution, is virtually unrecognized as an equally gifted experimentalist. In fact, it is to Charles Darwin and his son Francis, that we are indebted for the subsequent discovery of plant hormones in the twentieth century. A portion of their highly significant study is reprinted in the following paper.

The major finding reported here is that plant growth is contingent upon the production and diffusion of some active material elaborated by the growing tips in plants. This rather revolutionary concept arose from numerous observations in a lengthy series of ingeniously contrived experiments with a wide variety of different plants. The Darwins readily confirmed Candolle's earlier observations of stem and leaf movements induced by light. They further demonstrated, by capping the tips of young shoots with blackened glass tubes, that the tips did not curve toward the light source when the basal region was unilaterally illuminated.

Simple experiments and observations along such lines finally led the authors to express the view that the shoot is the seat of light "perception" from which a physiological influence is transmitted to lower regions.

LOCALISED SENSITIVENESS TO LIGHT, AND ITS TRANSMITTED EFFECTS

PHALARIS CANARIENSIS.—Whilst observing the accuracy with which the cotyledons of this plant became bent towards the light of a small lamp, we were impressed with the idea that the uppermost part determined the direction of the curvature of the lower part. When the cotyledons are exposed to a lateral light, the upper part bends first, and afterwards the bending gradually extends down to the base, and, as we shall presently see, even a little beneath the ground. This holds good with cotyledons from less than .1 inch (one was observed to act in this manner which was only .03 in height) to about .5 of an inch in height; but when they have grown to nearly an inch in height, the basal part, for a length of .15 to .2 of an inch above the ground, ceases to bend.

As with young cotyledons the lower part goes on bending, after the upper part has become well arched towards a lateral light, the apex would ultimately point to the ground instead of to the light, did not the upper part reverse its curvature and straighten itself, as soon as the upper convex surface of the bowed-down portion received more light than the lower concave surface. The position ultimately assumed by young and upright cotyledons, exposed to light entering obliquely from above through a window, is shown in the accompanying figure (Fig. 181); and here it may be seen that the whole upper part has become very nearly straight. When the cotyledons were exposed before a bright lamp, standing on the same level with them, the upper part, which was at first greatly arched towards the light, became straight and strictly parallel with the surface of the soil in the pots; the basal

FIG. 181.—*Phalaris Canariensis*: cotyledons after exposure in a box open on one side in front of a south-west window during 8 h. Curvature towards the light accurately traced. The short horizontal lines show the level of the ground.

part being now rectangularly bent. All this great amount of curvature, together with the subsequent straightening of the upper part, was often effected in a few hours.

After the uppermost part has become bowed a little to the light, its overhanging weight must tend to increase the curvature of the lower part; but any such effect was shown in several ways to be quite insignificant. When little caps of tinfoil (hereafter to be described) were placed on the summits of the cotyledons, though this must have added considerably to their weight, the rate or amount of bending was not thus increased. But the best evidence was afforded by placing pots with seedlings of Phalaris before a lamp in such a position, that the cotyledons were horizontally extended and projected at right angles to the line of light. In the course of 5½ h. they were directed towards the light with their bases bent at right angles; and this abrupt curvature could not have been aided in the least by the weight of the upper part, which acted at right angles to the plane of curvature.

It will be shown that when the upper halves of the cotyledons of Phalaris and Avena were enclosed in little pipes of tin-foil or of blackened glass, in which case the upper part was mechanically prevented from bending, the lower and unenclosed part did not bend when exposed to a lateral light; and it occurred to us that this fact might be due, not to the exclusion of the light from the upper part, but to some necessity of the bending gradually travelling down the cotyledons, so that unless the upper part first became bent, the lower could not bend, however much it might be stimulated. It was necessary for our purpose to ascertain whether this notion was true, and it was proved false; for the lower halves of several cotyledons became bowed to the light, although their upper halves were enclosed in little glass tubes (not

blackened), which prevented, as far as we could judge, their bending. Nevertheless, as the part within the tube might possibly bend a very little, fine rigid rods or flat splinters of thin glass were cemented with shellac to one side of the upper part of 15 cotyledons; and in six cases they were in addition tied on with threads. They were thus forced to remain quite straight. The result was that the lower halves of all became bowed to the light, but generally not in so great a degree as the corresponding part of the free seedlings in the same pots; and this may perhaps be accounted for by some slight degree of injury having been caused by a considerable surface having been smeared with shellac. It may be added, that when the cotyledons of Phalaris and Avena are acted on by apogeotropism, it is the upper part which begins first to bend; and when this part was rendered rigid in the manner just described, the upward curvature of the basal part was not thus prevented.

To test our belief that the upper part of the cotyledons of Phalaris, when exposed to a lateral light, regulates the bending of the lower part, many experiments were tried; but most of our first attempts proved useless from various causes not worth specifying. Seven cotyledons had their tips cut off for lengths varying between .1 and .16 of an inch, and these, when left exposed all day to a lateral light, remained upright. In another set of 7 cotyledons, the tips were cut off for a length of only about .05 of an inch (1.27 mm.) and these became bowed towards a lateral light, but not nearly so much as the many other seedlings in the same pots. This latter case shows that cutting off the tips does not by itself injure the plants so seriously as to prevent heliotropism; but we thought at the time, that such injury might follow when a greater length was cut off, as in the first set of experiments. Therefore, no more trials of this kind were made, which we now regret; as we afterwards found that when the tips of three cotyledons were cut off for a length of 2 inch, and of four others for lengths of .14, .12, .1, and .07 inch, and they were extended horizontally, the amputation did not interfere in the least with their bending vertically upwards, through the action of apogeotropism, like unmutilated specimens. It is therefore extremely improbable that the amputation of the tips for lengths of from .1 to .14 inch, could from the injury thus caused have prevented the lower part from bending towards the light.

We next tried the effects of covering the upper part of the cotyledons of Phalaris with little caps which were impermeable to light; the whole lower part being left fully exposed before a south-west window or a bright paraffin lamp. Some of the caps were made of extremely thin tin-foil blackened within; these had the disadvantage of occasionally, though rarely, being too heavy, especially when twice folded. The basal edges could be pressed into close contact with the cotyledons; though this again required care to prevent injuring them. Nevertheless, any injury thus caused could be detected by removing the caps, and trying whether the cotyledons were then sensitive to light. Other caps were made of tubes of the thinnest glass, which when painted black served well, with the one great disadvantage that the lower ends could not be closed. But tubes were used which fitted the cotyledons almost closely, and black paper was placed on the soil round each, to check the upward reflection of light from the soil. Such tubes were in one respect far better than caps of tin-foil, as it was possible to cover at the same time some cotyledons with transparent and others with opaque tubes; and thus our experiments could be controlled. It should be kept in mind that young cotyledons were selected for trial, and that these when not interfered with become bowed down to the ground towards the light. . . .

The summits of nine cotyledons, differing somewhat in height, were enclosed for rather less than half their lengths in uncoloured or transparent tubes; and these were then exposed before a south-west window on a bright day for 8 h. All of them became strongly curved towards the light, in the same degree as the many other free seedlings in the same pots; so that the glass-tubes certainly did not prevent the cotyledons from bending towards the light. Nineteen other cotyledons were, at the same time, similarly enclosed in tubs thickly painted with Indian ink. On five of them, the paint, to our surprise, contracted after exposure to the sunlight, and very narrow cracks were formed, through which a little light entered; and these five cases were rejected. Of the remaining 14 cotyledons, the lower halves of which had been fully exposed to the light for the whole time, 7 continued quite straight and upright; 1 was considerably bowed to the light, and 6 were slightly bowed, but with the exposed bases of most of them almost or quite straight. It is possible that some light may have been reflected upwards from the soil and entered the bases of these 7 tubes, as the sun shone brightly, though bits of blackened paper had been placed on the soil round them. Nevertheless, the 7 cotyledons which were slightly bowed, together with the 7 upright ones, presented a most remarkable contrast in appearance with the many other seedlings in the same pots to which nothing had been done. The blackened tubes were then removed from 10 of these seedlings, and they were now exposed before a lamp for 8 h.: 9 of them became greatly, and 1 moderately, curved towards the light, proving that the previous absence of any curvature in the basal part, or the presence of only a slight degree of curvature there, was due to the exclusion of light from the upper part. . . .

From these several sets of experiments, including those with the glass-tubes, and those when the tips were cut off, we may infer that the exclusion of light from the upper part of the cotyledons of Phalaris prevents the lower part, though fully exposed to a lateral light, from becoming curved. The summit for a length of .04 or .05 of an inch, though it is itself sensitive and curves towards the light, has only a slight power of causing the lower part to bend. Nor has the exclusion of light from the summit for a length of .1 of an inch a strong influence on the curvature of the lower part. On the other hand, an exclusion for a length of between .15 and .2 of an inch, or of the whole upper half, plainly prevents the lower and fully illuminated part from becoming curved in the manner (see Fig. 181) which invariably occurs when a free cotyledon is exposed to a lateral light. With very young seedlings the sensitive zone seems to extend rather lower down relatively to their height than in older seedlings. We must therefore conclude that when seedlings are freely exposed to a lateral light some influence is transmitted from the upper to the lower part, causing the latter to bend.

Transmission of the Phototropic Stimulus in the Coleoptile of the Oat Seedling. ~

by P. BOYSEN-JENSEN

From *Berichte d. Deutsche Botanische Gesellschaft*, Vol. 28, pp. 118–120 (1910), by permission of the editors. Translated by M. L. Gabriel and Olga Janowitz for this volume.

From their observations on Phalaris *the Darwins concluded that tropistic growth curvature in a basal region, following illumination of the shoot tip, depended upon the transmission of some influence from the tip downward. Nearly thirty years elapsed, however, before definitive evidence for the material nature of this influence was set forth by Boysen-Jensen in his now classical study of growth in the oat coleoptile. The crucial experiment involves the demonstration that the influence generated at the tip can pass across a tissue discontinuity. First he cut off the tips of young shoots. Then, after placing a layer of gelatin on the cut stumps he replaced the tips and exposed the latter to light. Within a short time a distinct curvature was noted, first in the tip region, and then later in the basal region. It was clearly apparent that the influence postulated by Darwin was of a material nature capable of diffusing through a gelatin barrier without impairment and that it distinctly altered the growth of distantly removed cells. The experiment is extravagantly simple, and illustrates how one frequently derives a penetrating insight without resorting to extensive gadgetry or complex equipment.*

IN ORDER TO discover whether the phototropic stimulus is transmitted through the fibrovascular bundles or through the parenchyma, Rothert cut both the fibrovascular bundles which are present in the coleoptile of the oat seedling (Avena) with a sharp knife. It turned out that the transmission of the stimulus was not inhibited by this procedure. When he illuminated one side of the tip a positive phototropic curvature occurred in the base which had been kept in the dark. Rothert concluded from his experiments that the heliotropic stimulus is transmitted through the parenchyma.

Later the question was very thoroughly investigated by Fitting. Like Rothert, he found that the transmission of the stimulus is not abolished by a transverse incision, regardless of its position in relation to the light, whether on the front, back, or sides of the oat coleoptile. Fitting concluded that the polarity which is induced in all parts (cells) of the perceptive organ by the external stimulus spreads out into the laterally unpolarized reaction zone so that all parts of it, as well as cells along the paths of stimulus transmission, become "polarized." Already before the publication of Fitting's paper I had performed several experiments in the Institute of Plant Physiology in Copenhagen which yielded different results. At the beginning of 1909 these experiments were continued in the Institute of Plant Physiology in Leipzig.

In my experiments it appeared that a very distinct curvature occurred in the darkened base when the incision was made in the illuminated side of the coleoptile; but when the incision was in the shaded part, no curvature occurred. The experiments were carried out in rather dry air indoors.

That the dryness of the atmosphere was not the cause of the discrepancy in the results was shown when I repeated the experiments under water. The results of these experiments were entirely the same as in air.

I then imitated Fitting's experimental conditions as precisely as possible. The experiments were performed under a glass cylinder in air saturated with water vapor, and the results were the same as in Fitting's experiments.

To sum up: When the seedlings are in a very moist atmosphere, transmission of a stimulus takes place, regardless of the position of the incision in relation to the light; but when the experiments are carried out either in dry air or under water, transmission of the stimulus occurs only when the incision is located on the illuminated side of the coleoptile; it does not take place when the incision is on the shaded side.

The positive results which I always obtained when the incision was on the illuminated side convinced me that my plants had not lost their sensitivity to light, their ability to transmit the stimulus, or their capacity to react. I therefore gathered the impression from my experiments that the stimulus is transmitted only on the shaded side of the coleoptile, and that, under favorable experimental conditions, it is able to spread across a wound.

In accord with this conclusion is the fact—already shown by Fitting—that the insertion of a sheet of mica into the incision inhibits the transmission of the stimulus, but only when the incision is situated on the shaded side. When, however, the mica sheet is replaced by a thin slice of *Calamus,* which has very wide vascular bundles and which permits the passage of water and dissolved substances, the transmission of stimuli takes place also when the incision is located on the shaded side.

My assumption became a certainty only when I succeeded in cutting off the tip of the coleoptile entirely, then in replacing it again and evoking a positive phototropic curvature in the darkened base by illuminating one side of the tip. The operation is performed in the following way: The coleoptile is cut through by two wedge-shaped incisions about one cm from the tip, without injuring the primary leaf which is inside the coleoptile. Then the tip of the coleoptile is taken off and the tip of the

primary leaf is removed down to about two mm above the wound; a small drop of gelatine solution is put on the tip of the truncated primary leaf and then the tip of the coleoptile is replaced in its former position. The coleoptile tip is tightly connected with the base by means of a ring of cocoa butter.

When the tip is unilaterally illuminated, a distinct stimulus transmission takes place and a strong curvature occurs in the dark base.

These experiments show that the transmission of the phototropic stimulus takes place only on the shaded side of the coleoptile and that the stimulus can be transmitted across a wound.

On Growth-accelerating Substances in the Coleoptile of Avena sativa. ᗜ

by F. W. WENT

Abridged from *Proc. Kon. Akad. Weten.*, Amsterdam, Vol. 30, pp. 10–19 (1926). Reprinted by permission of the author.

The experimental study of plant growth initiated by Boysen-Jensen's publications was soon extended and refined with numerous improvements by Paál. An important development from this work was the observation that if the decapitated tip was replaced asymmetrically, the shoot curved so that the side in contact with the displaced tip was convex. But the observed curvature, caused by the differential growth of the coleoptile, occurred in total darkness. Paál correctly inferred that normal growth is regulated by the symmetrically distributed diffusion of a material substance synthesized by the tip. Curvature, he reasoned, was caused by some inequality of distribution associated with the action of light or gravity.

A further step in the analysis of plant growth regulation was contributed by Went in 1926 in the paper which follows and in a more elaborate study published the following year. He permitted decapitated tips to remain in contact with agar for some time and found that when such agar blocks were placed on test stumps the usual curvatures were observed. These were in no way distinguishable from those caused by side illumination or asymmetric tip replacement. In fact, judging from the effects produced on the test stump, the agar block was physiologically equivalent to a functional tip. The curvature was shown to be proportional to the amount of material present in the agar; that is, it was proportional both to the number of tips placed on a given block and to the duration of contact.

The plant growth hormones have been termed auxins and this term has since been applied to include a large group of synthetic substances with similar physiological properties.

PAAL (1919), ON account of his experiments, has been the first to assume a regulation of the growth in the coleoptile of Avena. This regulation is seated in the tip and must be caused by the local formation of a substance which, partly by diffusion, moves in a basipetal direction. Arrived in the growing zone it there accelerates growth. This substance (or substances) I shall for the sake of brevity call growth-regulators. . . .

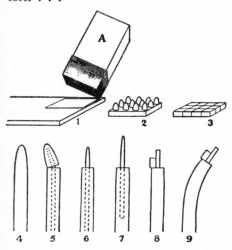

FIG. 1.—(From Went, Rec. trav. bot. néerl., vol. 25, pp. 1–116, 1928). Schematic representation of the method for analyzing growth substances. 1. Stamping out agar plate from an agar film. 2. Placing coleoptile tips on the agar. 3. The agar plate divided into twelve blocks. 4. Unilateral incision of the coleoptile. 5. and 6. Removal of the tips. 7. Pulling out the primary leaflet. 8. Agar block placed on one side. 9. Resulting curvature.

Paál's experiments had proved that diffusion of a phototropic stimulus also takes place through gelatine. I therefore placed a number of tips of coleoptiles of Avena closely together with their cut faces on a thin layer of gelatine. (Fig. 1) After about an hour I took off the tips again and placed the gelatine, cut into small blocks, on one side of decapitated plants. Already one hour later these plants began to show a negative curvature which after 3 hours had become strongly negative, sometimes amounting to an angle of 40° with the vertical. Gelatine on which no tips had been put, when placed on one side, gave no or a very feeble positive curvature, while gelatine on which coleoptile rings, cut off just below the tip, had stood, also produced no perceptible curvature. It was evident that I had obtained the more or less hypothetical growth-regulators. For the curvature produced by placing gelatine blocks on one side, indicates the difference in growth-rate on the two sides of the coleoptile. This difference is caused by the influence of the gelatine on the underlying half of the coleoptile. The more the growth of this half is accelerated the stronger the curvature will be. Already the first experiments showed that on this foundation a quantitative method could be worked out, in which the angle of curvature is the measure for the quantity of growth-regulators, diffusing from the tiplets into the gelatine. For, if the unilaterally placed blocks were from the same portion of gelatine, also the curvatures of the stumps, expressed as angles, were pretty much the same. Taking an average of the angles with six plantlets, the mean error was as a rule not larger than 20%, and sometimes much smaller. This is particularly striking, as phototropical curvatures often diverge widely. Two conclusions may be drawn: 1. the effect of a certain quantity of growth-regulators on different stumps is the same, and 2. the curvature of the stump is a means for quantitatively determining the amount of growth-regulators. So my experiments fall into two groups.

In the first place I am studying the formation and change of the growth-regulators by various external circumstances, the curvature of the stumps after one-sided application of the gelatine being used as the means of analysis, and secondly I am examining how the stump reacts on the presence of growth-regulators under different conditions. The method is briefly as follows: Coleoptiles are raised in a dark room at a constant temperature of 20° C. All manipulations are there made with red light. When the plants have attained the desired length (10—30 mm above the ground) the tips, having a length of 1 to 2 mm are cut off and placed for a few moments on moist filter-paper, in order to remove as well as possible the contents of the injured cells. They are then put close to each other on a thin slice of 10% gelatine. It is important always to place the same number of tips on equal surfaces, the tips should therefore all be cut off at the same length. They are removed from the gelatine after about an hour.

The gelatine obtained in this way is then cut into small blocks of about equal size, which by means of melted gelatine are stuck on one side of coleoptile stumps. Decapitation is carried out in the manner indicated by Stark and Drechsel (1922), the length of the cut-off portion being about 5 mm. The primary leaf is partly pulled out, so that it will not lift the gelatine block from the stump when it grows larger. After

this treatment the plantlets are left to themselves for about half an hour, because within this time the curvatures resulting from the operation manifest themselves; only those plants are used for the experiments that are still perfectly straight then. Already one hour after the gelatine with the growth-regulators has been put on, a distinct curvature is observed in the upper part of the stump. This is gradually transmitted downwards, so that after 3 hours a zone of ± 15 mm is curved. After 3 hours the plants are photographed by casting their shadow on sensitive paper. It is very easy to measure the curvature on the paper. . . .

If pure gelatine is placed on one side negative curvatures never occur: 50% of the plantlets remain straight and 50% bend slightly in a positive direction. The same result is obtained when coleoptile rings have previously stood on the gelatine, and it makes practically no difference whether these rings are cut out close under the tip or from lower parts of the coleoptile. Hence we infer that neither from the sectional surface nor from the ordinary coleoptile cells substances, having a marked influence on growth, diffuse into the gelatine. . . .

A few words must be said on the constancy of the growth-regulators. If gelatine into which they have diffused is left to dry in the air (with a constant moistness of 85%) they remain active, at least partly, also when kept for a longer period. After 2 days' drying of the gelatine they gave a curvature of 18°.2 ± 0°.2; after having been kept dry for 11 days the curvature was still 10° ± 1°.2, and even after 43 days it still produced negative curvatures. When diluting the gelatine containing the growth-regulators with an equal quantity of pure gelatine, its activity diminishes proportionally to the dilution. Undiluted it gave a curvature of 22°.5 ± 2°.0 (in another case 19°.5 ± 7°.9); diluted the curvature was 12° ± 1°.6

(8° ± 1°.6). This also points to their individuality as substances.

The experiments of Fitting (1907), who found that no stimuli were transmitted through a coleoptile disc that had been heated to 43° C., induced me to heat the gelatine to 40°, 60° and 90°. These experiments have a qualitative value only, as I did not make sufficient control experiments. Gelatine that had been heated for 1 minute to 90° was still quite able to produce curvatures, even as strongly as gelatine heated for 1 minute to 40°. Also when heated to 60° very fine curvatures were produced. Hence in Fitting's experiments only the transport of the stimulating substances, in this case the growth-regulators, can have been stopped, without the substances themselves having been destroyed. And this transport must for the greater part be ascribed to the living cells, as diffusion is not nearly sufficient to explain the rate of transport. Brauner (1922) therefore regards the protoplasmic streaming observed by him as a chief factor of transport. A theory of Paal to explain the transport-rate I consider less probable. Transport of the growth-regulators I understand as diffusion from protoplast to protoplast through the cell-wall, and for the rest as a mechanical distribution in the cell by protoplasmic streaming.

If by heating above 41° C. the protoplasmic streaming has been irreversibly checked, no transport of growth-regulators can take place in perceptible quantities.

Illumination of gelatine containing growth-regulators does not check their activity, but I have no quantitatively certain results on this point as yet.

I will deal now with the influence of external circumstances on the formation of the growth-regulators in the tip. It has already been stated that the length of the plantlets has scarcely any influence on the quantity produced.

One of the principal questions that may be answered by the present method

is: what influence has light on the formation of growth-regulators? The result of the experiments on this point might have been foreseen after Van Dillewijn's latest publication (1926). The growth-retardation observed by him after illumination from three sides with 800 metre-candle-seconds and the growth-acceleration stated after 80,000 m.c.s. could only be caused by a smaller and by a larger formation of growth-regulators. Ramaer (1926) could prove this growth-retardation and acceleration in a different way. And finally Sierp (1921) came to the same conclusion from his experiments. Because the growth-regulators formed during the illumination want some time before they have been so far conveyed downwards that an increase or diminution can make itself felt in the gelatine, I waited 30—40 minutes after illumination before cutting the tips and then kept them 45 minutes on the gelatine. The results of a few series of experiments are given in table 1. Only one series gave a completely discordant result, which I can only explain by assuming that the numbers of the experiments were interchanged by accident. I always illuminated vertically from above.

TABLE 1 (for explanation see text).

Quantity of light M.C.S.	Curvature of the stumps		
	Series I	Series II	Series III
0	11.5 ± 1.9	11 ± 1.8	8 ± 0.7
1000	6 ± 1.7	5.5 ± 0.5	4.5 ± 1.4
10000			11 ± 1.3
100000	15.5 ± 1.5	16 ± 1.1	10 ± 0.5
1000000			14 ± 0.3

From these data it appears very clearly that during a time of 35 to 80 minutes less growth-regulators diffuse from the tips (having a length of 1—1.5 mm) into the gelatin after applying 1000 m.c.s., but more after 100,000 m.c.s.

It was now also possible to imitate phototropic curves. To do this I first placed, as in all former experiments, on one side of the stump gelatine, treated with tips to which an illumination of e.g. 100,000 m.c.s. had been applied. Then on the other side a gelatine block was placed, on which tips had stood that had been illuminated with ten times less light. In this way a gelatine system was placed on the stump which, according to Blaauw's theory, as nearly as possible approached the unilaterally illuminated tip. The plantlets indeed bent themselves in perfect accordance with the figures obtained by Arisz (1915). With a difference of 1000 versus 0 m.c.s. a positive curvature (in 7 out of 9 plants, 2 remained straight) occurred, reckoned towards the 1000 m.c.s. With 10,000 versus 1000 m.c.s. the curvature was negative. With 100,000 versus 10,000 m.c.s. I found a positive curvature again, i.e. towards the 100,000 m.c.s.

PHOTOSYNTHESIS

CHRONOLOGY

ca ·1450   Cusa suggested that plants grew by assimilation of water.

1648   Publication of van Helmont's works, including account of an experiment on plant nutrition.

1727   Hales concluded that plants are nourished in part from the atmosphere.

1754   Bonnet noted the emission of bubbles by a submerged illuminated leaf.

1772   Priestley discovered the evolution of oxygen by plants.

1779   Publication of Ingen-Housz's *Experiments on Vegetables* showing that illumination was required for oxygen production.

1788   Senebier showed that it is the light and not the heat of the sun that is effective in photosynthesis.

1796   Ingen-Housz concluded that plants utilize carbon dioxide in their nutrition. He understood that plants carry on respiration concomitantly with photosynthesis.

1804   de Saussure published experiments that represent the first treatment of the subject using quantitative methods and modern chemical terminology.

1836   Daubeny investigated the efficiency of different parts of the spectrum in photosynthesis.

1837   Dutrochet recognized that chlorophyll was necessary for photosynthesis.

1840   Liebig pointed out that organic compounds in plants are synthesized from carbon dioxide of the atmosphere while nitrogenous compounds are derived from precursors in the soil.

1843   Liebig speculated that organic acids such as oxalic, tartaric, or malic were intermediates in the production of carbohydrates by plants.

1844   Draper showed that plants grown in solutions of sodium bicarbonate can liberate oxygen in the light.

1851–1855   Boussingault demonstrated that higher plants cannot utilize atmospheric nitrogen, but only nitrates from the soil.

1862   Sachs produced experimental evidence that starch was a product of photosynthesis.

1868   Boussingault pointed out that plants require oxygen for photosynthesis.

1882   Engelmann demonstrated that red light was the most effective in photosynthesis.

1883–1888   Engelmann discovered photosynthesis in purple bacteria.

1898   Barnes proposed the word "photosynthesis."

1901   Friedel found that powdered leaves can liberate oxygen when resuspended and illuminated.

1905   Blackman pointed out that photosynthesis involved several processes, its rate being determined by several possible limiting factors.

1906–1926   Willstätter and coworkers discovered the chemical structure of the chlorophyll pigments.

1913   Publication of Willstätter and Stoll's *Untersuchungen Ueber Chlorophyll*.

1919   Warburg found that the efficiency of photosynthesis was increased in intermittent light.

1922   Warburg and Negelein reported first measurements on the quantum efficiency of photosynthesis.

1923   Thunberg first characterized photosynthesis as an oxidation-reduction reaction in which carbon dioxide is reduced and water is oxidized.

1925   Molisch obtained the evolution of oxygen by illuminated preparations of dried leaves.

1930   van Niel suggested the parallelism between photosynthetic processes in bacteria and in green plants.

1936   Wood and Werkman discovered that cells kept in the dark are able to build up larger organic molecules from carbon dioxide.

1938   Hill found that cell-free suspensions of chloroplasts evolve oxygen when illuminated in the presence of ferric salts.

1939   Ruben, Hassid, and Kamen first applied radioactive tracers to the study of photosynthesis.

1940   Gaffron showed that algae can utilize molecular hydrogen for photosynthesis.

1940   Kausche and Ruska published first electron microscope pictures of chloroplasts.

1941   Ruben, Randall, Kamen, and Hyde reported that the oxygen liberated in photosynthesis comes from water.

1948   Calvin and Benson reported that the major intermediate compound in which photosynthetic carbon is fixed is phosphoglyceric acid.

Concerning the Elements of Wood, Plants, Flesh, Animals, and Liquids. ◆

by CARDINAL P. NICOLAI CUSA

From *Opera*, Vol. 1, folio 96, Paris: J. Badius, A. Ascensius, 1514. Translated by Ethyle R. Wolfe for this volume.

The two excerpts that follow describe one of the first experiments in modern biology. The first passage, by Cardinal Nicolai of Cusa (1401–1464) illustrates the difficulties that beset any attempt to explain chemical changes in terms of the four elements of the ancients, and foreshadows the downfall of that doctrine. It served possibly as the inspiration for van Helmont's classic experiment performed a century and a half later. Van Helmont's brief paragraph rewards careful attention for it is an epitome of scientific method. Noteworthy are his careful control of the experimental variables, his quantitative approach, and his implicit reliance on the principle of conservation of mass—three basic conceptions that are still the indispensable requisites for research in natural science.

IF SOMEONE WERE to put one hundred pounds of earth in an earthen pot and were thereafter to collect one hundred pounds from the plants or seeds which had first been weighed and then thrown into the earth, and should again weigh the earth, he would find that it was very little lessened in weight; from which he would conclude that the plants which were picked have their weight rather from water. Therefore waters thickened in the earth have taken on the properties of earth and by the work of the sun they have been condensed into the plants. If those plants were to be burned, would you not ascertain by inference from the variation in the weights of all how much earth more than one hundred pounds you would find, and that the water had produced it?[1]

[1] Cusa's meaning is that by burning, one would drive off the water, leaving a charcoal, or "earth." The mass of this residue might be accounted for in part by the mass of the seeds and in part by the loss of soil weight, but the remainder must, he reasoned, represent solid matter derived from the water imbibed by the plants. It is, however, by no means clear from the account that the experiment was actually performed. Had Cusa actually ashed the plant material completely, he would have found the weight of the ash equal to the decrease in soil weight. Thoroughly imbued with the dogma of the day, which maintained that all matter could be resolved into the four elements—earth, air, fire and water (air and fire having no appreciable weight in this scheme)—Cusa could scarcely be expected to have considered that a major fraction of the plant mass was derived from a seemingly weightless element such as air.—*Editors*.

By Experiment, that All Vegetable Matter is Totally and Materially of Water Alone. ❧

by JEAN-BAPTISTE VAN HELMONT

From *Ortus Medicinae*, pp. 108–109, Amsterdam, 1748. Translated by Naphtali Lewis for this volume.

THAT ALL VEGETABLE [matter] immediately and materially arises from the element of water alone I learned from this experiment. I took an earthenware pot, placed in it 200 lb of earth dried in an oven, soaked this with water, and planted in it a willow shoot weighing 5 lb. After five years had passed, the tree grown therefrom weighed 169 lb and about 3 oz. But the earthenware pot was constantly wet only with rain or (when necessary) distilled water; and it was ample [in size] and imbedded in the ground; and, to prevent dust flying around from mixing with the earth, the rim of the pot was kept covered with an iron plate coated with tin and pierced with many holes. I did not compute the weight of the deciduous leaves of the four autumns. Finally, I again dried the earth of the pot, and it was found to be the same 200 lb minus about 2 oz. Therefore, 164 lb of wood, bark, and root had arisen from the water alone.

Observations on Different Kinds of Air. ❧

by JOSEPH PRIESTLEY, LL.D., F.R.S.

Abridged from *Philosophical Transactions of The Royal Society of London*, Vol. 62, pp. 166–170 (1772). Reprinted by permission of The Royal Society.

During the eighteenth century it was generally assumed that plants were nourished exclusively through the roots by the absorption of water and humus from the soil. The first inkling that the atmosphere was in any way involved in plant nutrition was given to the world by Priestley. Unfortunately for his understanding of the experimental results he obtained, Priestley was under the sway of the prevailing phlogiston theory of Stahl, and he could only interpret the effect of plants in "restoring" air as a "phlogistication" of air that had been "dephlogisticated" by combustion or the respiration of animals. Unaware of the importance of illumination in this process, Priestley was unable to obtain consistent results when he repeated this work in later years. Priestley's discovery made it clear, however, that a balance between plant and animal activities was responsible for maintaining an atmosphere capable of supporting life. This important conception met with immediate widespread acceptance and stimulated a great deal of interest in photosynthesis.

I FLATTER MYSELF THAT I have accidentally hit upon a method of restoring air which has been injured by the burning of candles, and that I have discovered at least one of the restoratives which nature employs for this purpose. It is vegetation. In what manner this process in nature operates, to produce so remarkable an effect, I do not pretend to have discovered; but a number of facts declare in favour of this hypothesis. I shall introduce my account of them, by reciting some of the observations which I made on the growing of plants in confined air, which led to this discovery.

One might have imagined that, since common air is necessary to vegetable, as well as to animal life, both plants and animals had affected it in the same manner, and I own I had that expectation, when I first put a sprig of mint into a glass-jar, standing inverted in a vessel of water; but when it had continued growing there for some months, I found that the air would neither extinguish a candle, nor was it at all inconvenient to a mouse, which I put into it.

The plant was not affected any otherwise than was the necessary consequence of its confined situation; for plants growing in several other kinds of air, were all affected in the very same manner. Every succession of leaves was more diminished in size than the preceding, till, at length, they came to be no bigger than the heads of pins. The root decayed, and the stalk also, beginning from the root; and yet the plant continued to grow upwards, drawing its nourishment through a black and rotten stem. In the third or fourth set of leaves, long hairy filaments grew from the insertion of each leaf, and sometimes from the body of the stem, shooting out as far as the vessel in which it grew would permit, which, in my experiments, was about two inches. In this manner a sprig of mint lived, the old stem decaying, and new ones shooting up in its place, but less and less continually, all the summer season.

In repeating this experiment, care must be taken to draw away all the dead leaves from about the plant, lest they should putrefy, and affect the air. I have found that a fresh cabbage leaf, put under a glass vessel filled with common air, for the space of one night only, has so far affected the air, that a candle would not burn in it the next morning, and yet the leaf had not acquired any smell of putrefaction.

Finding that candles burn very well in air in which plants had grown a long time, and having had some reason to think, that there was something attending vegetation, which restored air that had been injured by respiration, I thought it was possible that the same process might also restore the air that had been injured by the burning of candles.

Accordingly, on the 17th of August, 1771, I put a sprig of mint into a quantity of air, in which a wax candle had burned out, and found that, on the 27th of the same month, another candle burned perfectly well in it. This experiment I repeated, without the least variation in the event, not less than eight or ten times in the remainder of the summer. Several times I divided the quantity of air in which the candle had burned out, into two parts, and putting the plant into one of them, left the other in the same exposure, contained, also, in a glass vessel immersed in water, but without any plant; and never failed to find, that a candle would burn in the former, but not in the latter. I generally found that five or six days were sufficient to restore this air, when the plant was in its vigour; whereas I have kept this kind of air in glass vessels, immersed in water many months, without being able to perceive that the least alteration had been made in it. I have also tried a great variety of experiments upon it, as by condensing, rarefying, exposing to the light and heat, &c. and throwing into it the effluvia of many different substances, but without any effect.

Experiments made in the year 1772, abundantly confirmed my conclusion concerning the restoration of air, in which candles had burned out by plants growing in it. The first of these experiments was made in the month of May; and they were frequently repeated in that and the two following months, without a single failure.

For this purpose I used the flames of different substances, though I generally used wax or tallow candles. On the 24th of June the experiment succeeded perfectly well with air in which spirit of wine had burned out, and on the 27th of the same month it succeeded equally well with air in which brimstone matches had burned out, an effect of which I had despaired the preceding year.

This restoration of air I found depended upon the vegetating state of the plant; for though I kept a great number of the fresh leaves of mint in a small quantity of air in which candles had burned out, and changed them fre-

quently, for a long space of time, I could perceive no melioration in the state of the air.

This remarkable effect does not depend upon any thing peculiar to mint, which was the plant that I always made use of till July 1772; for on the 16th of that month, I found a quantity of this kind of air to be perfectly restored by sprigs of balm, which had grown in it from the 7th of the same month.

That this restoration of air was not owing to any aromatic effluvia of these two plants, not only appeared by the essential oil of mint having no sensible effect of this kind; but from the equally complete restoration of this vitiated air by the plant called groundsel, which is usually ranked among the weeds, and has an offensive smell. This was the result of an experiment made the 16th of July, when the plant had been growing in the burned air from the 8th of the same month. Besides, the plant which I have found to be the most effectual of any that I have tried for this purpose is spinach, which is of quick growth, but will seldom thrive long in water. One jar of burned air was perfectly restored by this plant in four days, and another in two days. This last was observed on the 22d of July. In general this effect may be presumed to have taken place in much less time than I have mentioned; because I never chose to make a trial of the air, till I was pretty sure, from preceding observations, that the event which I had expected must have taken place, if it would succeed at all; lest, returning back that part of the air on which I made the trial, and which would thereby necessarily receive a small mixture of common air, the experiment might not be judged to be quite fair; though I myself might be sufficiently satisfied with respect to the allowance that was to be made for that small imperfection.

Experiments upon Vegetables.

by JOHN INGEN-HOUSZ

Excerpted from the book *Experiments upon Vegetables, Discovering Their Great Power of Purifying the Common Air in the Sun-shine, and of Injuring it in the Shade and at Night*, London, 1779.

In three months in the summer of 1778, during a leave of absence from his duties as physician to the Austrian court, Ingen-Housz performed about 500 experiments, the results of which he presented in his Experiments on Vegetables, Discovering Their Great Power of Purifying the Common Air in the Sun-shine, and of Injuring it in the Shade and at Night, *published the following year. Priestley had assumed that the purification of air by plants was a consequence of their growth. Now Ingen-Housz was able to demonstrate that sunlight was necessary for oxygen production, that only the leaves and petioles could photosynthesize, and that fruits or shaded plants respired like animals. Significant achievements indeed to show for a summer's work! At the time, Lavoisier's refutation of the phlogiston theory had just been accomplished, but his viewpoint had not yet supplanted the old doctrine. In this book, therefore, we find Ingen-Housz discussing his results in terms of the phlogiston theory. Years later, in his* Essay on the Nutrition of Plants and the Fruitfulness of the Earth *(1796), Ingen-Housz reinterpreted his earlier work in line with the new chemistry.*

I WAS NOT LONG engaged in this enquiry before I saw a most important scene opened to my view: I observed, *that plants not only have a faculty to correct bad air in six or ten days, by growing in it, as the experiments of Dr. Priestley indicate, but that they perform this important office in a compleat manner in a few hours; that this wonderful operation is by no means owing to the vegetation of the plant, but to the influence of the light of the sun upon the plant. I found that plants have, moreover, a most surprising faculty of elaborating the air which they contain, and undoubtedly absorb continually from the common atmosphere, into real and fine dephlogisticated air* [oxygen]; *that they pour down continually, if I may so express myself, a shower of this depurated air, which, diffusing itself through the common mass of the atmosphere, contributes to render it more fit for animal life; that this operation is far from being carried on constantly, but begins only after the sun has for some time made his appearance above the horizon, and has, by his influence, prepared the plants to begin anew their beneficial operation upon the air, and thus upon the animal creation, which was stopt during the darkness of the night; that this operation of the plants is more or less brisk in proportion to the clearness of the day, and the exposition of the plants more or less adapted to receive the direct influence of that great luminary; that plants shaded by high buildings, or growing under a dark shade of other plants, do not perform this office, but, on the contrary, throw out an air hurtful to animals, and even contaminate the air which surrounds them; that this operation of plants diminishes towards the close of the day, and ceases entirely at sun-set, except in a few plants, which continue this duty somewhat longer than others; that this office is not performed by the whole plant, but only by the leaves and the green stalks that support them; that acrid, ill-scented, and even the most poisonous plants perform this office in common with the mildness and the most salutary; that the most part of leaves pour out the greatest quantity of this dephlogisticated air from their under surface, principally those of lofty trees; that young leaves, not yet come to their full perfection, yield dephlogisticated air less in quantity, and of an inferior quality, than what is produced by full-grown and old leaves; that some plants elaborate dephlogisticated air better than others; that some of the aquatic plants seem to excell in this operation; that all plants contaminate the surrounding air by night, and even in the day-time in shaded places; that, however, some of those which are inferior to none in yielding beneficial air in the sun-shine, surpass others in the power of infecting the circumambient air in the dark, even to such a degree, that in a few hours they render a great body of good air so noxious, that an animal placed in it loses its life in a few seconds; that all flowers render the surrounding air highly noxious, equally by night and by day; that the roots removed from the ground do the same, some few however, excepted;*

but that in general fruits have the same deleterious quality at all times, though principally in the dark, and many to such an astonishing degree, that even some of those fruits which are the most delicious, as, for instance, peaches, contaminate so much the common air as would endanger us to lose our lives, if we were shut up in a room in which a great deal of such fruits are stored up; that the sun by itself has no power to mend air without the concurrence of plants, but on the contrary is apt to contaminate it.

These are some of the secret operations of plants I discovered in my retirement, of which I will endeavour to give some account in the following pages; submitting, however, to the judgement of the candid reader the consequences, which I thought might fairly be deduced from the facts I am to relate. . . .

All plants possess a power of correcting, in a few hours, foul air unfit for respiration; but only in clear daylight, or in the sunshine.

This remarkable property of plants is indeed very great; for in a few hours, nay even sometimes in an hour and an half, they purify so much a body of air quite unfit for respiration, as to be equal in goodness to atmospheric air. They will even do it when they are inclosed in a glass vessel, without any water. One leaf of a vine, shut up in an ounce phial, full of air fouled by breathing so that a candle could not burn in it, restored this air to the goodness of common air in the space of an hour and a half. But plants enjoy this privilege only in the day-time, and when they grow in unshaded places.

This power of plants extends itself even to the worst of all airs, in which an animal finds his destruction in a moment; such as is pure inflammable and highly phlogisticated air, which is little or scarcely at all diminishable by nitrous air. I observed some differences in various kinds of plants in this respect, and found that water plants seem to possess this quality in a greater degree than others. The willow tree and the *persicaria urens* were found eminent in producing this effect; and may it not be providentially ordained it should be so, as those plants grow better in marshy, low grounds, and even in stagnated waters, whose bottoms are generally muddy, and yield a great deal of inflammable air, which may be collected at the surface of the water by stirring up the ground, and may be kindled by throwing a burning paper upon the water, which is an amusing experiment by night? Plants, however, want longer time to correct this kind of air, at least that which is extracted from metals by vitriolic acid.[1]

All plants yield a more or less quantity of dephlogisticated air in the day-time, when growing in the open air, and free from dark shade.

The quantity of dephlogisticated air, and even the quality of it, which the leaves of plants give, seems to be different in different plants: though, indeed, this may depend in a great measure upon some particular circumstances, to which it is not easy to be sufficiently attentive. It seems, however, to be a general rule, that the leaves of all plants, growing in a place where they are not much shaded by other plants, buildings, &c. yield, in a clear day, dephlogisticated air; and that this air is yielded in greater abundance, and of a greater purity, when they grow in open places unincumbered by other plants higher than they are themselves.

I got in general a large quantity of air of a very good quality from some water plants, as from the *persicaria urens* and willow. The fir trees yielded also very fine air, and in abundance.

The *nasturtium Indicum* surpassed

them all in general, in regard as well to the quantity as to the quality. One hundred leaves of this plant, which are very thin, yielded, in two hours time, as much dephlogisticated air as would fill a cylindrical glass four inches and a half deep, and one inch and three quarters diameter; of which quantity gathered again afterwards from the same leaves, without taking them out of the water. . . . This quantity surpasses by far the bulk of the leaves themselves, and shews to how amazing a quantity the air may amount yielded in a fair day by a lofty tree.

The leaves being more or less crouded together, being exposed for a longer or shorter time, or sooner or later in the day, will occasion some difference in the quality and quantity of this air.

It seems that, in general, the finest air is obtained when the sun has passed the meridian.

Experiments tending to investigate to what degree plants may affect common air in the night, and by day time in shaded places.

Two handfuls of leaves of *French beans* were put in a jar of a gallon; it was kept inverted upon a dish, and some water poured upon it; next morning I found the air so much fouled that a candle could not burn in it. One measure of it with one of nitrous air occupied 1.39.[2]

---

[1] Plainly, Ingen-Housz does not distinguish hydrogen from methane—*Editors.*

[2] Nitrous air is nitric oxide, NO, which is very slightly soluble in water. It reacts with atmospheric oxygen to form water-soluble nitrogen dioxide: $2NO + O_2 \rightarrow NO_2$. Priestley had previously discovered this reaction and utilized it as a means of assaying the oxygen content of air by measuring the diminution in volume which occurred when nitric oxide was mixed with air. The numbers given by Ingen-Housz in this and subsequent experiments express relative volume as measured with the eudiometer, or gas burette. This instrument may best be described by quoting Ingen-Housz's own words in the introduction to his book:

Eudiometer, is a new word; it signifies an instrument by which we may judge of the

After having taken out some of the air for trial, I placed the jar with the remaining air and leaves in the sun from nine till eleven o'clock, when I found the air so much mended, that a candle could burn in it, and that one measure of it with one of nitrous air occupied 1.12.

After this I replaced it again in the sun till five in the afternoon, when I found the air so much mended as to be equal in goodness to common air.

Experiments showing that no part of

degree of salubrity of the common air. The invention of such an instrument belongs to Dr. Priestley. It consists chiefly of a glass tube, divided in equal parts; for instance, in two large divisions; each of which is divided into ten others, and each of these ten sub-divided again into ten parts: and a glass measure, containing exactly one of the great divisions of the tube. One measure of common air and one of nitrous air, put together in a separate glass vessel, and left by themselves till the diminution of the bulk of the two airs is compleated, and afterwards let up in the glass tube, indicates at once the exact diminution of the two joint measures. The degree of goodness of the common air is found to be in proportion to the diminution of the bulk of the two airs. . . .—*Editors.*

plants improve ordinary air, or yield dephlogisticated air, but the leaves and the green stalks.

The former experiments with flowers, roots, and fruits, are already above related. There remain only the green stalks or branches, not yet covered with the rough skin or bark, and the wood itself, to be examined.

I put some green stalks of a willow-tree, the leaves being stripped off, in a gallon jar filled with pump-water; the jar was exposed, inverted, as ordinary, upon a wall in a warm sun-shine during four hours. They became most beautifully covered with an infinite number of round air-bubbles. A great deal of dephlogisticated air was obtained, which gave, by the nitrous test, 1.96; 1.87; 1.83½; 2.68; 3.64.

Some branches of a mulberry-tree, covered with grey bark, were put in a gallon jar full of pump-water, and exposed to the sun. A moderate quantity of air was obtained, which, being put to the nitrous test, proved to be about the same quality with common air; its test was 2.01; 2.10; 3.10.

On the Influence of Carbonic Acid Gas on Mature Plants.

by N. TH. DE SAUSSURE

Excerpted from *Recherches Chimiques sur la Végétation*, Paris, 1804. Translated by M. L. Gabriel for this volume.

To appreciate the radical nature of the revolution in chemistry that took place at the turn of the nineteenth century, one has only to compare the preceding pages by Ingen-Housz with these excerpts from de Saussure's book Chemical Investigations on Vegetation *published only twenty-five years later. In the interval Lavoisier had established the nature of oxidation and the phlogiston theory had been forever over-*

thrown, Lavoisier had elucidated the chemical composition of carbon dioxide, and water had been synthesized from hydrogen and oxygen (Cavendish, 1784) and decomposed by electrolysis (Nicholson and Carlisle, 1800). The distinction between elements and compounds was still hazy, Dalton's formulation of the atomic theory being still four years in the future, and consequently de Saussure's interpretation of his results could not be completely correct. Nevertheless, this work stands as the first quantitative treatment of photosynthesis, expressed in what are almost modern terms.

PERCIVAL HAS OBSERVED that a mint plant nourished with water and placed in a current of air mixed with carbonic acid gas thrived better than a similar plant placed in a current of pure atmospheric air.

I attempted to confirm this observation and to determine the amount of carbonic acid which, mixed with atmospheric air, has a beneficial influence on the growing plant. With the aid of water I allowed peas to germinate until each plant reached a height of about one decimeter and weighed one gram. Thereupon for each experiment I placed three plants in a water glass so that only the roots were immersed in the liquid, and brought them together with various mixtures of ordinary air and carbonic acid gas in vessels, sealed with water, which were covered on the inside with a layer of oil when the vessels contained more than half their volume of carbonic acid gas. Three pea plants in each experiment had an atmosphere of 990 cc and themselves took up not a four-hundredth part. They were exposed to the direct rays of the sun for five or six hours daily and partly shaded whenever the light intensity was too great.

At the same time and in the same place I set up similar apparatus and placed them in weak and diffused light. These latter set-ups I have designated "exposure to shade."

RESULTS IN SUNLIGHT

The average gain in weight of the plants set out in the sun during ten days amounted to 425 mg for each pea plant in atmospheric air.*

With the same exposure these plants withered as soon as they came in contact with pure carbonic acid gas. They suffered the same fate in an atmosphere containing $3/4$ or $2/3$ the volume of carbonic acid gas.

They grew seven days in a vessel which contained half its volume of carbonic acid gas; after this they stopped growing. Plants kept in an atmosphere containing $1/4$ its volume of carbonic acid gas maintained themselves during the 10 days of the experiment, but grew only slightly. Each pea plant gained only about 265 mg.

In $1/8$ carbonic acid gas the average gain amounted to 371 mg. The average gain of each plant in an atmosphere of ordinary air of which carbonic acid gas comprised $1/12$ amounted to 583 mg. I have repeated this experiment many times; and the plants thrived consistently better in it than in pure atmospheric air. The plants growing in the latter did not change it perceptibly either in purity or in volume; those, however, which grew in the artificial mixture, transformed nearly all the carbonic acid gas to oxygen. . . .

---

* This weight gain must be attributed largely or perhaps entirely to the transport of water—that is, vegetation water—to the leaves, which developed during the course of the experiment and formed their solid substance out of the cotyledons, which were still thick and attached to the plant. These cotyledons contain three or four times less water than the leaves to whose development they contribute.

RESULTS IN SHADE

In the apparatus set up in the shade, the slightest amount of carbonic acid gas mixed with ordinary air was harmful to growing plants. In an atmosphere containing one-fourth the volume of carbonic acid gas they were dead after the sixth day. They maintained themselves, in the same exposure to light, for 10 days in an atmosphere containing $\frac{1}{12}$ part of carbonic acid gas, but their weight gain amounted to only 159 mg whereas in pure atmospheric air they gained 265 mg. . . .

The Consumption of Carbonic Acid Gas by Leaves Is Necessary for their Existence in the Sun.

Into a glass globe I introduced 31 g of lime [which absorbs carbonic acid gas]. I moistened it slightly in order to obviate any doubt as to its dehydrating qualities. Thereupon I introduced into the four-liter globe a leafy branch of a woody plant * which was set in the light and whose roots were in earth; I took pains to see that the leaves touched neither the lime nor the walls of the globe, the neck of which was carefully cemented to the branch. I attached a similar apparatus but without lime in the globe to a branch adjacent to the first. This branch preserved its fresh condition for longer than two months; not so, however, the branch growing in the presence of lime. Its leaves remained green for fourteen days; then they began to become dry, and after three weeks they fell off. The branch was not dead, for a month later it produced fresh leaves in the globe which had not been loosened. At this time, however, the lime no longer had any effect on the air, its surface being saturated with carbonic

---

* The plants with which I set up these experiments were honeysuckle (*Lonicera caprifolium*), plum (*Prunus domestica*), privet (*Ligustrum vulgare*) and peach (*Amygdalus persica*).

acid. I took it out and found that it effervesced when treated with acid.

These new formations of leaves show that the fall of leaves is not to be ascribed to deprivation of oxygen which is held by the lime through the absorption of carbonic acid gas, but merely to the absence of the latter. . . .

On the Decomposition of Carbonic Acid Gas by the Green Parts of Plants.

Priestley was the first to recognize that leaves possess the ability to improve air which has been vitiated by combustion or respiration, but he did not inquire into the cause of this phenomenon. Senebier discovered that leaves decompose carbonic acid gas by assimilating the carbon and separating the oxygen. He observed that fresh leaves placed in the sun in well-water or in water lightly impregnated with carbonic acid gas evolved oxygen as long as carbonic acid gas was present in the water. He saw that when leaves were placed in the light after forming gas in distilled water they did not produce any quantity of gas larger than could be contained in their volume. But the products of the breakdown of carbonic acid gas were not analyzed and it was not determined whether the amount of oxygen evolved was greater, less, or equal to that which goes into the formation of carbonic acid gas. The following experiments are devoted to the solution of this problem. . . .

FIRST EXPERIMENT

With Myrtle (*Vinca minor L.*)

Out of carbonic acid gas and ordinary air shown by the phosphoreudiometer [1] to contain 21/100 oxygen, I made up an artificial atmosphere which occupied 5.746 liters. Lime water showed it to contain $7\frac{1}{2}$ per cent of carbonic acid

---

[1] A kind of gas burette; see p. 160—*Editors.*

gas. This gas mixture was enclosed in a vessel which was sealed with wet mercury, i.e., mercury covered with a thin layer of water to prevent contact of the metal with the atmosphere of the plant; since I had previously established the fact that, as already reported by the Dutch chemists, mercury is harmful to plants in experiments of long duration.

Into this vessel I introduced seven myrtle plants each of which was two decimeters tall; their combined volume was 10 cc. Their roots were immersed in a separate vessel containing 15 cc of water; the quantity of this liquid was insufficient to absorb any significant amount of carbonic acid gas, especially at room temperature which never fell below 17° Réaumur [70°F.].

This apparatus was exposed for six consecutive days to the direct rays of the sun from 5 to 11 o'clock A.M., the light being partly shaded whenever it became too intense. On the seventh day I took out the plants, which had not undergone the slightest change. Taking into consideration all corrections, the volume of the atmosphere had not changed, at least so far as one can judge in a vessel of 1.3 decimeters in diameter, in which a difference of 20 cc can barely be estimated; the error cannot be greater than this.

Testing with lime water showed that carbonic acid gas was no longer present, whereas the eudiometer indicated 24½ per cent oxygen. I set up a similar apparatus with pure atmospheric air and the same number of plants; the air did not change either in purity or volume.

It is shown by the eudiometric observations adduced here that the mixture of carbonic acid gas and ordinary air contained, before the experiment:

4199 cc nitrogen
1116 cc oxygen
431 cc carbonic acid gas
———
5746 cc

The same air after the experiment contained:

4338 cc nitrogen
1408 cc oxygen
0 cc carbonic acid gas
———
5746 cc

The myrtle had therefore utilized or caused to disappear 431 cc of carbonic acid gas; had it been eliminated again as oxygen, a volume equal to that of the vanished carbonic acid gas should have been formed; since, however, the plants evolved only 292 cc of oxygen, they accordingly must have assimilated 139 cc of oxygen and formed 139 cc of nitrogen [2] in breaking down the carbonic acid gas.

A comparative experiment showed me that the seven myrtle plants which I had used had a dry weight of 2.707 grams before decomposing the carbonic acid gas; on being charred over a fire in sealed vessels, they yielded 528 mg of carbon. The plants which had decomposed carbonic acid gas, after having been dried and carbonized by the same method, yielded 649 mg of carbon. The decomposition of carbonic acid gas resulted, therefore, in a gain of 120 mg of carbon.

I similarly carbonized myrtle plants which had grown in air free of carbonic acid gas and found that the carbon content during the period of maintenance under the vessel had greatly decreased rather than increased. . . .

Plants nourished by pure water in the fresh air obtain carbon from the small amount of carbonic acid gas which occurs naturally in our atmosphere.

The preceding observations indicate that plants kept in enclosed vessels decompose carbonic acid gas if it is

---

[2] De Saussure's conclusion that nitrogen is formed is, of course, incorrect; the apparent increase in nitrogen resulted from errors of technique of which he was unaware.—*Editors.*

mixed with atmospheric air in a proportion higher than its normal occurrence.

It is now the suitable moment to inquire if this decomposition can also take place in the open air which contains hardly more than 1 per cent by volume of carbonic acid gas. Hassenfratz in a treatise on the nutrition of plants has attempted to support the view that plants growing in the open air in pure water increase in volume with the aid of water alone and that after their development they contain less carbon than is present in the seed. I have performed several experiments that have yielded results which precisely contradict those of this author. I shall present two examples.

FIRST EXPERIMENT

I immersed the roots of several peppermint plants (*Mentha piperita*) in jars filled with distilled water and these plants were allowed to grow in a planting box outside a window in the sun, but protected from rain. By uprooting and drying some of these plants at the same time and place, I convinced myself * that out of 100 parts grown in distilled water, 40.29 parts were dry substance, of which after carbonization 10.96 parts of carbon were left.

One hundred parts of peppermint, after 2½ months' growth in open air, weighed 216 parts by weight in the fresh state; so far this gain does not signify anything as it might be attributed to an increase in water content, as always occurs when plants grow in a place that is moister than that in which they had been growing previously. Upon drying

* The absolute weight of the plants growing in distilled water was 7.6 grams.

at air temperature the weight of the plants went down to 62 parts. The plants had therefore increased their dry substance with the aid of air and water by 21.71 parts. These 62 parts on being carbonized yielded 15.78 parts of carbon, or 4.82 parts more than they would have yielded if they had not been growing in distilled water. When I allowed the same plants to grow under similar conditions in a weakly illuminated place I found that they had lost a small amount of their carbon. Perhaps lack of light was the cause of the results obtained by Hassenfratz.

SECOND EXPERIMENT

I put four beans weighing 6.368 g into a glass case among pebbles and poured distilled water over them. At the end of a growth period of three months in the sun under the open sky the fresh bean plants, immediately after flowering, weighed 87.149 g. Upon drying the weight decreased to 10.721 g; during their growth in the open air the beans had nearly doubled the amount of their dry substance. On being charred in closed vessels these plants yielded 2.703 g of carbon; now, however, four beans of the same weight as those used in the experiment contained 1.209 g of carbon. The beans therefore had gained more than double the amount of carbon when they developed with the aid of water in the open air; it cannot be doubted that they accomplished this only through the decomposition of carbonic acid gas which was found in the atmosphere; because, as we have seen in the preceding paragraphs, plants grown in vessels filled with pure atmospheric air which is not renewed do not increase their carbon content.

On the Production of Oxygen by Plant Cells in a Microspectrum. ∿

by TH. W. ENGELMANN

From *Botanische Zeitung*, Vol. 40, pp. 419–426 (1882).
Translated by M. L. Gabriel for this volume.

Engelmann was not the first to concern himself with the question of relative effectiveness of different portions of the spectrum in photosynthesis, and later workers improved on the quantitative precision of the determinations by equalizing the amounts of energy supplied at different wavelengths. But from the standpoint of sheer elegance of technique, this experiment will always excite admiration. Especially ingenious was Engelmann's use of light transmitted through the cell itself to correct for the absorption spectrum of chlorophyll.

DURING THE PAST FALL and winter I have more closely investigated the dependence of oxygen production by green cells upon the wave length of the light by means of the bacterial method, utilizing for this purpose a microspectral apparatus designed to my specifications by Carl Zeiss. A brief report on this subject may be given here.

The apparatus, which is designed to throw a microscopically small spectrum in the plane of the object, is placed, when in use, in the position of the usual illuminating system of the microscope (mirror and diaphragm). It consists (1) of a plane mirror adjustable in any direction; (2) a double slit mechanism comprising (a) a bilaterally symmetrically movable slit, the width of which may be exactly adjusted between the limits of 0 and 2 mm to the nearest 0.001 mm by means of a micrometer screw; (b) two 'sGravesande blades movable at right angles to slit "a" for regulation of the length of the light slit; (3) a collimator lens; (4) an erecting prism; (5) an objective system for perfecting the spectral image of the slit. Since it is desirable to be able to change the absolute size of the spectrum according to the nature of the object and the requisite light intensity, the objective system is not fixed but various objectives can be screwed in. For Zeiss objectives A, B, and C, which are sufficient for most purposes, the absolute distances between Fraunhofer lines a and E [7185 Å and 5270 Å] are respectively 0.236, 0.180, and 0.092 mm.

The clearness of the spectrum is such that when sunlight is used (even much weakened) and a slit width of 15 μ and less, several hundred Fraunhofer lines are clearly visible. The intensity of illumination is sufficient, even with the use of objective A with an ordinary gas flame as light source, for observation of bacteria under high magnification with a permissible slit width of 10 μ and less.

For exact determination of the wavelength of the light when using a continuous spectrum, one utilizes the scale of an ocular micrometer which is calibrated with the solar spectrum for each combination of objectives.

The position of the spectrum in the microscopic field in relation to the scale may be adjusted by screws. With continuous spectra, sharp adjustment may be accomplished by using a sodium flame. . . .

The results to be reported here . . . have to do with the problem of the relative effectiveness of different wave-lengths of light in relation to the production of oxygen by cells containing chlorophyll.

In essence, the bacterial method is applicable to the solution of this problem by two different methods:—They may be distinguished as the methods of simultaneous and successive observation.

With the method of simultaneous observation one simultaneously observes the effect of different rays of the spectrum on the same object in different closely spaced positions, or upon different objects of the greatest possible similarity which are equally distributed through the spectrum. In the first case the object must have a regular, e.g., cylindrical or prismatic form, and a very regular structure especially in regard to the distribution of the chlorophyll. Filamentous algae, Oscillatoria, long diatoms or diatom colonies are especially suitable. But tissue sections may also be used. The object is placed in the microspectrum with its longitudinal axis at right angles to the direction of the Fraunhofer lines.

Hereupon, the following is observed:

On increasing the light intensity from zero, the bacteria in the immediate vicinity of the green cells, which had previously come to rest because of lack of oxygen, now begin to move, generally first in the red, usually between B and C [6869 Å—6563 Å] or close to C.

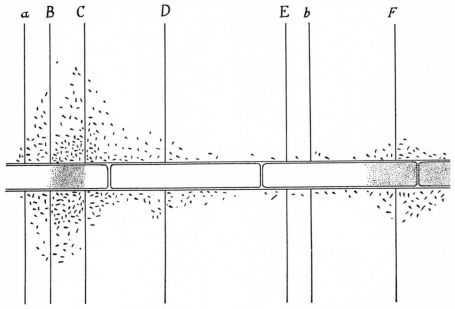

FIG. 1.—Portion of a *Cladophora* with swarming bacteria in a microspectrum of sunlight. The chloroplasts, which fill the cells uniformly, have been omitted. The absorption band between B and C, and the absorption at the violet end, beginning between b and F, are indicated (enlarged 200 X).

On further increase in the light intensity the effect spreads towards the beginning of the infra-red and in the violet. The original accumulation and rapidity of motion of the bacteria remain greatest in the red. With green cells (e.g., *Euglena, Oedogonium, Cladophora*), but not with brown (diatoms) and bluegreen (*Oscillaria*), a minimum around E [5270 Å] and a second maximum around F [4861 Å] may be observed in sunlight (not in gaslight).

If very many bacteria are present, one sees in such cases a sort of graphic representation of the relationship between the wave-length and the energy of assimilation [photosynthesis], in which the abscissa is represented by the object itself and the ordinates by the various heights of the bacterial accumulations, as the accompanying wood-cut shows.

In very great light intensities the differences become slighter, in that accumulation and velocity become very apparent in all parts of the spectrum. As long as the spectrum remains pure (narrow slit), however, the difference in favor of the red remains always noticeable.

Upon gradually diminishing the light intensity the phenomena described are repeated in reverse order.

In the method of successive observation, the selfsame object, which must be small, or at least narrow, is brought successively into the different parts of the spectrum and each time the smallest slit width is sought at which the bacteria immediately next to the object will move. Various modifications of this experiment could be applied, but they yield essentially similar results. The light source during a series of determinations must naturally remain constant, a condition which is easily fulfilled since for each measurement only one or several minutes are required. With good, that is, homogeneous and not oversensitive bacteria, this experiment yields especially precise measurements.

In the two tables following several results obtained in this way are reported.

The values representing the oxygen production in different regions of the spectrum are the minimal slit widths at which bacterial motility was observed, set down in inverse proportion. The maximum value is taken as equal to 100. The measurements were in each case taken in order proceeding from the red end toward the violet end and then again in reverse order; each number is the average of the two values thus obtained.

In the beginning of the infra-red no effect was observed. Oxygen production therefore begins at the outermost visible red. As the tables and many more confirming experiments show, it reaches its greatest magnitude between B and C [6869–6563 Å] and falls off with diminishing wave-length at first rapidly, later more slowly. In the sunlight spectrum this drop takes place more slowly than in that of gas-light. It reaches a minimum (at most about 10–20 per cent) for green cells (not for brown and blue-green) cells in the green, some-

a) Experiments with sunlight (subdued by one or two pieces of ground-glass)

	a	B½C	C½D	D	D½E	E½b	E½F	F	F½G	G
Euglena viridis (rounded resting condition) of 0.018 mm diameter	11	100	59	45	24	14	16	20	14	..
E. viridis. Another individual of 0.022 mm diameter	14	100	57	42	31	18	23	24	20	11
Green spore (resting condition) of 0.006 mm diameter	18	100	68	48	17	12	25	27	18	8
Navicula sp., 0.005 mm wide	..	100	..	65	..	36	..	20	..	..
Oscillaria sp., 0.005 mm wide	..	100	..	73	..	30	..	15.7	..	..

b) Experiments with gaslight.

	a	B½C	C½D	D	D½E	E½b	E½F	F	F½G	G
Euglena viridis (resting condition) of 0.012 mm diameter	30	100	40	23	11	8	4.5	3.5	..	..
E. viridis of 0.015 mm diameter	34	100	47	25	13	8	5	..	..	..
E. viridis of 0.023 mm diameter	30	100	53	30	10.5	8	5.5	..	..	..
Green spore (resting condition) of 0.006 mm diameter	30	100	50	32	..	12	..	6	..	1
Oedogonium sp. (Cell 0.012 mm wide)	35	100	44	30	10.5	6.5	5	3	2	..
Pinnularia, 0.018 mm wide	20	100	40	24.5	19	13.5	8	4.5	2	..
Oscillaria, 0.0056 mm wide	..	100	74	39	13	9.5	...	5.9	..	..

where between E and b [5270 Å and 5180 Å] and a second maximum in the blue somewhere near F [4861 Å]. If one takes into account the much more considerable amount of dispersion in the blue part of the prismatic spectrum, it follows that for sunlight the assimilatory [photosynthetic] effect of blue light at F hardly falls short of that of the red between B and C. With electric light and magnesium light the former should markedly surpass the latter. This fact will have to be taken into account in judging the results of culture experiments in electric light.

As may be seen, the results obtained by the bacterial method deviate essentially from these obtained by the methods (gas analysis, gas bubble counts) heretofore used by trustworthy investigators (Draper, Sachs, Pfeffer), in that the greatest effect is not in the yellow at D [5892 Å], but is located in the red between B and C and next (with sunlight and green cells) in the blue at F. . . .

The discrepancy is . . . readily and adequately explained by the circumstance that with the methods heretofore employed (gas analysis, gas bubble counts), macroscopic objects must be used, so that one is dealing with the effect of light on a number of successive chlorophyll-containing layers; in the deeper ones, the absorption of light by the more superficial layers has an effect. Now this absorption, as known, and as may be very clearly demonstrated by microspectral analysis of a single chloroplast, occurs chiefly in the red rays between B and C, which according to my experiments are precisely the most effective, as are the equally very effective blue rays of F (and beyond). Now since the production of oxygen by the most superficially situated chlorophyll layer comprises in general only a relatively small part of the total oxygen production of the leaf or whole plant, the maximal effects of the latter can no longer fall between B and C and at F, but the maximum effect, in general, is rather to be expected in the yellow to green.

The correctness of this consideration was corroborated by experiments with the bacterial method using light which was transmitted through a dilute solution of chlorophyll or through a thin green leaf: for every absorption band of the chlorophyll, a corresponding minimum of oxygen production could easily be demonstrated. Indeed, in a microspectrum of ordinary light this influence of the absorption showed itself in any cell that was rich in chlorophyll and not too thin, in that the thickest accumulation and most rapid motion of the bacteria *under* the cell, i.e., on the side facing the light source, was in the red, while *above* the cell it took place in the yellow to green.

For example, in a *Cladophora* cell

0.028 mm thick, the relative magnitude of oxygen production in different parts of the sunlight spectrum measured as follows:

	for B-C	D	D½-E	E-b	F	F½-G
Under surface of the cell	100.0	48.5	37.0	24.0	36.5	10.0
Upper surface of the cell	36.5	94.0	100.0	52.0	22.0	12.0

In the fact that the bacterial method virtually eliminates the effect of light absorption, or at least makes it possible easily to correct for this effect, lies one of its essential advantages over previous experiments.

Photosynthesis of Bacteria.

by C. B. VAN NIEL

Reprinted from *Contributions to Marine Biology* (A report of the 1929 meeting of the Western Society of Naturalists) pp. 161–169, with the permission of the publishers, Stanford University Press.

In large measure, the progress of a science can be measured by the extent to which its various lines of investigation have converged so as to bring the phenomena it describes within a common conceptual scheme. Such a sign of maturity in biology has been the achievement of biochemists in recent times in laying bare the uniformity of protoplasmic systems throughout the living world. In the field of photosynthesis, a brilliant example of this synthetic approach is the following paper, in which van Niel has clarified the nature of photosynthesis and has pointed out the biochemical unity underlying the metabolic processes of a diversity of organisms that are capable of utilizing light energy in their nutrition. The implication from van Niel's work that the oxygen liberated in photosynthesis comes from the decomposition of water was confirmed experimentally by Ruben and others in 1941.

IT WAS LAVOISIER who made the fundamental discovery of the importance of atmospheric oxygen in life processes. As no living organism was known which could live without oxygen, he naturally concluded that O_2 was, without exception, necessary for the sustenance of life; metabolism was looked upon as a process of "slow combustion" of organic matter. This point of view held until Pasteur, in studying the microscopic living beings, discovered organisms which were able to live and to develop in the complete absence of free O_2 and formulated his genial conception: *"La fermentation c'est la vie sans air."* Here was a substitute for the "slow combustion"; here were processes which evolved in the total absence of one of the integral factors of any combustion.

Yet there should be something in common in these two widely divergent phenomena of living matter; the "slow combustion" as well as the "fermentation" would appear to represent merely two different aspects of this common feature. Especially the work and clear insight of Max Rubner made us familiar with the idea that the most important function of both was the liberation of energy. It was this same idea of the function of organic matter as a source of energy for living organisms which, as early as 1887, led Winogradsky to his brilliant conception of the function of inorganic substances as the combustible matter or source of energy in the metabolism of lower organisms.

This conception was based on Winogradsky's experiments on the sulphur bacteria and has been proved conclusively, as far as the colorless forms are concerned, by Keil in 1912. Among the sulphur bacteria studied by Winogradsky were also those forms which had been known, since the time of Ray Lankester, Cohn, Warming, etc., as purple bacteria, characterized by purplered colored cells. He showed that these organisms also converted hydrogen sulphide into sulphates and, therefore, concluded that their metabolism was similar. Now these purple bacteria behave like true anaërobes, and for the oxidation process would need O_2. Winogradsky's observations on the favorable influence of minute green organisms (green bacteria) led him to the hypothesis that these latter provided it.

As early as 1882, Engelmann had made the important observation that the purple bacteria were extremely sensitive to light, and therefore put forward the idea that they were capable of converting CO_2 in the light with the liberation of oxygen—a theory which he believed he had proved in 1887. By the use of Engelmann's motile bacteria method,

Ewart and Buder later confirmed Engelmann's results. All attempts, however, to demonstrate the liberation of oxygen by methods other than Engelmann's failed.

Skene, after having proved in 1914 that these organisms can grow in a purely mineral medium containing H_2S under almost anaërobic conditions, went back to Winogradsky's hypothesis as to the function of the green bacteria, but Bavendamm made this appear highly improbable on the basis of his experimental results with cultures which, according to him, did not contain green bacteria. This situation is most clearly and critically discussed in Buder's excellent paper on the biology of the bacteriopurpurin and the purple bacteria, which was published in 1919. Therein Buder comes to the following conclusions:

The difficulty which at the present time exists in trying to explain the metabolism of the *Thiorhodaceae* seems to be based on the fact that one is inclined to ascribe an assimilatory function to the pigment according to Engelmann; whereas, on the other hand, we have to consider with Winogradsky the oxidation of the H_2S as a fundamental link of their metabolism—the more so because Skene's experiments and the analogy with the colorless sulphur bacteria also support this. Thus we would then have two sources of energy for the reduction of the CO_2, the light, and the chemical energy liberated during the oxidation of the H_2S. Up to now one seems to have been afraid to assume the existence of photo- and chemosynthesis independently side by side. From an energetic viewpoint I cannot see any difficulty in the way of this assumption. . . .

Buder then points out that the assumption of a photosynthetic activity is almost a necessary consequence of the observed facts; these organisms, however, in contradistinction to the green plants, would use the oxygen liberated for the oxidation of H_2S.

Yet there remains one great difficulty in the way of this, as Buder calls it, well-founded assumption. Buder discusses in detail the possibility of a purely chemosynthetic activity, and sees the superiority of the purple bacteria over the colorless forms in the fact that the former under anaërobic conditions can provide themselves with the necessary oxygen by a photosynthetic decomposition of CO_2. Bavendamm, following Buder's ideas, states:

As the red sulphur bacteria can develop in the absence of oxygen and require CO_2, but also need oxygen for the oxidation of the H_2S, we must assume that the pigments play a rôle similar to the chlorophyll, i.e., that the purple sulphur bacteria can assimilate CO_2 in the light with a simultaneous liberation of oxygen. . . . Thus they can also live during certain periods in places with little or no oxygen, which is impossible for the colorless forms. . . . When H_2S is lacking—under which conditions the colorless forms must die—the red forms still have the other source of energy at their disposition.

And yet, on the next page, Bavendamm states very definitely:

For both groups, the colorless and the purple sulphur bacteria, the H_2S is absolutely necessary.

To my mind the problem of the metabolism of the purple sulphur bacteria lies right here. We must account for the fact that they cannot live except in the presence of both H_2S and light. It is true that from an energetic point of view there is no objection to the assumption that a photo- and chemosynthetic mode of life might exist side by side independently. This would mean, however, that the organisms, once being capable of assimilating (reducing) CO_2 by means of photosynthesis, should be able, also, to develop in a medium free from H_2S.

Obviously, this is not true, and there seems to be only one possible explanation of it. It might be assumed that only part of the necessary CO_2 could be reduced by photosynthetic activity, and that the chemosynthetic reaction would have to furnish the additional supply. But if we calculate, on the basis of Winogradsky's data for the colorless sulphur bacteria, the quantity of CO_2 which can be reduced chemosynthetically with the aid of photosynthetically liberated oxygen, we find that 80 molecules of CO_2 must be reduced photosynthetically in order to furnish the necessary oxygen for the chemosynthetic reduction of only one molecule of CO_2. Quantitatively, then, it appears that there is no necessity for the existence of a chemosynthetic reaction. In fact it would be absurd to assume that this chemosynthetic reaction—made possible only by a previous photosynthetic production of oxygen—would provide the necessary energy for the reduction of part of the CO_2 which, for some obscure reason, could not be reduced photosynthetically.

Hence, the function of the H_2S as an independent source of energy having become highly improbable, we must find another explanation for the fact that there is, apparently, no photosynthetic activity in the absence of this compound.

What is photosynthesis? It has long been known that during photosynthesis a reaction takes place which may, schematically, be represented by the formula

$$CO_2 + H_2O = CH_2O + O_2$$

Thus we may say that it represents a typical oxidation-reduction process. CO_2 is reduced, H_2O is oxidized. It was Thunberg who first applied to this process the theory of oxidation and reduction phenomena developed by H. Wieland. According to Wieland's concept all oxidation reactions involve the transference of hydrogen from one molecule, the donor, to another compound, the acceptor. Thunberg pointed out that the reduction of the CO_2 during photosynthesis took place according to Wieland's general scheme, in other words, the CO_2 would act as the hydrogen acceptor, the H_2O as hydrogen donor, and that, consequently, the oxygen developed must be regarded as dehydrogenated H_2O.

H_2A	$+$	B	$\rightarrow$	A		BH_2
(donor)		(acceptor)		(oxid. prod.)	$+$	(red. prod.)
$2H_2O$	$+$	CO_2	$\rightarrow$	O_2		H_2O+CH_2O
(donor)		(acceptor)		(oxid. prod.)	$+$	(red. prod.)

A survey of the large number of oxidation-reduction reactions known to be accomplished by micro-organisms led Kluyver and Donker to their theory of the "unity in biochemistry" based. upon Wieland's ideas and on Boeseken's dislocation theory of catalytic action. This theory may be briefly formulated as follows:

Each special organism can bring about a specific activation of certain hydrogen atoms in the substratum. When the activation has reached a certain point, this activated hydrogen can be transferred to an acceptor, which, in its turn, is also activated.

The value of this theory as a working hypothesis has been shown by many important contributions in the field of microbial metabolism. It allows, here, a tentative explanation of the metabolism of the purple sulphur bacteria. For if we consider carbon dioxide assimilation (or reduction) in the light of this concept, it follows that, during the well-known photosynthetic reactions of the green plants, the hydrogen of the water molecule is sufficiently activated to be transferred to the carbon dioxide. And it is equally conceivable that other organisms can bring about the activation of hydrogen atoms to the same degree only when they act upon certain other hydrogen compounds.

In this connection attention may be directed to the oxidation of the dextrose molecule by various micro-organisms, all with oxygen as the hydrogen-acceptor. Alsberg has shown that *B. Savastanoi* converts this sugar into gluconic acid only. But Kluyver and de Leeuw have proved that *Acetobacter suboxydans* oxidizes both dextrose and gluconic acid into oxygluconic acid. We may say, therefore, that *B. Savastanoi* can accomplish the first step but cannot go farther and activate the hydrogen of the gluconic acid sufficiently to cause its transfer to the acceptor. *Acetobacter suboxydans,* on the other hand, can accomplish this but is unable to activate the oxygluconate-hydrogen sufficiently, although a great many microbes are known which are capable of oxidizing the dextrose or the oxygluconic acid still further.

For the process of photosynthetic carbon dioxide assimilation (or reduction) we may then say that the reaction

$$CO_2 + 2H_2A = CH_2O + H_2O + 2A$$

requires various and special compounds of hydrogen for various and special organisms. From which it follows that the photosynthetic activity of the chlorophyll-bearing organisms, in which H_2A represents H_2O, represents only one very special instance of a group of possible photosynthetic activities. This would mean that the purple sulphur bacteria can use H_2S as a hydrogen donor but cannot use H_2O.

I wish now to show that the results obtained are in complete agreement with this hypothesis.

If, in the case of the purple bacteria, chemosynthetic and photosynthetic activity occurred side by side, we would have the following reactions going on:

Chemosynthetic $\left\{ \begin{array}{l} 40\ H_2S + 80\ O_2 = 40\ H_2SO_4 \\ CO_2 + 2\ H_2O = CH_2O + H_2O + O_2 \end{array} \right\}$

Photosynthetic $\quad CO_2 + 2\ H_2O = CH_2O + H_2O + O_2$

These processes being independent of each other, there would not be any quantitative relationship between the end-products H_2SO_4, O_2, and reduced

CO_2. But if, on the other hand, the H_2S is regarded as the hydrogen donor for the reduction of CO_2 in the photo-synthetic process, according to the equation:

$$CO_2 + 2 H_2S = CH_2O + H_2O + 2S$$

or

$$2 CO_2 + H_2S + 2 H_2O = 2 CH_2O + H_2SO_4$$

a very definite quantitative relationship between the reaction products—reduced CO_2 and S or H_2SO_4—is required, and the fact that these organisms cannot live except in the presence of H_2S is also explained. The results of a quantitative study of this relationship, with pure cultures, are given in the following tables. Details as to methods of cultivation or determination will not be included.

THIOSPIRILLUM SPEC. 1. (ECTOTHIOFORM, BECKING)

All figures represent mg. per 100 cc.

	H_2S Oxidized	H_2SO_4 Produced		CO_2 Reduced	
		Calculated	Found	Calculated	Found
Exp. 1. Analyzed after 14 days.....	12.7	36.7	35.8	33.0	32.1
Exp. 2. Analyzed after 24 days.....	24.8	71.5	70.9	64.2	63.8
Exp. 3. Analyzed after 25 days.....	24.8	71.5	70.2	64.2	63.1
Exp. 4. Analyzed after 47 days.....	24.8	71.5	71.4	64.2	63.9

CHROMATIUM SPEC. 3. (ENDOTHIOFORM, BECKING)

	H_2S Oxidized	H_2SO_4 Produced		CO_2 Reduced	
		Calculated	Found	Calculated	Found
Exp. 1. Analyzed after 27 days.....	8.8	25.5	24.7	22.9	20.7
Exp. 2. Analyzed after 34 days.....	17.2*	49.6	43.3†	44.5	39.2
Exp. 3. Analyzed after 42 days.....	18.7	53.9	51.4†	48.4	46.8
Exp. 4. Analyzed after 48 days....	18.7	53.9	53.4	48.4	48.9

* Not all of the H_2S used.
† SO_4 = below calculated amount: cells still contain sulphur-droplets.

CHLOROBIUM LIMICOLA NADSON (GREEN BACTERIA)

	H_2S Oxidized	H_2SO_4 Produced		CO_2 Reduced	
		Calculated	Found	Calculated	Found
Exp. 1. Analyzed after 14 days.....	26.2	75.4	No soluble sulphur compounds other than H_2S	16.9	18.8
Exp. 2. Analyzed after 17 days.....	26.2	75.4		16.9	17.2
Exp. 3. Analyzed after 30 days....	46.9	135.2		30.4	28.7
Exp. 4. Analyzed after 36 days...:	46.9	135.2		30.4	31.0

Examination of these tables will show, first of all, that, within the limits of error, in not a single instance was the amount of CO_2 reduced greater than the calculated amount. This, in itself, might prove that a CO_2 assimilation in the conventional sense does not take place, especially when it is considered (1) that all of the cultures were continuously illuminated, thus ruling out any possibility that the amount of CO_2 assimilated might equal the amount "respired"; and (2) that the cultures were analyzed after different periods, so that, if the first analysis showed complete oxidation of the H_2S, the cultures later examined would, with certainty, have been "growing" in the absence of any compound which could have been oxidized with the O_2 liberated by the CO_2-reduction process. In this respect the first series is of interest. After 23 days a fresh supply of Na_2S solution was added to the cultures 2, 3, and 4. After 24 hours only, this quantity was completely oxidized; and even after twenty-four days the quantity of CO_2 reduced was exactly the same as that after only one day.

The second series is of interest in that it shows that when the H_2S is not yet completely oxidized (Exps. 2 and 3), as can be determined from a comparison of the quantity of H_2SO_4 produced and calculated as well as by microscopic examination revealing sulphur globules in the cells, the quantity of CO_2 reduced also remains below the calculated amount.

The third series, carried out with a pure culture of green bacteria, shows further that here we deal with organisms which entirely lack the power to dehydrogenate the first oxidation product of the H_2S, the sulphur. It was not possible to make accurate sulphur determinations, since representative samples cannot be taken owing to the slimy consistency of the bacterial development. However, the determined amount of re-duced CO_2 checks so well with the amount calculated, on the basis of the equation

$$CO_2 + 2\ H_2S = CH_2O + H_2O + 2\ S,$$

that there can be little doubt that this is, actually, the process occurring. The fact that these cultures do not contain any trace of soluble sulphur compounds also supports this statement. It is true that in this case some doubt might arise as to whether the sulphur production might not be a secondary process, caused by the oxygen liberated during a "normal" photosynthesis. However, the analogy between these bacteria and the true purples, the fact that the CO_2 reduced is *never greater than that calculated* on the basis of the foregoing equation, together with the fact that they do not develop at all when H_2S is absent, so strongly supports the idea that this, too, is an "abnormal" photosynthetic process, i.e., one in which other hydrogen donors take the place of H_2O, that it seems entirely justifiable to conclude that this equation actually represents the metabolism of the green bacteria.

Consequently we have at present the experimental evidence of the existence of at least two photosynthetic processes which are fundamentally different from that of the green plants. But there is more. When we direct our attention to that group of organisms which has been called "Athiorhodaceae," we find microbes that apparently require organic substances. But what can we say here about the function and influence of light?

It is interesting to consider the few facts which, up to the present, have been established. The observation that these organisms, wherever found in crude cultures, behave like true anaërobes and seem to develop only in the light, plus the knowledge that they certainly can grow under aërobic conditions and in the dark (Molisch), led me to compare their development in the light and in the dark under both aërobic and anaëro-bic conditions.

Here the fact was established that, whereas under aërobic conditions the cultures seemed not to be influenced by light, the anaërobic cultures developed *in the presence of light only.* We may therefore conclude that the acceptor-action of the oxygen can be substituted for by some other compound only when illuminated. Is this the CO_2?

In the present status of this problem the available facts do not yet allow of this conclusion. The difficulty presented by this group of purple bacteria, of which only a limited number of repre-sentatives is known, is that, up to the present time, we have not yet been able to obtain a good development in media which can be analyzed afterward. The organisms grow abundantly only in media containing complex organic N-compounds, such as peptone, yeast autolysate, etc., so that a complete pic-ture of the changes taking place during development can be obtained only after analyses which, for the present at least, seem impossible. They do not develop in media containing H_2S only. They need organic matter, and when small quanti-ties of H_2S are added to the organic media they are always quantitatively re-coverable afterward. Therefore, here too the liberation of oxygen by an ordi-nary photosynthetic activity is out of the question.

What particular influence the light may have upon the components of the medium, which become available as hy-drogen acceptors only when illuminated, remains an open question. However, it is probable that the continued study of the metabolism of this group will give additional information with regard to the further possibilities of photosyn-thesis.

At present we are more or less aware of some of the factors influencing and even governing photosynthesis, especially in so far as they pertain to conditions outside of the cell. We also know some-thing about the inner factors. But from the data available it is still impossible to decide which ones of these factors are really indispensable. We have nothing but hypotheses and theories.

And here, especially, lies the impor-tance of the study of these "abnormal" photosynthetic processes, because a com-parison of the factors and conditions which are required for their accomplish-ment will enable us to find those charac-teristics which are common to all. It will then be possible to derive the funda-mental laws underlying all photosyn-thetic processes and to correlate these into a general view.

In considering photosynthesis as a process in which CO_2 is reduced by hydrogen from some compound H_2A, it must be kept in mind that this reaction requires the activation of the CO_2 as well as that of the H_2A. And then it must be possible to find that hydrogen compound which requires either no acti-vation at all (H_2S in the case of the green bacteria?) because it is, in itself, active enough, or which requires the same activation as the CO_2. In such a case it might become possible to carry out photosynthesis with only one cata-lyst, which has an oxidation-reduction potential suitable for this activation, and, therefore, to carry out photosynthesis independent of the living cell.

Oxygen Produced by Isolated Chloroplasts. ～

by R. HILL

Abridged from *Proceedings of the Royal Society of London*, Series B, Vol. 127, pp. 192–210 (1939). Reprinted by permission of The Royal Society and the author.

Many elementary text-books still represent photosynthesis by an equation which erroneously gives the impression that the process is a single chemical reaction in which carbon dioxide combines with water to form carbohydrate and oxygen. But from the early years of the twentieth century evidence had already been accumulating to show that several reactions with independent characteristics must participate in photosynthesis, and that these were separable into a phase dependent upon light and others which could proceed in the dark. It soon began to appear that the evolution of oxygen, the chlorophyll, and light were somehow connected, for Friedel in 1901 and Molisch in 1925 discovered that when suspensions of dried leaves are illuminated, minute amounts of oxygen are liberated. By providing a hydrogen acceptor and refining the techniques, R. Hill became the first to obtain significant and continued oxygen production from illumination chloroplasts. This reaction has since been known as the Hill reaction. It is the first component of the photosynthetic system to have been made to operate in vitro. *Hill was unable to say definitely where the oxygen came from, although the suspicion already was prevalent that water was being decomposed with the aid of light energy. A clear answer to this question was not possible until isotopic tracers became available during World War II.*

INTRODUCTION

THE SUBCELLULAR * EVOLUTION of oxygen under illumination has been known in the case of green plants for many years. The effect, however, was always insignificant compared with the original photosynthetic activity of the cell. The oxygen could only be detected by using certain bacteria which show either motility or luminescence with traces of this gas. But to this method we owe the classical investigations of Engelmann who showed that in the living cell oxygen appeared in the neighborhood of the illuminated chloroplast and the experiments on the isolated chloroplasts of *Funaria hygrometrica* by Haberlandt, who demonstrated the production of oxygen in light. . . .

* The term *subcellular* is used here to imply a degree of organization less than that of the whole cell.

The same problem was approached in a somewhat different manner by Molisch (1925). The leaves of many phanerogams were allowed to dry slowly in air and finally over a dehydrating agent. This produced a stable preparation which, if ground up in water, would show an evolution of oxygen in light which could be detected by the bacterial methods. Molisch showed that these preparations were thermolabile, indicating an enzymic process. . . .

This subcellular evolution of oxygen is then the only property specific for green plant tissue which is at the moment open to biochemical investigation. So far the oxygen had been detected qualitatively by two methods, both using bacteria. Two questions then naturally arise: can molecular oxygen be proved by an independent method, and can the activity of preparations from green tissue be measured and compared with the activity of the living cell?

It happens that there is one reagent which can be used to detect and measure traces of oxygen with certainty in a liquid medium. This reagent is haemoglobin, and it has this rare property of combining with molecular oxygen without being oxidized by it. The absorption spectra of oxyhaemoglobin and haemoglobin are very different and oxyhaemoglobin possesses so strong an absorption of light that it can be used in a dilution corresponding to concentrations of oxygen from 10^{-5} to 10^{-4}M. But as oxyhaemoglobin is a dissociable compound, the method is limited by the affinity of the haemoglobin for oxygen. However, it has this advantage, that not only can the amount of oxygen evolved be determined but also the pressure of oxygen obtaining in the fluid. . . .

The fresh suspensions of chloroplasts obtained by crushing leaves in sucrose solution would not, on illumination, evolve measurable amounts of oxygen even in the presence of CO_2. But in the presence of an aqueous extract of acetone-treated leaf, oxygen was evolved in the light. These two findings substantiate the observations of the earlier workers and at the same time justify the contentions of Kny (1897) that the chloroplast was not perhaps a complete photosynthetic system in itself.

The present paper is devoted to an examination of this oxygen-producing property of chloroplasts. The results obtained show that for the purpose of biochemical investigation the activity of chloroplasts removed from the cell is significant, being about one-tenth the activity of the living leaf.

General procedure: The fresh leaves of a plant are crushed with a pestle and mortar in sucrose solution. The resulting mass is strained through glass-wool. The suspension of chloroplasts is then introduced into an evacuated Thunberg tube containing haemoglobin and desired reagents. The tube is then illuminated and oxygen estimated spectroscopically as oxyhaemoglobin. . . .

[Details of procedure given by the author here and in later sections have been omitted in this abridgment.]

THE MEASUREMENT OF OXYGEN EVOLVED

The chloroplasts were suspended in a liquid medium containing a known quantity of haemoglobin in a vacuum tube. The relative concentrations of haemoglobin and oxyhaemoglobin were determined in a spectro-colorimeter which has been described elsewhere. This method of measurement was used previously for spectroscopic determination of oxygen dissociation curves. The presence of 0.2–0.5 $\times$ 10^{-4} M chlorophyll, while showing a strong band in the red, does not interfere with the part of the spectrum used. . . .

If no oxygen is added from outside, an increase in saturation of the haemoglobin is a measure of the oxygen liberated from some source in the fluid. The affinity of muscle haemoglobin for oxygen is so high that the concentration of free oxygen in the solution is negligible under the conditions used. . . . Not only can the quantity of oxygen liberated be calculated but also the pressure of oxygen in apparent equilibrium with the system at any moment. Both these quantities it is of importance to measure.

[In the experimental part of this paper Hill demonstrates that isolated chloroplasts evolve oxygen in light when in the presence of leaf extracts or certain ferric salts, and do not evolve oxygen from carbon dioxide. In particular the chloroplasts will cause a photoreduction of ferric oxalate to ferrous oxalate; the oxygen evolved corresponds to the iron reduced.]

EVOLUTION OF OXYGEN BY MESOPHYLL CELLS OF LAMIUM ALBUM

The cell suspension obtained from the leaf by centrifuging contained also free chloroplasts. It was introduced into a tube containing haemoglobin and all the oxygen removed by evacuation. In order to produce a measurable output of oxygen it was necessary to add some CO_2. 0.2 c.c. of a saturated solution of CO_2 in air-free water was added to the tube through the side arm. The rate of O_2 production per unit of chlorophyll obtained by these preparations was only half that obtained from the chloroplasts in ferric oxalate under similar conditions. Allowing for the presence of inactive chloroplasts outside the cells, the active chloroplasts inside the cells did

not greatly exceed the rate of O_2 production of the isolated chloroplasts in the ferric oxalate. Moreover, the CO_2 remaining in the fluid after evacuation is shown to be very small in amount. Hence the oxygen evolved by the isolated chloroplasts in ferric oxalate must all come from the change from ferric to ferrous iron and not from CO_2—as indeed is shown by the relation of the original ferric iron concentration and the oxygen evolved. To remove with certainty all the CO_2 from a suspension of chloroplasts before they have become inactive is at present impossible, but this is at the moment an essential step in elucidating the mechanism of the formation of oxygen. The probability is, however, that CO_2 does not take part in the production of oxygen from ferric salts as no difference was found after attempting to remove all the CO_2 at pH 6.8 by evacuation, and after the addition of CO_2.

DISCUSSION

The first question to decide is whether the isolated chloroplasts are acting in a catalytic capacity or whether they possess some store of oxygen which is only liberated in light. Inman considered that the oxygen he had detected came from a store of oxygen-producing substance. Kautsky points out that ferric oxalate causes decomposition of peroxides in light. This latter effect would be far the simplest qualitative explanation of the experiments where ferric oxalate is concerned.

The reaction would be of the type

$$2\mathrm{Fe}^{\cdots} + R\!\!\begin{array}{c}\mathrm{O}\\ \Big|\\ \mathrm{O}\end{array}\!\! 2H_2O \rightarrow 2\mathrm{Fe}^{\cdot\cdot} + R(OH)_2 + O_2 + 2H \ . \tag{1}$$

In the present experiments only half the oxygen for this reaction is obtained. It is possible that some oxygen is lost by other oxidations; yet this is improbable because the oxygen/iron ratio is constant

for a series of experiments with different initial concentrations of ferric iron.

The second inference from the experiments is that if there is a store of a peroxide it must be at least 1/10 M in the chloroplasts, because at least 5 mol. of O_2 can be liberated per molecule of chlorophyll. This large quantity of a peroxide would be of great interest if it could be detected by a direct method, but so far there is no evidence for it.

The third inference from the experiments is that there is something which can be extracted from leaves which contains neither $Fe^{\cdot\cdot\cdot}$ nor oxalate; this however behaves towards chloroplasts very much like ferric oxalate. We will therefore leave aside the question of the store of oxygen-giving substance and

consider the chloroplast as a catalytic system.

The conclusion, then, to be drawn from the present investigation is that light energy can be utilized by a subcellular system containing chlorophyll; the work done can be measured in terms of the production of molecular oxygen and reduction of a ferric complex salt.

With potassium ferric oxalate the photochemical reaction in presence of chloroplasts gives nearly the theoretical yield of molecular oxygen for the reaction

$$4K_3Fe(C_2O_4)_3 + 2H_2O + 4K = 4K_4Fe(C_2O_4)_3 + 4H^{\cdot} + O_2. \qquad (2)$$

In the dark the reaction will proceed in the reverse direction. . . .

A suspension of chloroplasts will also evolve oxygen under illumination when in presence of other ferric complex salts with organic acids, and also from extracts of leaves that contain calcium ions and do not give reactions for iron salts. Thus the chloroplasts are not specific for ferric oxalate. The ferric oxalate could then be regarded simply as a reagent to demonstrate a property of the

chloroplast. This might be compared to the use of indophenol reagent by Keilin in measuring the activity of the oxidase cytochrome system in the respiration of cells. There must therefore be some primary substance which is reduced, while at the same time giving oxygen. If this primary substance is A, and the reagent B, such as ferric oxalate, represented in terms of hydrogen transport, we have the following reactions.

$$2A+2H_2O\rightarrow2AH_2+O_2, \qquad (3)$$

$$AH_2+B\rightarrow BH_2+A. \qquad (4)$$

These two reactions together will represent the type of reaction (2). It must be concluded that the substance A is not easily removed from the chloroplasts because great dilution of the suspending fluid did not diminish the rate of reaction with ferric oxalate.

With chloroplasts alone we obtain no oxygen either because A is present in small amount or that a catalyst is needed to oxidize AH_2. But if a reagent is added which will reoxidize AH_2 sufficiently fast, O_2 can accumulate, but this is only possible if the reduction of the reagent B is more rapid than the oxidation by molecular oxygen. Thus the conditions are limited in which it is possible to produce a measurable oxygen

output with the preparations of isolated chloroplasts.

In the absence of a reagent B, no oxygen evolution could be detected, that is, it would be less than $1/10$ mm. of mercury pressure. CO_2 was also found to exert no influence on the evolution of oxygen in the case of substances which could be reduced. The next most important step would be to ascertain whether CO_2 is actually the primary substance A, giving oxygen in the experiments. This cannot be decided directly from the results of the present work. If, however, CO_2 is the primary substance concerned with oxygen output by isolated chloroplasts, it follows directly from the experiments that the first product of reduction of the CO_2 must be as rapidly oxidized as it is formed, and hence it could not be normal carbohydrate. Also it must react with ferric oxalate at great speed. Again, if CO_2 is the primary substance undergoing reduction, the chloroplasts must have the greater part of the photosynthetic mechanism intact. This last assumption is rendered unlikely by the behaviour with cyanide and other poisons. Thus while it is not possible to show directly that CO_2 plays a part in this system giving oxygen, there is circumstantial evidence against this assumption. . . .

This subcellular evolution of oxygen, then, does not represent normal assimilation and very probably has no direct connexion with carbon dioxide. Yet the activity of the system is relatively high and oxygen as a photochemical product is a characteristic of photosynthesis in green plants.

The most suggestive view is to regard the chloroplast as containing a mechanism, the activity of which can be measured apart from the living cell, which under illumination simultaneously evolves oxygen and reduces some unknown substance which is not carbon dioxide. This substance is capable of rapid reoxidation, being the converse of reaction (3)

$$2A\,H_2 + O_2 \rightarrow 2H_2O + 2A. \quad (5)$$

Organisms are known which can assimilate CO_2 in the dark while oxidizing inorganic compounds, that is, during the progress of a reaction of the type of (5). Thus it is proved that CO_2 can be reduced by living cells when free oxygen is present quite independently of light and chlorophyll derivatives. So that reactions (3) and (5) provide, qualitatively at least, a means of carbon assimilation; the net production of oxygen in the process will then be a function of the CO_2 reduced. This type of process will obviously have a low efficiency. The substance A in the chloroplast is, however, assumed to be of the type of a respiratory catalyst. This mode of linking assimilation with a part of respiration may give a high efficiency at low light intensities. The autotrophic anaerobes, which have no possibility of carrying out reaction (5) directly, obtain their energy by a system similar to the green plant. The oxygen, however, never appears as such because it is removed by hydrogen donators in the growth medium, and when these are fully oxidized assimilation ceases.

This hypothesis acknowledges the reduction of CO_2 as being a rather general phenomenon in organisms independently of photosynthesis, and yet it can explain the nature of a similar type of pigment system in the green plant and in autotrophic anaerobes for utilizing radiant energy.

Heavy Oxygen (O^{18}) as a Tracer in the Study of Photosynthesis. ❧

by SAMUEL RUBEN, MERLE RANDALL,
MARTIN KAMEN, and JAMES LOGAN HYDE

Reprinted from the *Journal of the American Chemical Society*, Vol. 63, pp. 877–879 (1941), by permission of the editor and authors.

Ingen-Housz was probably the first to suggest that photosynthesizing plants decomposed carbon dioxide, retaining the carbon and exhaling the oxygen. This view, which was entirely speculative, held sway for more than a century though it was not testable by any known means. In 1930 van Niel pointed out that it was possible to regard the photosynthetic processes carried out by certain bacteria and the assimilation of carbon by green plants as modifications of a basically similar system involving hydrogen transfer. On this view, the oxygen liberated in photosynthesis ought to be derived from the decomposition of water. In 1941, the following paper by Ruben and his coworkers announced experimental evidence that this was so. The reader should be cautioned that the conciseness of this report makes the experimental procedure appear deceptively simple. The results here presented have been substantiated in the main by subsequent researchers, but various technical considerations have led to some controversy as to the precise proportion of oxygen that can be proven to be derived from water.

IT IS GENERALLY AGREED that the net reaction for green plant photosynthesis can be represented by the equation

$$CO_2 + H_2O + h\nu \xrightarrow{\text{Chlorophyll}} O_2 + (1/n)(C \cdot H_2O)n \qquad (1)$$

and also that very little is known about the actual mechanism. It would be of considerable interest to know how and from what substance the oxygen is produced. Using O^{18} as a tracer we have found that the oxygen evolved in photosynthesis comes from water rather than from the carbon dioxide.

The heavy oxygen water used in these experiments was prepared by fractional distillation and was distilled from alkaline permanganate before use. The isotopic oxygen content was determined by the method of Cohn and Urey using carbon dioxide and a mass spectrometer. Heavy oxygen carbonate was prepared by allowing a solution of potassium acid carbonate ($KHCO_3$) in heavy oxygen water to come to approximate isotopic equilibrium, adding a nearly equivalent quantity of potassium hydroxide and distilling off the water, finally drying in an oven at 120°. Isotopic analysis of this carbonate or of the carbonate in a solution, was performed by rendering the solution sufficiently alkaline to prevent exchange and precipitating calcium carbonate. The calcium carbonate after filtering, washing and drying at 120°, was calcined at red heat in an evacuated platinum bulb connected to the gas handling system of the mass spectrometer, and the evolved carbon dioxide analyzed for heavy oxygen.

Young active *Chlorella* cells were suspended in heavy oxygen water (0.85% O^{18}) containing ordinary potassium bicarbonate and carbonate. Under these conditions the oxygen exchange between the water and bicarbonate ion is slow but readily measurable. The isotopic ratio in the evolved oxygen was measured with a mass spectrometer. In other experiments the algae were allowed to carry on photosynthesis in ordinary water and heavy oxygen potassium bicarbonate and carbonate. The results of these experiments are summarized in Table I.

It is apparent that the O^{18}/O^{16} ratio of the evolved oxygen is identical with that of the water. Since the oxygen in OH, COOH, O—O, C=O, etc., groups exchanges but very slowly with water at room temperature and moderate pH, it seems reasonable to conclude that the oxygen originates solely from the water. While this conclusion makes it possible to reject many of the suggestions proposed in the past it does not enable a choice to be made between the several more recent hypotheses. However it is of interest to note that van Niel has specifically suggested that the oxygen may arise by a dehydrogenation of water.

We have also attempted to ascertain whether the evolution of oxygen was a reversible reaction. The algae were suspended in ordinary potassium bicarbonate and carbonate solution and photosynthesis allowed to proceed in the

TABLE I

Isotopic Ratió in Oxygen Evolved in Photosynthesis by *Chlorella* [a]

Expt.	Substrate	Time between dissolving KHCO₃ + K₂CO₃ and start of O₂ collection, minutes	Time at end of O₂ collection, minutes	Percent. O^{18} in HCO₃⁻ +		
				H₂O	CO₃⁻	O₂
1	0.09 M KHCO₃ +0.09 M K₂CO₃	0		0.85	0.20	..
		45	110	.85	.41[b]	0.84
		110	225	.85	.55[b]	.85
		225	350	.85	.61	.86
2	0.14 M KHCO₃ +0.06 M K₂CO₃	0		.20		..
		40	110	.20	.50	.20
		110	185	.20	.40	.20
3	0.06 M KHCO₃ +0.14 M K₂CO₃	0		.20	.68	..
		10	50	.20		.21
		50	165	.20	.57	.20

[a] The volume of evolved oxygen was large compared to the amount of atmospheric oxygen present at the beginning of the experiment. [b] These are calculated values.

Table II

Isotopic Ratio in Oxygen Evolved in Photosynthesis
by *Chlorella* in Presence of Oxygen

O_2 present in gas space at beginning, ml.	O_2 produced in photosynthesis by 200 mm.^{3} algae, ml.	Obsd.	Percent O^{18} at end of experiment Calcd. for no exchange
2.29 ($O^{18} = 0.20\%$)	1.55 ($O^{18} = 0.85\%$)	0.43	0.46
3.64 ($O^{18} = .20\%$)	1.18 ($O^{18} = .85\%$)	.34	.36
1.44 ($O^{18} = .85\%$)	0.73 ($O^{18} = .20\%$)	.59	.62
4.81 ($O^{18} = .85\%$)	1.22 ($O^{18} = .20\%$)	.69	.71

presence of heavy oxygen. In other experiments the algae evolved heavy oxygen in the presence of light oxygen. The results are shown in Table II.

There is no indication of exchange reactions involving oxygen. The experimental errors are such that an exchange involving less than $5 \cdot 10^{-8}$ mol of oxygen with each cu. mm. of algae would not be detected.

Similar experiments with *Chlorella* and yeast were performed in order to determine whether the oxidation (respiration) reactions utilizing oxygen were reversible. The results are summarized in Table III.

Here also there is no indication for an exchange reaction involving molecular oxygen.

Table III

Isotopic Oxygen Ratio in Respiration with *Chlorella* and Yeast

Respiring system	O_2 ($O^{18} = 0.85\%$) present at start of expt., ml.	O_2 utilized in respiration, ml.	Per cent O^{18} in O_2 at end of experiment Obsd.	For no exchange
Chlorella cells in dark for 90 minutes	0.82	0.11	0.85	0.85
Yeast cells for 60 minutes	4.5	2.4	.84	.85

Part Five

~~

EMBRYOLOGY

THE GERM CELL THEORY

1779   Blumenbach classified spermatozoa as Infusoria.

1780   Spallanzani performed experimental artificial fertilization in amphibians, silkmoth, and dog. Concluded from filtration experiments that spermatozoa were unnecessary for fertilization. Described cleavage in frog.

1805   Treviranus asserted that spermatozoa were analogous to the pollen of plants.

1822–1826 E. Geoffrey St. Hilaire experimentally produced abnormal development in chicks, providing an argument against preformation.

1824   Prévost and Dumas reported that the spermatozoa were essential agents in fertilization.

1825   Dumas repeated Spallanzani's filtration experiments and confirmed the necessity of spermatozoa for fertilization.

1827   von Baer first demonstrated the mammalian ovum; he regarded the sperm cells as "Entozoa," i.e., parasites, and named them spermatozoa.

1828   Publication of von Baer's *The Embryology of Animals* which strongly opposed preformationism.

1835–1838 Peltier maintained spermatozoa to be differentiated body cells.

1837   Dujardin asserted that the spermatozoa are produced by the seminiferous tubules of the testis.

1840   Lallemand held that the spermatozoa are produced by the seminiferous tubules.

1840   Barry expressed the belief that the spermatozoon enters the egg.

1841   Kölliker traced the histogenesis of the spermatozoa and proved that they are differentiated tissue cells.

1853   Newport observed the penetration of the vitelline membrane of the frog egg by the sperm.

1856   Pringsheim observed sperm penetration of the egg of *Oedogonium*.

1868   Darwin elaborated the theory of pangenesis and gave it its name.

1875   Hertwig showed that the head of the spermatozoon becomes a pronucleus and combines with the female pronucleus as the zygote nucleus.

1879   Union of the gamete nuclei in syngamy was reported by Fol in an animal and by Schmitz in a plant.

1883   van Beneden demonstrated that the sperm and egg are haploid and that fertilization restores the diploid chromosome number.

1892   Publication of Weismann's *Das Keimplasma*.

Experiments on the Generation of Insects. ∾

by FRANCESCO REDI

Reprinted from *Experiments on the Generation of Insects* by F. Redi, translated from the 1688 Italian edition by Mab Bigelow. The Open Court Publishing Company, Chicago, 1909, by permission of the publisher.

No fruitful approach to the problems of development was possible as long as it was thought that living things could spring de novo from slime or putrefaction. The framing of rational hypotheses of the emergence of patterns of organic structure from the germ cells depended upon acceptance of the fact that such patterns were necessarily inherited from parents and that life flows across the generations in an uninterrupted stream. In this context, Redi's experimental refutation of the doctrine of spontaneous generation holds a fundamental place in the history of embryology. Despite the clarity of Redi's results, the spontaneous generation theory survived. But its adherents were obliged to shift their ground to the realm of microbiology where the decisive final battles were fought by Pasteur and Tyndall in the nineteenth century.

ALTHOUGH CONTENT TO BE CORRECTED by any one wiser than myself, if I should make erroneous statements, I shall express my belief that the Earth, after having brought forth the first plants and animals at the beginning by order of the Supreme and Omnipotent Creator, has never since produced any kinds of plants or animals, either perfect or imperfect; and everything which we know in past or present times that she has produced, came solely from the true seeds of the plants and animals themselves, which thus, through means of their own, preserve their species. And, although it be a matter of daily observation that infinite numbers of worms are produced in dead bodies and decayed plants, I feel, I say, inclined to believe that these worms are all generated by insemination and that the putrefied matter in which they are found has no other office than that of serving as a place, or suitable nest, where animals deposit their eggs at the breeding season, and in which they also find nourishment; otherwise, I assert that nothing is ever generated therein. . . .

At the beginning of June I ordered to be killed three snakes, the kind called eels of Æsculapius. As soon as they were dead, I placed them in an open box to decay. Not long afterwards I saw that they were covered with worms of a conical shape and apparently without legs. These worms were intent on devouring the meat, increasing meanwhile in size, and from day to day I observed that they likewise increased in number; but, although of the same shape, they differed in size, having been born on different days. But all, little and big, after having consumed the meat, leaving only the bones intact, escaped from a small aperture in the closed box, and I was unable to discover their hiding place. Being curious, therefore, to know their fate, I again prepared three of the same snakes, which in three days were covered with small worms. These increased daily in number and size, remaining alike in form, though not in color. Of these, the largest were white outside, and the smallest ones, pink. When the meat was all consumed, the worms eagerly sought an exit, but I had closed every aperture. On the nineteenth day of the same month some of the worms ceased all movements, as if they were asleep, and appeared to shrink and gradually to assume a shape like an egg. On the twentieth day all the worms had assumed the egg shape, and had taken on a golden white color, turning to red, which in some darkened, becoming almost black. At this point the red, as well as the black ones, changed from soft to hard, resembling somewhat those chrysalides formed by caterpillars, silkworms, and similar insects. My curiosity being thus aroused, I noticed that there was some difference in shape between the red and the black eggs [pupæ],[1] though it was clear that all were formed alike of many rings joined together; nevertheless, these rings were more sharply outlined, and more apparent in the black than in the red, which last were almost smooth and without a slight depression at one end, like that in a lemon picked from its stalk, which further distinguished the black egg-like balls. I placed these balls separately in glass vessels, well covered with paper, and at the end of eight days, every shell of the red balls was broken, and from each came forth a fly of gray color, torpid and dull, mis-

shapen as if half finished, with closed wings; but after a few minutes they commenced to unfold and to expand in exact proportion to the tiny body, which also in the meantime had acquired symmetry in all its parts. Then the whole creature, as if made anew, having lost its gray color, took on a most brilliant and vivid green; and the whole body had expanded and grown so that it seemed incredible that it could ever have been contained in the small shell. Though the red eggs [pupæ] brought forth green flies at the end of eight days, the black ones labored fourteen days to produce certain large black flies striped with white, having a hairy abdomen, of the kind that we see daily buzzing about butchers' stalls. . . .

I continued similar experiments with the raw and cooked flesh of the ox, the deer, the buffalo, the lion, the tiger, the dog, the lamb, the kid, the rabbit; and sometimes with the flesh of ducks, geese, hens, swallows, etc., and finally I experimented with different kinds of fish, such as sword-fish, tun, eel, sole, etc. In every case, one or other of the above-mentioned kinds of flies were hatched, and sometimes all were found in a single animal. Besides these, there were to be seen many broods of small black flies, some of which were so minute as to be scarcely visible, and almost always I saw that the decaying flesh and the fissures in the boxes where it lay were covered not alone with worms, but with the eggs from which, as I have said, the worms were hatched. These eggs made me think of those deposits dropped by flies on meats, that eventually become worms, a fact noted by the compilers of the dictionary of our Academy, and also well known to hunters and to butchers, who protect their meats in Summer from filth by covering them with white cloths. Hence great Homer, in the nineteenth book of the Iliad, has good reason to say that Achilles feared lest the flies would breed worms in the wounds of dead

---

[1] Throughout this work Redi uses the word "uova" where the context shows that pupa is meant. In this he followed Harvey, who called any embryonic mass an "egg."—*Translator.*

Patrocles, whilst he was preparing to take vengeance on Hector.

Having considered these things, I began to believe that all worms found in meat were derived directly from the droppings of flies, and not from the putrefaction of the meat, and I was still more confirmed in this belief by having observed that, before the meat grew wormy, flies had hovered over it, of the same kind as those that later bred in it. Belief would be vain without the confirmation of experiment, hence in the middle of July I put a snake, some fish, some eels of the Arno, and a slice of milk-fed veal in four large, wide-mouthed flasks; having well closed and sealed them, I then filled the same number of flasks in the same way, only leaving these open. It was not long before the meat and the fish, in these second vessels, became wormy and flies were seen entering and leaving at will; but in the closed flasks I did not see a worm, though many days had passed since the dead flesh had been put in them. Outside on the paper cover there was now and then a deposit, or a maggot that eagerly sought some crevice by which to enter and obtain nourishment. Meanwhile the different things placed in the flasks had become putrid and stinking;

the fish, their bones excepted, had all been dissolved into a thick, turbid fluid, which on settling became clear, with a drop or so of liquid grease floating on the surface; but the snake kept its form intact, with the same color, as if it had been put in but yesterday; the eels, on the contrary, produced little liquid, though they had become very much swollen, and losing all shape, looked like a viscous mass of glue; the veal, after many weeks, became hard and dry.

Not content with these experiments, I tried many others at different seasons, using different vessels. In order to leave nothing undone, I even had pieces of meat put under ground, but though remaining buried for weeks, they never bred worms, as was always the case when flies had been allowed to light on the meat. One day a large number of worms, which had bred in some buffalo-meat, were killed by my order; having placed part in a closed dish, and part in an open one, nothing appeared in the first dish, but in the second worms had hatched, which changing as usual into egg-shape balls [pupæ], finally became flies of the common kind. In the same experiment tried with dead flies, I never saw anything breed in the closed vessel.

Experiments upon the Generation of Animals and Plants.

by L. SPALLANZANI

Abridged from *Expériences pour Servir à L'Histoire des Animaux et des Plantes*, Geneva, 1785. Translated by M. L. Gabriel for this volume.

Spallanzani was an adherent of the ovist school of preformationists. He held that the foetus was preformed in the unfertilized egg and that the semen served merely to stimulate the egg to grow into the visible animal. In view of this, the experiments reprinted here, particularly that on the filtration of semen, are interesting in showing how experiments carefully performed and objectively reported may contribute to scientific advance quite regardless of the validity of the theories their author holds.

Is FERTILIZATION effected by the spermatic vapor?

It has been disputed for a long time and it is still being argued whether the visible and coarser parts of the semen serve in the fecundation of man and animals, or whether a very subtle part, a vapor which emanates therefrom and which is called *aura spermatica,* suffices for this function. It cannot be denied that doctors and physiologists defend this last view, and are persuaded in this more by an apparent necessity than by reason or by experiments. They rely upon the observations of some anatomists who have found the vagina of some pregnant women very narrow or perfectly closed; they dwell upon other observations which would have one believe that the semen does not penetrate into the uterus. They reflect upon the orifice of the egg canals or the Fallopian tubes, so narrow that a very fine probe cannot enter there, and which can hardly allow the passage of air; from which they conclude that the seminal liquid of the male, ejaculated into the organs of generation of the females, cannot arrive at the ovaries where the embryos are lodged;[1] but that they must be fertilized by the part of the semen which evaporates, and which they call *aura spermatica.* They further believe that this fertilization must be accomplished by the vapor which communicates with the ovaries by means of the circulation, or by the opening of the uterus and the tubes. Despite these reasons, many other authors hold the contrary opinion, and believe that fertilization is accomplished by means of the material part of the semen. They suspect that the entrance of

the vagina and the tubes is enlarged by the heat produced during copulation, and they confirm this suspicion by the finding of semen in the uterus and in the ovaries—they take no account of observations which show that often the uterus of females is without seminal liquid even after copulation, whether because the uterus has been examined too late after mating, and the seminal liquid has already left, or because the quantity of this liquid which penetrates the uterus is so small that it has escaped observation.

These reasons advanced for and against do not appear to me to resolve the question; for it has not been demonstrated that the spermatic vapor itself arrives at the ovaries just as it is not clear whether the material part of the semen that arrives at the ovaries and not the vaporous part of the semen is responsible for fertilization. Therefore, in order to decide the question, it is important to employ a convenient means to separate the vapor from the body of the semen and to do this in such a way that the embryos are more or less enveloped by the vapor; for then if they are born, this would be an evident proof that the seminal vapor has been able to fertilize them; or, on the other hand, they might not be born, and then it will be equally sure that the spermatic vapor alone is insufficient and that the additional action of the material part of the sperm is necessary. This procedure, which seems to me to have been completely ignored, is that which I have deemed it necessary to employ.

I have elsewhere demonstrated that the seminal liquid continues to fertilize even though it is diluted with a very large quantity of water. A small drop of

---

[1] It was not known then that fertilization takes place in the oviduct.—*Editors.*

water of $\frac{1}{50}$ of a ligne [1 ligne=2.25 mm] drawn from a volume of water of 18 oz, in which there had been infused 3 grains of semen, is quite adequate to fertilize a tadpole [2] [egg]. This experiment seemed to favor the spermatic vapor idea since spermatic vapor is nothing but the semen itself extremely attenuated; but the facts which I am going to relate evidently prove the contrary.

In order to bathe tadpoles thoroughly with this spermatic vapor, I put into a watch glass a little less than 11 grains of seminal liquid from several toads. Into a similar glass, but a little smaller, I placed 26 tadpoles [eggs] which, because of the viscosity of the jelly, were tightly attached to the concave part of the glass. I placed the second glass on the first, and they remained united thus during five hours in my room where the temperature was 18°. The drop of seminal liquid was placed precisely under the eggs, which must have been completely bathed by the spermatic vapor that arose; the more so since the distance between the eggs and the liquid was not more then 1 ligne. I examined these eggs after five hours and I found them covered by a humid mist, which wet the finger with which one touched them; this was however only a portion of the semen, which had evaporated and diminished by a grain and a half. The eggs had therefore been bathed by a grain and a half of spermatic vapor; for it could not have escaped outside of the watch crystals since they fitted together very closely. But in spite of this, the eggs, subsequently placed in water, perished.

Although the experiment overthrows the spermatic vapor theory, it was nevertheless unique and I wished to repeat it. One grain and a half of this vapor, tak-

ing example from the spermatic liquid, should have been able to fertilize several thousand eggs, and surely, by consequence, 26. I tried to increase the dosage and I succeeded, using the same technique, simply by increasing the atmospheric temperature. I therefore put 11 grains of this semen into a larger watch glass and I attached, by means of their jelly, 26 eggs to the concavity of another smaller glass, taking care that the spermatic drop and the eggs corresponded perfectly, and were both in the middle of the glasses; I then placed them one on the other, as in the previous experiment, and I exposed them to the sun in a window, tempering its action by an interposed sheet of glass which prevented the heat from exceeding 25° so as not to hinder fertilization in case this could take place. At the end of four hours the eggs were so bathed with this vapor that they were covered with very noticeable droplets; but in spite of this, they did not develop. I again repeated this second experiment in the same circumstances, not only to assure myself of the result but in order to see whether the remainder of this semen, of which a part had been reduced to vapor, had preserved its fertilizing power. Half of these eggs, bathed by the spermatic vapor, perished in the water into which I placed them; but the other half, which I had taken care to moisten with the residue of the semen after evaporation, succeeded well; all the tadpoles hatched. I draw two conclusions from these facts; one, that the spermatic vapor of the semen of the toad is incapable of fertilization; the other, that the remainder of the semen, after a considerable evaporation, entirely preserves its fertilizing powers. . . .

Having previously used spermatic vapor produced in closed vessels, I wished to see what would happen in open vessels in order to eliminate a doubt produced by the idea that the circulation of air was perhaps necessary to

---

[2] In conformity with his preformationist views, Spallanzani uses "tadpole" for the unfertilized as well as the fertilized egg.— *Editors.*

fertilization; but fertilization did not succeed any better than in the preceding experiments.

The last experiment of this type was to collect several grains of spermatic vapor and to immerse a dozen eggs in it for several minutes; I touched another dozen eggs with the small remnant of semen which remained after evaporation, and which did not weigh more than half a grain; eleven of these tadpoles hatched successfully although none of the twelve that had been plunged into the spermatic vapor survived.

The conjunction of these facts evidently proves that fertilization in the terrestrial toad is not produced by the spermatic vapor but rather by the material part of the semen. As might be supposed I did not do these experiments only on this toad, but I have repeated them in the manner described on the terrestrial toad with red eyes and dorsal tubercles, and also on the aquatic frog, and I have had the same results. I can even add that although I have only performed a few of these experiments on the tree frog, I have noticed that they agree very well with all the others. . . .

Shall we, however, say that this is the universal process of nature for all animals and for man? The small number of facts which we have does not allow us, in good logic, to draw such a general conclusion: One can at the most think that this is probably so, more especially as there is not a single fact to the contrary, and the question of the influence of the spermatic vapor in fertilization is at least definitely decided in the negative for several species of animals, and with a great probability for the others.

Having succeeded in artificially fertilizing several viviparous animals which are naturally fertilized outside the body of the female [sic], it remained for me therefore to see whether it was possible to fertilize artificially animals which are naturally fertilized only in the body of

the females and to seek for this purpose an animal which was large, like a cat, a sheep, or a dog. I did not believe this very difficult, after my success with silkworms, which are fertilized within the body of the female, and I resolved to make the attempt upon a bitch.

The bitch which I chose was a water spaniel of medium size. She had previously whelped, and I suspected that she would not be long in coming into heat; I immediately enclosed her in a room where she was obliged to remain a long time, and in order to be sure of the results I myself fed and watered her: I alone kept the key to the door which imprisoned her; at the end of the thirteenth day of this confinement, the bitch gave evident signs that she was in heat, as was apparent from the swelling of the external genital organs, and by a flow of blood; from the 23rd day, she appeared to have a strong desire to mate: it was then that I attempted the artificial fertilization in the following manner. I had at that time a young dog of the same species [breed]; he supplied me, by spontaneous emission, with 19 grains of seminal liquid, which I injected without delay into the uterus of the bitch, with a small sharply pointed syringe, introduced into the uterus; and since the natural temperature of the seminal liquid is perhaps a necessary condition for the success of the fertilization, I took the precaution to bring the syringe to the temperature of the seminal liquid of the dog, which is approximately 30° Réaumur. Two days after this injection, the bitch ceased to be in heat, and at the end of twenty days the belly appeared swollen; therefore on the 26th day I set her at liberty. The belly continued to grow, and 62 days after the injection of the seminal liquid the bitch delivered three very lively puppies, two male and one female, which by their form and their color resembled not only the mother, but also the male which had furnished me with seminal liquid. The success of this experiment gave me a pleasure which I have never experienced in any of my philosophical researches.

A SPERM SUSPENSION, FILTERED THROUGH VARIOUS BODIES, LOSES ITS FERTILIZING POWER

Filtration produces upon a sperm suspension in water the same effect as shaking. If one filters water containing a suspension of sperm through cotton, through rags, or through cloth, it loses much of its fertilizing power and it loses it entirely if one filters it through several blotting papers. If one filters this water through two papers, and if one fertilizes tadpole eggs with the filtered water not as many tadpoles are born as when it has not been filtered. They are born in still fewer numbers if one has filtered the water through three papers. The diminution of births is greater still if one filters this water through four papers. Finally, filtration performed through six or seven layers of paper prevents the birth of tadpoles fertilized by this water.

If the paper through which there has recently been filtered a sperm suspension is squeezed out into pure water where one puts unfertilized eggs, these hatch out very successfully, which proves that the filtration deprives a sperm suspension of its fertilizing power, insofar as the seminal liquid which it had contained remains upon the blotting papers; then one causes it to come out by squeezing it.[3]

-----

[3] Despite the fact that these results point so clearly to the spermatozoa as the agents of fertilization, Spallanzani failed to associate the residue on the filter paper with spermatozoa, having previously come to the erroneous conclusion that semen devoid of spermatozoa was still capable of fertilization. Later workers (Prévost and Dumas, 1824; Newport, 1851) repeated and confirmed this experiment and drew the conclusion that to our twentieth century hindsight seems so obvious.—*Editors.*

Researches on the Impregnation of the Ovum in the Amphibia; and on the Early Stages of Development of the Embryo. ❧

by GEORGE NEWPORT, selected and arranged from the author's manuscript by GEORGE V. ELLIS

Reprinted from *Philosophical Transactions of The Royal Society of London,* pp. 229–244, (1854) by permission of The Royal Society.

Although Leeuwenhoek had held that fertilization was accomplished by entry of a sperm cell into the egg, this assertion was unsupported by observation. The question of sperm entrance therefore remained a hotly contested matter until the middle of the nineteenth century. Of a number of reports which describe sperm entrance in various organisms, the account of Newport appears to be the most reliable. This paper is also

interesting for its descriptions of frog cleavage, and especially for New-
port's discovery that the first cleavage plane coincides with the median
plane of the adult body.

IN A NOTE DATED April 18th, 1853 . . . I recorded the fact that, "through the adoption of a different mode of examination" from that which I had previously employed, I had seen the spermatozoon pass through the gelatinous covering and the vitelline membrane of the egg into the vitelline chamber and the yelk. This fact of the penetration of the spermatozoon into the yelk is of such importance as to make it necessary for me to state, with precision, all the circumstances connected with it, and to detail the exact course I have pursued. . . .

MODE OF PROCEEDING.

I have elsewhere mentioned that I employed a glass cell to contain the egg whilst it was examined, with the view of keeping it in one position, and preventing the movement derived from accidental causes: it is made of a section of a piece of barometer tube, from one-eighth to one-fourth of an inch deep and three lines in diameter in the clear, which is cemented on a plate of glass of convenient size. This piece of apparatus, which I name a *tube-cell*, is of a size sufficient to contain only a single egg after its covering is fully expanded. For the purpose of making an observation, the egg is to be placed in the centre of the cell, immediately after removal from the body of the frog, and before it has come into contact with any fluid; by this proceeding the gelatinous envelopes adhere so firmly to the glass as to render the egg almost or quite immoveable, when the jelly expands on the subsequent addition of water. In order that the proper focal distance of high magnifying powers may be obtained, I commonly use a cell which allows the object-glass to be immersed in the fluid. . . .

To ascertain the fact of the impregna-tion of the ovum by penetration, it was then necessary to invent some means by which the egg could be examined laterally with the compound microscope. The great difficulty to be overcome was the tendency of the dark surface of the fecundated ovum to maintain a vertical position, with the consequent rotation or rather gravitation of the whole mass of the yelk, whenever there was any change in the position of the cell. I contrived for this purpose a cell or box larger than the one before described, which may be designated a *cistern box;* and with it I could note all the changes that took place whilst the egg was quite undisturbed. . . . During the use of this box the microscope is placed horizontally; and a camera is attached to the eyepiece to allow of the immediate delineation of the changes seen. . . .

If the following points are attended to, the entrance of the spermatic body may be readily seen. The eggs are to be passed uninjured from the frog, and are to be attached immediately to the inner surface of the glass plate in the moveable front of the cistern box; the front of the box is to be replaced and the objects brought into focus, and then the box is to be filled with spermatozoic water. As soon as the fluid touches the eggs, these imbibe it and expand, but they remain firmly attached to the glass. In order that the success of the experiment may be ensured, equal parts of the sperm and water may be used, and within a few minutes after the former has been obtained; this will cause a large number of spermatozoa to enter the egg; but as the mixture is too opake for the satisfactory observation of the phenomena, I remove it at the end of two or three minutes by means of a siphon, and supply its place with pure water. By this time many of the sperm bodies have begun to enter the ovum, and their transit to the vitelline chamber is facilitated by the endosmose of the water.

When these circumstances have been attended to, spermatozoa may be sometimes seen at the *zona pellucida* of the envelope within the first minute, though only those that encounter the egg at right angles; but in from four to five minutes many may be visible, according to the number contained in the water. After the lapse of some time, varying with the temperature, the formation of the *chamber* may be noticed over the centre of the dark surface of the yelk: it is usually at this stage, and for a short time afterwards, that the spermatozoa are first detected in, or passing into, the vitelline chamber.

Penetration of the Spermatozoon into the Yelk

The fact of the penetration was first observed on the 25th of March, 1853, not only into the chamber, but also into the substance of the yelk; and as soon as I was satisfied of it, the following precise observations were made.

First set of observations.—An observation was begun at 11^h 28^m A.M. with the temperature 60° FAHR. of the room, though possibly it was three or four degrees higher to the eggs, from the radiation of the lamp.

Within five minutes an abundance of spermatozoa could be observed sticking in the vitelline membrane.

At twelve minutes the number was greatly increased, and extended around all the circumference of the membrane within focus: some were still in motion, and passing slowly on through the gelatinous envelope with their characteristic serpentine movement.

At seventeen minutes the number of the spermatozoa sticking in the vitelline membrane appeared to be lessened.

At twenty-two minutes the yelk had changed its position, the dark part being uppermost; and I could distinctly see some spermatozoa sunk in the vitelline membrane and shining through it, as in former observations, but I could not yet detect any within the cavity of the yelk: some of the bodies, both those in the yelk membrane and those in the jelly, were perishing, as the curling up of the tails showed.

In thirty minutes the yelk had begun to separate from its envelope (forming the *chamber*), and in the small space thus forming at the middle of its upper surface, I saw two spermatozoa in motion.

At thirty-seven minutes the space was increased and more spermatozoa were in it.

At 1^h 4^m the bodies were still moving, though the greater number were folded up both in the chamber and on the yelk, but some had their tails projecting out of the yelk membrane; the chamber had attained to half of its future dimensions.

At 1^h 22^m all motion had ceased, and there was a heaving of the yelk. From this period till segmentation began, the spermatozoa in the chamber became gradually fainter, till they appeared to change into fine elementary granules, and then disappeared; but some of those that entered the dark surface of the yelk remained for more than twenty minutes after its first cleavage, whilst others that were sticking in the vitelline membrane were perceptible for many hours.

In the glass box were three other eggs, in all of which the same facts could be noted. The segmentation of the yelk began at the end of three hours and thirty minutes at the temperature stated. I may mention, that in each egg two spherical bodies, to be presently described,[1] were present, and that these exist in all perfectly or imperfectly fecundated eggs.

The observations were repeated on the evening of the same day on a set of

---

[1] A later section of this paper, not reprinted here, contains a lengthy description of these bodies. There is no doubt that Newport had observed the polar bodies of the frog egg.— *Editors.*

four eggs; and were repeated on the three following days with precisely similar results. . . .

From the facts stated above, and before detailed in my former papers, the conclusion seems to be arrived at, that the fructifying of the egg depends on the force or power residing in the sperm body to make its way through the thick coverings of the yelk; and that, this being the case, an explanation will be afforded of the failure of the fluid to occasion fecundation when those bodies are deficient in number or well-being, or are deprived of the power of moving: and at the same time the penetrating power may afford a clue to the inability of filtering paper, even when it is twice or thrice folded, to stop their progress through it.

The action of the spermatozoon is influenced by the temperature of the air, and by mechanical impediments to its passage into the egg.

With respect to temperature, I have frequently referred to its influence in expediting or retarding the development of the embryo, and the following general statement may be given in support of it. A given number of eggs, at a mean temperature of 61° FAHR., will advance in *four* days as far as a corresponding set, at a mean temperature of only 47° FAHR., will reach in fourteen days. Further, the embryos exposed to the low temperature mentioned above die and decompose, whilst in a running stream, and in a natural state, they would come to maturity, and this difference appears to be owing to the more perfect aëration of the water in the natural than in the artificial development.

On the production of the Body and Head of the Embryo from definite portions of the Yelk.

Repeated observations have demonstrated that in one part of the yelk the head, and in another the body and tail of the forthcoming being begin. This appointment of the parts is further in-

dicated, very early, by conditions in the yelk cleavage—conditions so constant that I am able to predicate soon after the completion of the horizontal cleft, or at the beginning of the fourth change, where the head, and where the tail of the future embryo will be placed. In support of this statement the changes in the egg undergoing segmentation must be referred to, but they will be traced, here, only to the point indicatory of the diagnosis to be made.

To ascertain the correctness of the following statement it will be necessary to put the impregnated eggs, dark surface uppermost, in *tube-cells,* and to mark on these where the future head and body should be, according to the deduction from changes in the segmenting yelk.

First change.—In eggs kept at a temperature of 60° FAHR., the first change begins at about the end of four hours, and consists in a cleft that runs vertically round the egg. This cleft may be called *axial* from its position, as it will afterwards appear, to the body of the future embryo. It begins in the centre of the dark surface in a slight depression, so that in some instances the canal may be almost detected: then suddenly a sulcus appears on each side of the depression, and quickly extends outwards around the yelk, though it is deepest and most strongly marked above. In the egg of the Frog as in that of the Newt, the halves are not always of equal size in this stage, but this disproportion is obviated in the second division.

Second change.—Another cleft now surrounds the egg crossing the first at right angles, and this may be named *crucial.* An interval of about an hour elapses before its appearance, and its commencement is not seen at the same instant on each side of the axial line, but is perceived first at one side. After this, as after the axial cleft, the pieces into which it divides the yelk are unequal in size; but these variations have in general but little influence on the result obtained by the segmentation. . . .

Third change.—In this a third cleft is formed horizontally around the egg, nearly midway between the upper and under surfaces: this may be called from its position, the *equatorial* cleft.

Fourth change.—About two hours after the completion of the crucial cleft, a new series of changes is set up in the egg. The clefts no longer include the whole circumference of the egg, but are confined to the splitting of the larger into smaller pieces after a binary plan: and this process does not begin at once over the whole surface, but appears first in a given spot, and then pursues a definite course; thus each of the two pieces seen from above on one side (behind) of the crucial cleft become subdivided, producing four segments on one side of that line, whilst there are only two on the other. When this subdivision is nearly completed, and not till then, a corresponding change takes place in the two segments on the other side (in front) of the sulcus.

When this stage of the segmentation of the yelk is arrived at, the position of the body and head of the coming being can be determined with certainty, so that it is not necessary to follow further the changes during segmentation. If the cell be marked opposite the first commencing post-crucial subdivisions, and then set aside for the formation of the embryo, the trunk and tail of the developing being will be found to originate in this first-subdividing part behind the crucial sulcus, and the head to be produced in the part on the other side, or in front of the sulcus, in which the secondary segmentation last appears.

On the correspondence of the primary cleft of the Yelk with the axis of the future Embryo.

I have been long aware that the axis of the embryo was in the line of the first cleft of the yelk, but my endeavour to show this was not always satisfactory, in consequence of the difficulty of making the egg keep a given position, whilst it was free to move; but since I have employed the tube-cell I have obtained the desired evidence with great ease. The results of the following observations will support my statement.

Obs. 1.—I took an egg that had just divided for the first time, and placed it in a glass cell only sufficiently large to contain it when the jelly was fully expanded, and filled the cell with water. The dorsal surface turned uppermost, as usual, consequently I had under my eye the whole surface, and could watch the changes with the microscope. I marked the plate of glass supporting the cell with a line parallel to the primary cleft of the yelk, and indicated the position of the ends of the sulcus by other marks. The whole was placed in a temperature of 60° FAHR.

At the time of the closing-in of the dorsal laminæ, I found the correspondence between the axis of the embryo and the line of the first cleft to be exact. As I knew however that some movement would be excited, I made a drawing of the appearances. In twelve more hours the dorsal sulcus was nearly closed, and the embryo had passed to the left of the line marked on the glass, viz. to about an angle of 30°. A second drawing was made to remove doubts.

On the day after, the embryo had moved still further round. Finally, the embryo was perfected, like those of the same set that were left in mass in water. . . .

Although these observations have shown that the axis of the body of the future embryo corresponds primarily with the first cleft in the yelk, . . . at times, the axis deviates to the left or right of that line.

On the power of the Spermatozoon to influence in artificial impregnation the direction of the first cleft of the Yelk.

In connexion with the influence of

the spermatozoon on the egg, I determined to try whether the artificial application of that body to different parts of the egg's surface could affect the position of the first cleft of the yelk.

Obs. 1.—Several eggs were placed, March 29, in separate tube-cells, with each turned on its side so that both the dark and the white surface were exposed. Very recent spermatic fluid was then applied, by means of a pin's head, to the lower part of the dark surface, and the cell was carefully marked close to the spot, to show where the egg was touched.

The eggs rotated in the usual way, so as to bring upwards the dark surface, and at the end of one hour and a half only two eggs were fecundated. In these the spherical vesicles had the usual position and appearance, and were directed outwards across the centre of the flat surface of the yelk to that side of the egg to which the spermatic fluid had been applied. After the formation of the primary cleft, the cells were marked and set aside for the production of the embryo.

April 3. Each egg has formed an embryo, and in each instance with the head to the side of the egg touched.

Obs. 2.—Four eggs were placed in separate cells as before, and only two became fruitful.

In one the primary cleft was in the precise line of the spot touched, although the egg subsequently diverged to the left; and the head corresponded to the part fecundated. In the other egg the cleft was about ten degrees to the left of the part impregnated, and the head was also turned to the part touched with the fluid.

Obs. 3.—Four other eggs were taken, but two of them were sterile; and in the development of one the head deviated remarkably from the usual position.

The first cleft in one (*a*) was about six degrees to the right; and in the other (*b*) about five degrees to the left of the point touched. Both formed embryos: in

one (*a*) the head was at the end of the cleft nearest the point touched, but in the other (*b*) at the end furthest from the same point. The peculiarity in this last experiment I cannot explain; possibly there might be some want of precision in conducting it.

Similar experiments were repeated four other times, and the results showed that the first cleft of the yelk is in a line with the point of the egg artificially impregnated, and that the head of the young frog is turned towards the same point. But in this set, as in the other, the nascent being in the course of its development deviated to the right or the left of a line through the centre of the spot fecundated.

In another set of experiments the spermatic fluid was applied to an unknown part of the egg.

On taking my last female frog (April 5, 1853) I found the white part so dark in colour (not a very unusual change), that the usual black surface could not be well distinguished. Accordingly the eggs were put into separate cells, and the fluid was applied and the cell marked in the usual way, without a knowledge of what was the spot touched.

Experiment 1.—Six eggs were used: all were fecundated, and segmented in about three hours and a half in an atmosphere varying from 61° to 64° FAHR. The following is the result:—

The axis of the embryo was in one in a line with the part touched, in four diverging slightly to the left, and in one to the right of that line. The head was in four nearest to the spot fecundated, and in two furthest from it.

Experiment 2 with five eggs: all of these were fruitful. The axis coincided exactly with the impregnated point in three, and diverged slightly to the left in two eggs. The head was nearest the same point in four, and furthest from it in one embryo.

Experiment 3.—Five eggs were employed, and being fertilized, gave the following result:—

The axis coincided with the given point in one, and diverged more to the right or left in the other instances. The head was nearest the side to which the spermatic fluid was applied in four, and furthest from it in one.

From these and other experiments it results; that, when part of the black surface of the egg was certainly touched with the spermatic fluid, the head of the future embryo was turned towards it in ten eggs, and removed from it in only one; and that the axis of the embryo nearly coincided at first with the line of the point touched, though it afterwards deviated to the left or right of that line (most to the left), the distance not exceeding fifteen degrees.

When however the part of the egg to which the spermatic fluid was applied was not known, the axis kept much the same position as before, but the head was far distant from the impregnated spot in four out of sixteen instances.

The Continuity of the Germ-plasm as the Foundation of a Theory of Heredity. ∿

by AUGUST WEISMANN

Abridged from *Essays upon Heredity and Kindred Biological Problems,* Vol. I (1889), authorized translation edited by E. B. Poulton, S. Schönland, and A. E. Shipley (Oxford: Clarendon Press, 1889–1892) 2 volumes.

The demonstration that the sperm and the egg act as the agents of the parents in initiating development of the offspring left unsolved the basic problem of the relationship of these cells to the rest of the organism and the mechanism by which the heritable characteristics of the species are delegated to these cells, to be realized again in subsequent generations in infinitely repeatable succession. This problem had occupied the attention of many biologists; Darwin's untenable theory of pangenesis is perhaps the most famous of a number of unsuccessful attempts to solve it. The only theory to survive the discovery of Mendelian inheritance was that of the continuity of the germ plasm proposed by the brilliant theoretician August Weismann. Weismann correctly perceived that heredity must depend upon the preservation of a molecular pattern and he predicted the necessary existence of meiosis. Another corollary of his theory, the rejection of the Lamarckian theory of the inheritance of acquired characteristics, has profoundly influenced the thinking of most biologists since his time.

INTRODUCTION

WHEN WE SEE THAT, in the higher organisms, the smallest structural details, and the most minute peculiarities of bodily and mental disposition, are transmitted from one generation to another; when we find in all species of plants and animals a thousand characteristic peculiarities of structure continued unchanged through long series of generations; when we even see them in many cases unchanged throughout whole geological periods; we very naturally ask for the causes of such a striking phenomenon: and inquire how it is that such facts become possible, how it is that the individual is able to transmit its structural features to its offspring with such precision. And the immediate answer to such a question must be given in the following terms:—"A single cell out of the millions of diversely differentiated cells which compose the body, becomes specialized as a sexual cell; it is thrown off from the organism and is capable of reproducing all the peculiarities of the parent body, in the new individual which springs from it by cell-division and the complex process of differentiation." Then the more precise question follows: "How is it that such a single cell can reproduce the *tout ensemble* of the parent with all the faithfulness of a portrait?" . . .

My present task is not to deal with the whole question of heredity, but only with the single although fundamental question—"How is it that a single cell of the body can contain within itself all the hereditary tendencies of the whole organism?" . . .

Now if it is impossible for the germ-cell to be, as it were, an extract of the whole body, and for all the cells of the organism to dispatch small particles to the germ-cells, from which the latter derive their power of heredity; then there remain, as it seems to me, only two other possible, physiologically conceivable, theories as to the origin of germ-cells, manifesting such powers as we know they possess. Either the substance of the parent germ-cell is capable of undergoing a series of changes which, after the building-up of a new individual leads back again to identical germ-cells; *or the germ-cells are not derived at all, as far as their essential and characteristic substance is concerned, from the body of the individual, but they are derived directly from the parent germ-cell.*

I believe that the latter view is the true one: I have expounded it for a number of years, and have attempted to defend it, and to work out its further details in various publications. I propose to call it the theory of "The Continuity of the Germ-plasm," for it is founded upon the idea that heredity is brought about by the transference from one generation to another of a substance with a definite chemical, and above all, molecular constitution. I have called this substance "germ-plasm," and have assumed that it possesses a highly complex structure, conferring upon it the power of developing into a complex organism. I have attempted to explain heredity by supposing that in each ontogeny a part of the specific germ-plasm contained in the parent egg-cell is not used up in the construction of the body of the offspring, but is reserved unchanged for the formation of the germ-cells of the following generation.

It is clear that this view of the origin of germ-cells explains the phenomena of heredity very simply, inasmuch as heredity becomes thus a question of growth and of assimilation,—the most fundamental of all vital phenomena. If the germ-cells of successive generations are directly continuous, and thus only form, as it were, different parts of the same substance, it follows that these cells must, or at any rate may, possess the same molecular constitution, and that they would therefore pass through exactly the same stages under certain conditions of development, and would form the same final product. The hypothesis of the continuity of the germ-plasm gives an identical starting point to each successive generation, and thus explains how it is that an identical product arises from all of them. In other words, the hypothesis explains heredity as part of the underlying problems of assimilation and of the causes which act directly during ontogeny; it therefore builds a foundation from which the explanation of these phenomena can be attempted.

It is true that this theory also meets with difficulties, for it seems to be unable to do justice to a certain class of phenomena, viz., the transmission of so-called acquired characters. I therefore gave immediate and special attention to this point in my first publication on heredity, and I believe that I have shown that the hypothesis of the transmission of acquired characters—up to that time generally accepted—is, to say the least, very far from being proved, and that entire classes of facts which have been interpreted under this hypothesis may be quite as well interpreted otherwise, while in many cases they must be explained differently. . . . It is not my intention, on the present occasion, to enter fully into the question of acquired characters; I hope to be able to consider the subject in greater detail at a future date. But in the meantime I should wish to point out that we ought, above all, to be clear as to what we really mean by the expression "acquired character." An organism cannot acquire anything unless it already possesses the predisposition to acquire it: acquired characters are therefore no more than local or sometimes general variations which arise under the stimulus provided by certain external influences. If by the long-continued handling of a rifle, the so-called *"Exercierknochen"* (a bony growth caused by the pressure of the weapon in drilling) is developed, such a result depends upon the fact that the bone in question, like

every other bone, contains within itself a predisposition to react upon certain mechanical stimuli, by growth in a certain direction and to a certain extent. The predisposition towards an *"Exercierknochen"* is therefore already present, or else the growth could not be formed; and the same reasoning applies to all other "acquired characters."

Nothing can arise in an organism unless the predisposition to it is pre-existent, for every acquired character is simply the reaction of the organism upon a certain stimulus. Hence I should never have thought of asserting that predispositions cannot be transmitted, as E. Roth appears to believe. For instance, I freely admit that the predisposition to an *"Exercierknochen"* varies, and that a strongly marked predisposition may be transmitted from father to son, in the form of bony tissue with a more susceptible constitution. But I should deny that the son could develop an *"Exercierknochen"* without having drilled, or that, after having drilled, he could develop it more easily than his father, on account of the drilling through which the latter first acquired it. . . . I am also far from asserting that the germ-plasm—which, as I hold, is transmitted as the basis of heredity from one generation to another—is absolutely unchangeable or totally uninfluenced by forces residing in the organism within which it is transformed into germ-cells. I am also compelled to admit that it is conceivable that organisms may exert a modifying influence upon their germ-cells, and even that such a process is to a certain extent inevitable. The nutrition and growth of the individual must exercise some influence upon its germ-cells; but in the first place this influence must be extremely slight, and in the second place it cannot act in the manner in which it is usually assumed that it takes place. A change of growth at the periphery of an organism, as in the case of an *"Exercierknochen,"* can never cause such a change in the molecular structure of the germ-plasm as would augment the predisposition to an *"Exercierknochen,"* so that the son would inherit an increased susceptibility of the bony tissue or even of the particular bone in question. . . . If we consider that each so-called predisposition (that is, a power of reacting upon a certain stimulus in a certain way, possessed by any organism or by one of its parts) must be innate, and further that each acquired character is only the predisposed reaction of some part of an organism upon some external influence; then we must admit that only one of the causes which produce any acquired character can be transmitted, the one which was present before the character itself appeared, viz., the predisposition; and we must further admit that the latter arises from the germ, and that it is quite immaterial to the following generation whether such predisposition comes into operation or not. The continuity of the germ-plasm is amply sufficient to account for such a phenomenon, and I do not believe that any objection to my hypothesis, founded upon the actually observed phenomena of heredity, will be found to hold. If it be accepted, many facts will appear in a light different from that which has been cast upon them by the hypothesis which has been hitherto received,—a hypothesis which assumes that the organism produces germ-cells afresh, again and again, and that it produces them entirely from its own substance. Under the former theory the germ-cells are no longer looked upon as the product of the parent's body, at least as far as their essential part—the specific germ-plasm— is concerned: they are rather considered as something which is to be placed in contrast with the *tout ensemble* of the cells which make up the parent's body, and the germ-cells of succeeding generations stand in a similar relation to one another as a series of generations of

unicellular organisms, arising by a continued process of cell-division. It is true that in most cases the generations of germ-cells do not arise immediately from one another as complete cells, but only as minute particles of germ-plasm. This latter substance, however, forms the foundation of the germ-cells of the next generation, and stamps them with their specific character. . . . It seems to me that this theory of continuity of the germ-plasm deserves at least to be examined in all its details, for it is the simplest theory upon the subject, and the one which is most obviously suggested by the facts of the case, and we shall not be justified in forsaking it for a more complex theory until proof that it can be no longer maintained is forthcoming.[1]

THE GERM-PLASM

I entirely agree with Strasburger when he says, "The specific qualities of organisms are based upon nuclei"; and I further agree with him in many of his ideas as to the relation between the nucleus and cell-body: "Molecular stimuli proceed from the nucleus into the surrounding cytoplasm; stimuli which, on the one hand, control the phenomena of assimilation in the cell, and, on the other hand, give to the growth of the cytoplasm, which depends upon nutrition, a certain character peculiar to the species." "The nutritive cytoplasm assimilates, while the nucleus controls the assimilation, and hence the substances assimilated possess a certain constitution and nourish in a certain manner the cyto-idioplasm and the nuclear idioplasm. In this way the cytoplasm takes part in the phenomena of construction, upon which the specific form of the organism depends. This constructive activity of the cyto-idioplasm depends upon the regulative influence of the nuclei." The nuclei therefore "determine the spe-

---

[1] A remarkably clear statement illustrating the principle of parsimony in logic.—*Editors.*

cific direction in which an organism develops."

The opinion—derived from the recent study of the phenomena of fertilization —that the nucleus impresses its specific character upon the cell, has received conclusive and important confirmation in the experiments upon the regeneration of Infusoria, conducted simultaneously by M. Nussbaum at Bonn, and by A. Gruber at Freiburg. Nussbaum's statement that an artifically separated portion of a *Paramaecium,* which does not contain any nuclear substance, immediately dies, must not be accepted as of general application, for Gruber has kept similar fragments of other Infusoria alive for several days. Moreover, Gruber had previously shown that individual Protozoa occur, which live in a normal manner, and are yet without a nucleus, although this structure is present in other individuals of the same species. But the meaning of the nucleus is made clear by the fact, published by Gruber, that such artificially separated fragments of Infusoria are incapable of regeneration, while on the other hand those fragments which contain nuclei always regenerate. It is therefore only under the influence of the nucleus that the cell substance re-develops into the full type of the species. In adopting the view that the nucleus is the factor which determines the specific nature of the cell, we stand on a firm foundation upon which we can build with security.

If therefore the first segmentation nucleus contains, in its molecular structure, the whole of the inherited tendencies of development, it must follow that during segmentation and subsequent cell-division, the nucleoplasm will enter upon definite and varied changes which must cause the differences appearing in the cells which are produced; for identical cell-bodies depend, *ceteris paribus,* upon identical nucleoplasm, and con-

versely different cells depend upon differences in the nucleoplasm. The fact that the embryo grows more strongly in one direction than in another, that its cell-layers are of different nature and are ultimately differentiated into various organs and tissues,—forces us to accept the conclusion that the nuclear substance has also been changed in nature, and that such changes take place during ontogenetic development in a regular and definite manner. This view is also held by Strasburger, and it must be the opinion of all who seek to derive the development of inherited tendencies from the molecular structure of the germ-plasm, instead of from preformed gemmules.

We are thus led to the important question as to the forces by which the determining substance of nucleoplasm is changed, and as to the manner in which it changes during the course of ontogeny, and on the answer to this question our further conclusions must depend. The simplest hypothesis would be to suppose that, at each division of the nucleus, its specific substance divides into two halves of unequal quality, so that the cell-bodies would also be transformed; for we have seen that the character of a cell is determined by that of its nucleus. Thus in any Metazoon the first two segmentation spheres would be transformed in such a manner that one only contained the hereditary tendencies of the endoderm and the other those of the ectoderm, and therefore, at a later stage, the cells of the endoderm would arise from the one and those of the ectoderm from the other; and this is actually known to occur.[2] In the course of further division the nucleoplasm of the first ectoderm cell would again divide unequally, *e. g.,* into the nucleoplasm containing the

---

[2] Localization of embryonic potentials for development, to the extent implied in this statement, is certainly not a general phenomenon.—*Editors.*

hereditary tendencies of the nervous system, and into that containing the tendencies of the external skin. But even then, the end of the unequal division of nuclei would not have been nearly reached; for, in the formation of the nervous system, the nuclear substance which contains the hereditary tendencies of the sense-organs would, in the course of further cell-division, be separated from that which contains the tendencies of the central organs, and the same process would continue in the formation of all single organs, and in the final development of the most minute histo-logical elements.[3] This process would take place in a definitely ordered course, exactly as it has taken place throughout a very long series of ancestors; and the determining and directing factor is simply and solely the nuclear substance, the nucleoplasm, which possesses such a molecular structure in the germ-cell that all such succeeding stages of its molecular structure in future nuclei must necessarily arise from it, as soon as the requisite external conditions are present.

[3] For an experimental refutation of this theory, see the papers of Driesch, Spemann and Mangold in this volume.—*Editors*.

On the Nature of the Process of Fertilization and the Artificial Production of Normal Larvae (*Plutei*) from the Unfertilized Eggs of the Sea Urchin.

by JACQUES LOEB

Reprinted from the *American Journal of Physiology*, Vol. 31, pp. 135–138 (1899), by permission of the editor.

Towards the close of the nineteenth century the behavior of the germ cell nuclei in meiosis and fertilization had been laid bare by the researches of van Beneden, Hertwig, Fol, and others. The question of the function of the sperm cell in fertilization now engaged a great deal of attention. Among early reports of the experimental induction of parthenogenesis (though not the first) was this short paper by Jacques Loeb. Loeb was a champion of the biochemical interpretation of vital activity. In this conviction he was heir to the viewpoint taught with great influence by Justus von Liebig (1802–1873), one of the founders of physiological chemistry, who insisted that all life phenomena could be explained in physical and chemical terms. Loeb did much to disseminate this doctrine in the United States and much of the teaching in American biology today echoes his influence.

1. FORMER RESEARCHES had led me to suspect that changes in the state of matter (liquefactions and solidifications) might play an important rôle in the mechanics of life phenomena. While studying the absorption of liquids by muscle I found

that, to all appearances, a $\frac{n}{8}$ solution * of $CaCl_2$ favors the formation of solid compounds in the muscle, while an equi-molecular solution of KCl favors the formation of more liquid compounds. Na-ions rank between the K- and Ca-ions. In these phenomena, however, much depends upon the concentration of the salts. We know that the enzymes of coagulation and liquefaction are greatly influenced in their action by the Ca-, Na-, K-, and Mg-ions. Ca favors coagulation and Mg does the reverse. Between these come the two other ions. In this case also much depends upon the concentration.

I have made a series of studies on the mechanics of life phenomena, which will be published shortly in this Journal. I wish now to deal only with one part of these studies, namely, that referring to the nature of the process of fertilization.

I found that in $\frac{5}{8}n$ solutions † of $CaCl_2$, NaCl, KCl, and $MgCl_2$ the segmentation of fertilized eggs of sea urchins (Arbacia) proceeded best in $MgCl_2$, next best in KCl, while $CaCl_2$ proved to be the most injurious in the series.

Seven years ago I, and later, Norman, found that if the concentration of sea water be raised sufficiently by the addition of certain salts, a segmentation of the nucleus takes place without any segmentation of the protoplasm. Such eggs, however, when brought back into normal sea water, divide into as many cells as there are preformed nuclei. This year I tried the effects of equimolecular solutions of $MgCl_2$, KCl, NaCl, and $CaCl_2$ upon this process of nuclear division (in which the nuclear membrane is apparently liquefied), and found that the influence of the four salts (or rather

* I propose to substitute in the future the $\frac{n}{8}$ solution of NaCl for the 0.7 per cent solution. It is time that we were rid of percentage solutions in physiology.

† Approximately the concentration of sea water.

kations) followed the order mentioned above.

We know that enzymes as a rule require a slight degree of acidity or alkalinity for their action. I showed last year that the addition of a small amount of H-ions to sea water retards or prevents segmentation, while a small amount of HO-ions favors and accelerates the development of the Arbacia egg.

2. It has been known for some time that the *unfertilized* eggs of echinoderms, worms, and arthropods begin to segment when left for a comparatively long time in sea water. This has generally been considered a pathological phenomenon. Mead succeeded in causing a segmentation of the unfertilized egg of a marine worm, Chætopterus, by the addition of a very small amount of KCl to sea water. Morgan tried the effect of more concentrated sea water on the unfertilized eggs of sea urchins with results similar to those obtained by me previously with the same methods in fertilized eggs. If the unfertilized eggs are brought back from the more concentrated sea water into normal sea water, they break up into as many cells as there are nuclear masses preformed in the more concentrated solution. But in none of these cases did the cell divisions of the unfertilized eggs lead to the formation of a blastula. A heap of cells, at the best about sixty, were formed and then everything stopped. We cannot utilize these observations for the theory of fertilization, for the simple reason that the essential element of the process of fertilization, namely, the formation of an embryo, was lacking. In the case of tumors or galls we have cell division and even growth, and yet these cell divisions do not result in the formation of an embryo.

3. Some recent observations suggested to me that something in the constitution of the sea water prevented the unfertilized eggs of marine animals from developing parthenogenetically. Last year

I found that the striped muscles of a frog beat rhythmically (like the heart) if put into a $\frac{n}{8}$ NaCl or NaBr solution. It is only the presence of K- and Ca-ions in the blood that prevents striated muscles from contracting rhythmically in the body. Romanes had observed that if the margin (with the nerve ring) in Hydromedusæ be cut off, the centre no longer contracts rhythmically. I found this summer that this is due solely to the presence of K- and Ca-ions in the sea water. In a $\frac{5}{8}n$ solution of NaCl or still better of NaBr the centre continues to beat spontaneously. In applying this and any more recent observations on the relative influence of the various ions upon segmentation to the problem of artificial parthenogenesis it seemed to me that by making two changes in the constitution of sea water the eggs of the sea urchin might be able to produce perfect embryos without being fertilized. These changes were either a reduction of the Na- and Ca-ions or an increase in the Mg (or K) ions or both. I think that a great number of variations in this sense might bring about the desired effect, but the end of the season allowed me to try only a limited number of variations. Without going into details (which may be reserved for the full report) I will state briefly that the mixture of about 5000 $\frac{10}{8}n$ MgCl$_2$ with about 5000 c.c. of sea water was able to bring about the same effect as the entrance of a spermatozoon. The unfertilized eggs were left in such a solution for about two hours. When brought back into normal sea water they began to segment and form blastulæ, gastrulæ, and plutei, which were normal in every respect. The only difference was that fewer eggs developed, and that their development was slower than in the case of the normal development of fertilized eggs. With each experiment a series of control experiments was made to guard against the possible presence of spermatozoa in the sea water.

Unfertilized eggs of the same female were brought into normal sea water, and in solutions with too little MgCl$_2$. Neither in the normal sea water nor in any of these solutions with too little MgCl$_2$ did one single egg develop into a blastula or show anything more than the beginning of a segmentation after a long time.

4. From these experiments it follows that the unfertilized egg of the sea urchin contains all the essential elements for the production of a perfect pluteus. The only reason that prevents the sea urchin from developing parthenogenetically under normal conditions is the constitution of the sea water. The latter either lacks the presence of a sufficient amount of the ions that are necessary for the mechanics of cell division (Mg, K, HO, or others), or it contains too large a quantity of ions that are unfavorable to this process (Ca, Na, or others), or both. All the spermatozoon *needs* to carry into the egg for the process of fertilization are ions to supplement the lack of the one or counteract the effects of the other class of ions in the sea water, or both. The spermatozoon *may*, however, carry in addition a number of enzymes or other material. The ions and not the nucleins in the spermatozoon are essential to the process of fertilization (which may interest those who believe with me that physiologists ought to pay a little more attention to inorganic chemistry). I have no doubt that the same principles hold good for the process of fertilization of other, if not all, the marine animals, although the ions involved will probably differ in various species.

Finally we may ask the question, whether we may expect to produce artificial parthenogenesis in mammalians. Janósik has found segmentation in the unfertilized eggs of mammalians. This is similar to the fact mentioned above, that the unfertilized eggs of sea urchins may show a segmentation if they stay long enough in the sea water. I consider it possible that only the ions of the blood prevent the parthenogenetic origin of embryos in mammalians, and I think it further not impossible that a transitory change in the ions of the blood may also allow complete parthenogenesis in mammalians.

A Successful Ovarian Transplantation in the Guinea-Pig, and its Bearing on Problems of Genetics.

by W. E. CASTLE and JOHN C. PHILLIPS

Reprinted from *Science*, Vol. 30, p. 312 (1909), by permission of the editor and senior author.

It would be difficult to imagine a more rigorous test of Weismann's theory of the germ plasm than the experiment described below. According to this theory the germ cells are insulated, as it were, from the activities of the somatic tissues about them, and are thus enabled to transmit the hereditary pattern unaltered by environmental factors. The achievement of Castle and Phillips in verifying this principle by experiment was an influential force in casting the doctrine of the inheritance of acquired characteristics into disrepute.

TRANSPLANTATION OF the ovary from one animal to another has often been attempted, and with varying degrees of success. The object has usually been to observe the effects of the transplantation upon the animal into which the foreign ovary was introduced. Recently, however, the experiment has been repeated by students of genetics, to discover, if possible, what the effect would be upon the germ-cells, of a transfer from their normal environment to the body of a different individual. The most noteworthy results thus far reported are those of Guthrie on hens, and of Magnus on rabbits. Each apparently working without knowledge of the other's work has obtained what seems to be a modification of the coloration of the offspring, due to influence exerted by the foster-mother upon the germ-cells liberated within her body from the introduced ovary. But in the work of neither of these experimenters does the nature of the result obtained preclude the possibility that the ova liberated may have come from regenerated ovarian tissue of the mother herself rather than from introduced ovarian tissue. The theoretical importance of this point led us about a year ago to plan experiments which should not be open to the objection which we have stated. We therefore undertook the transfer of ovarian tissue from a·Mendelian dominant to a Mendelian recessive individual. For if in such a case germ-cells were liberated which bore the dominant character, we should know that they could have come only from the introduced tissue, since recessive individuals are themselves incapable of liberating dominant germ-cells.

We are now able to report partial success. The ovaries were removed from an albino guinea-pig about five months old, and in their stead were introduced the ovaries of a black guinea-pig about one month old. The albino upon which the operation had been performed was then placed with an albino male guinea-pig, and six months later bore two black-pigmented young.

In all recorded observations upon albino guinea-pigs, of which we have ourselves made many hundred, albinos when mated with each other produce only albino young. Accordingly there seems no room for doubt that in the case described the black-pigmented young derived their color, not from the albino which bore them, but from the month-old black animal which furnished the undeveloped ovaries, for transplantation into the albino. As regards the important question whether, in such an experiment as this, the germ-cells are modified in character by the changed environment within which they are made to grow, our results are at variance with those of Guthrie and Magnus. *We can detect no modification.* The young are such as might have been produced by the black guinea-pig herself, had she been allowed to grow to maturity and been mated with the albino male used in the experiment.

We have now under observation about seventy-five other guinea-pigs, as well as a number of rabbits, upon which similar operations have been performed. From some of these we hope to obtain further results.

EMBRYONIC DIFFERENTIATION

CHRONOLOGY

1759	Publication of *Theoria Generationis* by Casper Friedrich Wolff.
1874	Wilhelm His in *Ueber unsere Körperform* suggested mechanical explanations for morphological changes in the embryo.
1877	Dareste described the successful production of developmental monstrosities by experimental means.
1883	Roux described the time of determination of the main axes of the frog embryo.
1884	Pflüger, by allowing frog eggs to cleave under pressure, showed that abnormal cleavage patterns do not preclude formation of a normal embryo.
1888	Roux's experimental production of a half-embryo by killing one blastomere of the two-celled frog embryo.
1891	Driesch isolated blastomeres of the sea urchin egg by shaking and obtained complete embryos.
1893	Hertwig obtained twin embryos in the newt by constricting the egg.

1894–1897   Born made heteroplastic grafts of parts of frog and toad embryos.

1895   Roux's *Archiv für Entwicklungsmechanik der Organismen* was founded.

1897   Hertwig centrifuged frog eggs and demonstrated the effect of yolk distribution on cleavage.

1900   Herbst used calcium-free sea water to separate blastomeres of the sea urchin.

1901–1903   Spemann's constriction experiments on newt eggs.

1903   Roux showed that the point of entrance of the sperm marks the future mid-ventral line of the frog.

1904   Harrison obtained induction of the lens by the optic cup.

1907–1910   Stockard produced cyclopia in *Fundulus* by lithium and other agents.

1911   Goodale introduced vital staining of the amphibian embryo as a method of tracing the fate of embryonic parts.

1921   Spemann described the "organizer" effect of the amphibian dorsal lip region.

1924   Stöhr obtained development of an embryonic heart by self-differentiation of trunk mesoderm tissue.

1925   Vogt constructed maps of the prospective fate of parts of the amphibian blastula.

1933–1934   Spemann, Needham, and others showed that cell-free extracts from the organizer region retained powers of evocation.

1933   Holtfreter produced exogastrulae, an important tool for clarifying embryonic induction.

1933–1935   Chemical studies of Needham, Waddington, and others led to the belief that the evocator was probably a sterol.

1935   Hörstadius showed the existence of a double gradient of "animalization" and "vegetalization" in the echinoderm egg.

1938 ff.   Brachet showed that ribonucleic acids are accumulated in regions of high morphogenetic activity.

1941   Publication of Child's *Patterns and Problems of Development,* an analysis of development from the viewpoint of the gradient concept.

1952   Brachet suggested that movements of microsomes (which contain ribonucleic acid) from the archenteron roof to the overlying ectoderm are involved in neural induction.

The Potency of the First Two Cleavage Cells in the Development of Echinoderms. ❧

by HANS DRIESCH

From *Zeitschrift für wissenschaftliche Zoologie*, Vol. 53, pp. 160–178 (1891). Abridged and translated by M. L. Gabriel for this volume.

The preformation theory enjoyed a revival in more sophisticated guise in the mosaic theories of development of Roux and Weismann, which proposed that differentiation of the embryo is accomplished by organ-forming determinants pre-packaged in the egg and differentially distributed to the blastomeres during cleavage. These hypotheses are an instructive example of the significant viewpoint that it is not the truth of a hypothesis but its testability by practical means that lends it scientific value. Roux and Weismann turned out to be wrong, but the focussing of attention upon the problem of differentiation led to important advances in experimental embryology. In the following paper Driesch demonstrated the capacity of a portion of an embryo to develop into a whole, thus effectively refuting the Roux-Weismann position. The ability of an embryo to regulate its development in compensation for missing parts, exhibited in these results and in a number of other cases, subsequently led Driesch to adopt the vitalistic view that non-material principles or "entelechies" control the processes of development and provide for the harmonious interplay of the parts. Most embryologists, however, have had no difficulty in explaining regulation in terms of known physiological processes, making superfluous Driesch's mystical interpretation.

"THOUGH THE PRIMORDIUM of a part admittedly originates in a specific period of development, it would be more accurate to say that the primordium is already present in the flat germinal disc [blastoderm] though not demarcated morphologically and therefore not recognizable as such. By tracing back, we may determine the location of each primordium even in the period of incomplete or imperfect morphological differentiation; indeed, if we wished to be consistent, this determination could be carried back to the fertilized, and even to the unfertilized, egg. The principle that the blastoderm contains the organ primordia in a two-dimensional pattern, and conversely that every point on the germinal disc comes to be located in a later organ, I call the *Principle of Organ-forming Germinal Regions*."

In these words His set forth the

principle thus named by him. Following this line of thought, Roux discerningly discussed the difference between evolution [1] or metamorphosis of diversity, and epigenesis, or the new formation of diversity, and decided the question, in the case of the frog's egg, in favor of "evolution" in his well-known investigations on half-embryos.

A paper of Chabry which has not become very generally known is the only other investigation of this kind known to me. With a very refined apparatus constructed for the purpose, Chabry killed individual blastomeres— among others one of the first two cells. This operation is pertinent here. Chabry was essentially concerned with ascertaining descriptive-morphological relationships, his experiments being primarily intended for this purpose. This explains why the French investigator nowhere refers to the fundamental result of his experiment: namely, that from the unoperated blastomere there developed *not a left or right half-embryo, but always an entire embryo of half size,* from which, to be sure, certain organs of minor importance (otoliths, suckers) were missing.

His exposition and illustrations make this certain: The result *is essentially contradictory to that of Roux.* I must note that I became aware of Chabry's work after completion of my own experiments.

My objective in this work has been to repeat Roux's experiments with modified method on a hardy material easy to work with and easy to observe; all three conditions are met in the fullest degree by the echinoids, which have indeed served as a basis for so many investigations. I experimented on *Echinus microtuberculatus.*

Whereas the present work is related in content to the above-mentioned experiments of Roux, the method has been borrowed from the excellent cell experiments of the Hertwig brothers. These investigators detached portions of unfertilized eggs by shaking and successfully reared them. Boveri, as is known, used the same method to produce his "sexually produced organisms without maternal properties," although for other reasons he was unable to carry out the experiments exactly. These experiments —which, it may incidentally be noted, refute His's point of view, especially as regards the unfertilized egg—showed that the echinoid egg, at any rate, has an appreciable resistance, and that fragmentation does not necessarily entail death. It was therefore natural to employ the method of mechanical shaking to investigate Roux's problem with our animals in order to isolate completely eggs (the first two blastomeres) which have spontaneously separated though encased in a common membrane.

At an average temperature of about 15° C. the first cleavage in *Echinus* eggs sets in from $1\frac{1}{2}$ to 2 hours after artificial fertilization. . . .

The shaking was carried out in glass vessels 4 cm long and about 0.6 cm in diameter. 50–100 eggs were placed in a small amount of water. In order to be successful, one must shake very hard, for about 5 or more minutes with all one's might; even then one obtains in favorable instances about 10 isolated blastomeres and about as many eggs whose membranes are still intact, but within which both cells are more or less separated from one another. . . .

The contents of the shaking vessel must be poured into fresh sea water as quickly as possible, since the water naturally has become much warmer and has evaporated. With the help of a magnifying glass and a fine pipette, isolated cells or strongly pulled-apart two-cell stages were taken out of the shaken material and two or three were placed in the familiar square salt cellars;

_____
[1] The word is used here in the sense of unfolding of preformed structures.—*Editors.*

on each there was placed a cover with a hanging drop of fresh water in order to prevent concentration of the sea water by evaporation. After being set up, each container was carefully searched with magnifying glass and microscope to see whether the pipette had not introduced other objects besides the ones intended; then each vessel was recorded in the protocol.

During cleavage the preparations were examined under the microscope as often as possible, during later development usually each morning and always once every evening. . . .

CLEAVAGE

A few words about the normal behavior as it has been made known by Selenka's excellent investigations.

Two meridional cleavages are followed by an equatorial division, and the embryo now consists of eight cells of equal size. Four of these then constrict off smaller cells towards one pole, while the others divide almost meridionally (Fig. 1) so that the embryo consists of 16 cells and shows a pronounced polarity, one pole being occupied by the four easily recognized small cells. Further divisions lead to stages with 28, 32, 60, 108 cells (Selenka), the four small cells constricted off at the 16-cell stage continuing for some time to mark the animal pole clearly. In the blastula I was unable to observe with certainty any differences among the cells. Therefore, at a late stage of development before the epithelial flattening (by close union of the cells) has led to the blastula proper, the *Echinus* embryo consists, especially in the half with the small-celled pole, of concentric rings of cells.

Now, how do blastomeres of the two-cell stage cleave after isolation by shaking, assuming they are viable?

I shall describe next the conditions observed in the preponderant majority of cases. I have not observed a fully spherical rounding-up of the isolated cell like

that which occurs in Ascidia, according to Chabry. Although the surface which would normally be flat does round up, the radius of its curvature remains considerably greater than the originally free surface of the hemisphere. The cell now divides into two and then, at right angles to this, into four parts (Fig. 2). Normal control specimens simultaneously fertilized at this time show the eight equal cells mentioned, each of the same size as these four. . . .

About 5½ hours after fertilization, the untreated embryos have divided into 16 parts, in the manner already described, whereas the isolated blastomeres have divided into eight parts.

We now come to the really interesting part of the experiment in that the last division gives rise to a typical half of a 16-cell stage (Fig. 3 and 4), as described above (Fig. 1), as though absolute self-differentiation had occurred; it is actually half of the structure shown in Selenka's figure.

I shall now describe the normal course of behavior of my blastomeres; I will deal with the abnormalities (¼ of the cases) later.

I have carefully followed the formation of a half-embryo of 16 cells, i.e., a typical half of a 32-cell stage; each of the normal concentric rings of cells is present, but each consists of half the number of cells. The whole structure already has the appearance of an open hemisphere with an opening directed polewards. . . .

In the majority of cases here described as normal, on the evening of the day of fertilization, the half-embryo presented the appearance of a typical, many-celled open hemisphere, though often the opening appeared somewhat constricted (Fig. 5). As especially characteristic, I will mention one case which by chance was equivalent to the Roux-Chabry experiment: Upon shaking, the blastomeres did not become isolated, but one was killed. The surviving cell, which developed in

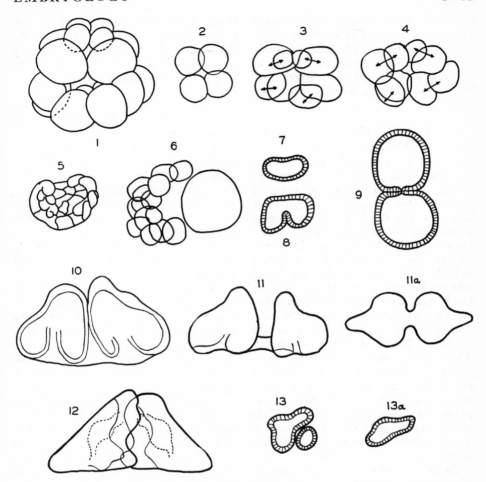

the manner described into a typical half-embryo, in the afternoon had the form of a hemisphere attached to the dead half (Fig. 6); in the evening its edges were clearly curled inward.

The cleavage of isolated blastomeres of the two-cell stage of Echinus multituberculatus *therefore results in a half-formation, as described by Roux for operated frogs' eggs.* . . .

The first time I was fortunate enough to make the observations described above, I awaited in excitement the picture which was to present itself in my dishes the next day. I must admit that the idea of a free-swimming hemisphere or perhaps even a half-gastrula with its ar-

chenteron opened lengthwise seemed rather extraordinary; I felt sure the formations would die. Instead, however, the following morning I found typical, actively swimming blastulae of half size in the dishes.

THE BLASTULA

. . . I have succeeded 30 times in observing small free-swimming blastulae arising from cleavage of isolated blastomeres as described above; the rest, about 20, died during cleavage or were sacrificed for the sake of observation with higher magnification. At this stage nearly all of them were still transparent and of completely normal structure but half-sized. I was unable to distinguish any difference in size between these cells and those of normal blastulae, as nearly as I can estimate, hence the number of cells was probably half the normal number, as the cleavage would indeed suggest.

THE GASTRULA AND
THE PLUTEUS

In healthy specimens invagination at the vegetal pole usually began by the end of the second day; on the morning of the third day vigorous small gastrulae swam about in the dishes. As mentioned, I succeeded in observing this 15 times. On one of the following days the experimental specimens as well as control animals kept under similar conditions take on bilateral form: the archenteron has become curved and has approached one spot on the ectoderm; at the same time one side in the vicinity of the blastopore begins to stretch lengthwise. This process leads to a shape which might be compared to a three-sided prism; the right and left sides of the animal correspond to the base of the prism, the dorsal region as well as the future mouth and anus areas comprise its three lateral surfaces (cf. each half of figure 11).

Altogether nine cases were seen of this prismatic gastrula stage, often with clear indications already present of the mouth area and the later pluteus arms.

The ectodermal mouth and anus are formed at this time; previously the primordium of the coelom plus hydrovascular vessels, at first single but later separate, have arisen. On account of the small size and active swimming of the larvae it was impossible to trace the mode of origin of these structures, but in five cases I was able to see its result: the typical division into three parts of the intestine, and, right and left of the mid-gut, a structure which must be a coelomic sac.

Three of the formations finally became actual plutei distinguishable from normal ones only in size.

It is therefore proven by these experiments that under appropriate conditions *each of the first two blastomeres of* Echinus microtuberculatus *can give rise to a normally developed larva, whole in form; i.e., a part-formation, not a half-formation.*

This fact contradicts fundamentally the theory of organ-forming germinal regions. . . .

However one considers the matter, one cannot escape the fundamental difference in the part which the same germinal material is called upon to play depending upon whether one whole formation or two part formations arise from it—and this can be effected artificially. . . .

Compared with Roux's results, my findings show a difference between the behavior of the sea urchin and the frog. Still, this difference may not be so fundamental. If the blastomeres of the frog were really isolated and removed from the other half—which was probably not dead in Roux's experiment—might they not behave like my echinoid cells? The cohesion of the blastomeres which display the law of minimal surfaces is much greater in the frog than in my material.

I have tried in vain to isolate amphibian blastomeres; let those who are more skillful try their luck at it.

The Development of Lateral and Dorso-ventral Embryo Halves with Delayed Nuclear Supply. ⌇

by HANS SPEMANN

From *Zeitschrift für wissenschaftliche Zoologie*, Vol. 132, pp. 105–134 (1928). Abridged and translated by M. L. Gabriel for this volume.

There is an apparent contradiction between the fact of the progressive differentiation of the parts of an embryo and the genetic identity of the cells which must result from the precision of the mitotic mechanism. The solution of this problem has not yet been fully accomplished, but direction was given to the search by Hans Spemann's discovery of the capacity of the gray crescent region of the amphibian egg to organize an embryonic axis, and by his demonstration of widespread mutual interactions between neighboring regions in the developing embryo. In this early paper Spemann offered an especially forceful argument for the genetic equivalence of the cleavage nuclei and showed that cytoplasmic localizations must be involved in differentiation. The success of the method employed incidentally attests to Spemann's marvelous technical skill in experimentation.

I. INTRODUCTION

THE EXPERIMENTS TO be described below no longer have the same interest that they would have had some decades ago when heated controversy raged over Weismann's theory of heredity.

According to this strictly preformationist theory, the development of the embryo is basically an unfolding—in the most literal sense—of the nuclear substance. The latter was regarded as not merely making possible all the processes by which the fertilized egg is transformed into the differentiated organism, but as fully determining and guiding them. The zygote nucleus, the carrier of the collective hereditary properties, was thought to become dismantled step by step into its simpler component parts by genetically unequal divisions in a strictly regular sequence determined solely by intrinsic factors. In this way the individual regions of the embryo are supplied with nuclei of quite specific potencies, and their further development is determined by the activation of these *Anlagen.*

This theory was attacked from various sides and indeed it was its fundamental premise, the genetically unequal division, that was disproven. Driesch (1891) showed that fragments of embryos could give rise to entire larvae—in other words that their potency was more extensive than their normal fate.

Later Driesch (1892), Born (1893), and O. Hertwig (1893) disturbed the normal cleavage by pressure exerted upon the egg; the successive nuclear generations thus became displaced into abnormal regions of the embryo and should have directed these into abnormal paths of development if they really were genetically unequal as Weismann postulated; this did not occur. Boveri (1896, 1900) finally demonstrated that random distribution of chromosomes must also occur in normal development, since the nature of the mitotic mechanism does not provide for the orderly allocation of unlike daughter chromosomes.

These experiments of Driesch, Born, and O. Hertwig in which abnormal nuclear divisions were produced by deformations of the egg were complemented by an experiment of J. Loeb (1894) in which this was achieved in an especially clear manner. Eggs of *Arbacia* are transferred 10 minutes after artificial fertilization to one-half strength dilution of sea water for a short time. The water taken in by osmosis then causes the egg membrane to burst. Thereupon a part of the egg substance flows out through the narrow opening, whereas the rest remains inside the membrane. In this way an enucleate half is constricted off from the egg half which contains the nucleus, the two halves remaining connected by a more or less thin cytoplasmic bridge. Cleavage begins in the nucleated half; sooner or later a nucleus wanders across into the other half and causes it to develop. The results are double-formations or twins; i.e., the half with delayed nuclear supply also possesses the capacity to form an entire embryo, even though it has received only a derivative of the cleavage nucleus.

In the summer of 1913, when I was teaching Otto Mangold the technique of constricting *Triton* eggs, it occurred to me that it ought to be possible by this means to keep the nucleus within one half of the unfertilized egg for a time so that it would begin its cleavages there. Only later would a daughter nucleus wander across the cytoplasmic bridge into the enucleate half and initiate cleavage there. . . .

II. MATERIAL AND METHODS

Eggs of *Triton taeniatus* were used, either artificially fertilized or gathered shortly after they were laid on aquarium plants. Such eggs show a small light-colored area with a dark spot, the first and shortly afterwards also the second polar body under which the egg nucleus lies, and one or more small dark spots, the points of entry of spermatozoa. The constriction was carried out in the manner described several times previously. By means of the landmarks mentioned one can tell which half contains the egg nucleus, and whether it has received at least one spermatozoon. In order to be able to identify both halves later on, the constricted egg was so oriented that the knot of the ligature was located on the underside and to the right of the egg nucleus; then the end of the ligature located on the side of the observer was cut off shorter than the other one. Only those eggs were further observed in which both halves were almost of equal size and in which both the outer membrane and the vitelline membrane were undamaged. . . .

III. DESCRIPTION OF THE EXPERIMENTS [1]

Exp. 1. *Triton taeniatus* 1914, J3

The egg was artificially fertilized on April 24, 1914, at 8.55 A.M. and constricted about ¼ hour later, at 9.09 A.M.; the light spot with the first polar body ("polar spot") and the closely adjacent point of entry of a spermatozoon were located on the same side of

---

[1] Only two of a number of experimental protocols can be reprinted here.—*Editors.*

the ligature. On this side the first cleavage furrow cut through obliquely about 6¾ hours after fertilization (3.38 P.M.). The embryo at this stage thus consisted of two cells, one of which represented about ¼ of the egg, while the other consisted of two parts, separated by the constriction furrow, the smaller of which contained the nucleus. About 1¾ hours later, at 5.20 P.M., the second cleavage followed; the smaller cell divided in two, and from the larger a small part constricted off by a furrow which lay exactly under the ligature. Obviously, therefore, a nucleus had migrated across the bridge into the hitherto enucleate half on the other side of the ligature.

The embryo now consisted of four cells, three smaller ones on one side of the ligature and a larger one on the other side. The furrow under the ligature cut in so deeply that with a somewhat stronger constriction the embryo would have been cut completely in two; here, however, they reunited shortly. One and one-fourth hours later, at 6.36 P.M., the three smaller cells of the more advanced half had divided again; the division of the larger cell began somewhat over ½ hour later, at 7.13 P.M. This delay, caused by the greater mass of the dividing cell, increased the lead of the other half, still clearly recognizable the following day when both halves were in advanced cleavage. In the course of further development the two halves separated from each other entirely. Out of one a well-formed embryo developed; out of the other a rounded ventral piece, not further differentiated, a sure sign that the constriction had taken place in a frontal plane.

In this embryo therefore, as a result of the retention of the nucleus in one side, the other half received, not one of two daughter nuclei as is normal, but one of four nuclei, or to put it briefly, ¼ rather than ½ cleavage nucleus. And

it was just this half from which the embryo developed, while the advanced half with ¾ cleavage nuclei gave rise to the ventral piece.

Experiment 3. *Triton taeniatus* 1914 N7

The egg was artificially fertilized on April 15, 1914 at 11.24 A.M. and about ¼ hour later, at 11.41 A.M., it was constricted as tightly as possible; the egg nucleus and several spermatozoa lay close together in one half. About 6½ hours after fertilization, at 5.50 P.M., the first cleavage furrow cut through one half obliquely; an hour later, at 6.55 P.M., the second cleavage appeared, exactly perpendicular to the first. An hour later, at 8.00 P.M., the horizontal furrow was observed to form and it was completed at 8.30 P.M. A cleavage alongside the ligature had not as yet formed. The embryo now consisted of two halves separated from one another by a deep constriction furrow, one half cleaved and the other uncleaved. The former was comprised of four vegetal and three animal cells; the fourth animal cell was connected by a narrow stalk with the other embryo half. At all events, all eight nuclei were located on one side of the ligature. At the next division a furrow finally cut through the connecting stalk; a nucleus representing 1/16 of the zygote nucleus had therefore crossed over into the hitherto enucleate embryo half and initiated its development.

It took nearly two hours until, at about 11.40 P.M., the first cleavage furrow appeared here; the other half had in the meantime divided at least twice. Both halves were almost entirely separated. The constriction had been a median one and twins developed whose age difference persisted a long time. They were raised to an age of 140 days. On preservation, on Sept. 2, 1914, no difference between them was any longer recognizable. This shows that a twin embryo with 1/16 of a zygote nucleus developed exactly as well as one having $^{15}/_{16}$ cleavage nuclei. . . .

IV. DISCUSSION OF THE RESULTS

In order to understand the further development of both egg halves, one must look back at the condition of both first blastomeres of *Triton taeniatus* when they are separated from one another by a constriction along the first cleavage furrow. As is well known, either both develop into embryos of half size but normal proportions, or only one of them does so while the other one forms a ventral fragment without axial organs. This is doubtlessly connected with the fact that the median plane of the embryo is already determined this early and can have various orientations toward the first cleavage plane and also to the plane of the constriction. This can be established with certainty by slight constriction during the two-cell stage. The two distinctive cases are those where the first cleavage plane represents the median plane of the embryo and those where it takes place perpendicular to the median plane, almost in a frontal plane, which separates the dorsal and ventral halves. If one divides normal embryos at the beginning of gastrulation in these two planes, i.e., either median or frontal, then in the first instance one obtains twin embryos of half size which can be normally proportioned if regulation has proceeded well; in the latter case, on the other hand, one obtains an embryo only from the dorsal half and out of the ventral half there arises a ventral piece containing the three germ layers, but without axial organs. . . .

Since exactly the same formations, that is, either twins or embryo and ventral piece, arise also from eggs which have been constricted before the appearance of the first cleavage and completely separated into two parts after nucleation of the retarded half, it follows that the constriction sometimes separates halves of more or less equal potency, and sometimes halves of more or less different potency. . . .

A $\frac{1}{4}$, $\frac{1}{8}$, $\frac{1}{16}$ cleavage nucleus coming from a lateral embryo half, can therefore initiate cleavage and normal development in a hitherto enucleate embryonic half so that the embryo with delayed nucleation can even reach metamorphosis. This, however, contradicts Weismann's theory according to which such a nucleus should contain only the corresponding fragments of all the organ *anlagen*.

My experiment involving medial constriction therefore affords for the egg of Triton confirmation of Loeb's results with the sea urchin egg (p. 216). In the case of frontal constriction, on the other hand, the results go beyond these findings as a result of the unequal potency of the dorsal and ventral egg halves. Since the formation of an embryo involves greater function than formation of a ventral fragment without axial organs, we need to take into consideration only the cases where the dorsal half was retarded and yielded a normal embryo out of a fragment of the cleavage nucleus while the ventral half, in spite of having a better nuclear supply, did not proceed beyond the formation of a ventral fragment.

. . . Although the ventral half contains a larger proportion of the zygote nucleus than the dorsal half it always forms less. Whereas the dorsal half is capable of forming an embryo always with one-eighth and under certain conditions with one-sixteenth of the cleavage nucleus it is useless for the ventral half to possess fifteen-sixteenths and even thirty-one thirty-seconds of the cleavage nucleus; it never becomes more than a fragment. *It therefore depends upon the egg cytoplasm and not upon the nuclei as to which part of the embryo a portion of the egg will develop (Spemann 1914).* The most likely assumption is that it is the material localized in the region of the "gray crescent" whose presence or absence is decisive for the fate of both embryo halves. Further experiments will be necessary to decide this point. . . .

The probabilities are all in favor of the fact that the lack of a gray crescent, and consequently the later absence of a center of organization, is responsible for the inability of the ventral fragment to form axial organs; since if one implants an organizer into the ventral lip of the blastopore then the ventral half forms axial organs (also after separation of the dorsal half, H. Bautzmann 1928). It is therefore not the necessary *anlagen* which are missing but the stimulus for their activation. And these organizing capacities themselves are present in the ventral ectoderm; one can evoke them by transplantation into an organizing environment. This something which normally arouses its activity—perhaps a substance—is manifestly localized in the gray crescent.

Experimental Analysis of the Development of the Balancer in Urodeles; an Example of the Interspecific Induction of Organs.

by O. MANGOLD

From *Naturwissenschaften*, Vol. 19, pp. 905–911 (1931), by permission. Abridged and translated by M. L. Gabriel for this volume.

A particularly illuminating example of the type of experimental analysis of development introduced by Spemann is the following paper by his student Mangold. Subsequent to Spemann's discovery of the primary organizer it became clear that many organs were called forth in development by "commands" or inductions exerted by neighboring parts. The organized embryo, it was learned, results from an interplay between the embryonic materials of which the organs are molded and the localities or "fields" in which these materials come to lie. From the repertory of responses of which the materials are capable, certain ones are aroused to activity by specific influences emanating from these fields. Mangold, in the researches presented here, shed light on the nature of this interaction. By combining tissues from different species he was able to show that the fields of one embryo are able to evoke the differentiation of cells of an amphibian embryo of a different order, but that these organ-forming cells respond to stimulation in terms which are limited by their genetic endowment. Although in the years following this preliminary experimental investigation continued attempts have been made to lay bare the physiological basis of these events, the metabolic processes which are involved are still quite obscure.

IN THE FOLLOWING account the development of the Urodele balancer will be causally analyzed. . . . Inasmuch as in the analysis we have combined forms with (*Triton*) and without (axolotl) balancers, there have emerged facts which may be significant for understanding the induction process and the phylogenetic origin of these structures.

A. Analysis of the development of the balancer in urodeles possessing balancers.

The larvae of the majority of urodeles, shortly before they leave the jelly envelope, develop on both sides, ventrocaudal of the eye, a long, somewhat club-shaped filament which serves to attach and support the larva, and which is cast off upon the development of the gills and anterior extremity. It consists of a relatively thick two-layered epidermis, the cells of which produce a very sticky secretion; a strong basal membrane, which is connected with the palatoquadrate, is derived from mesenchyme, and lends great elasticity to the organ; and the mesenchyme, which is formed (at least in part) from the head ganglion crest. A nerve and a blood-vessel run through the mesenchyme. The balancer is easily distinguished by its shape, its characteristic mode of development, its structure, and its stickiness, and it is therefore best suited for experimental investigation.

With regard to the point in time during development when the material of the balancer becomes determined as to its fate, we are to some extent oriented by the experiments of Harrison on *Amblystoma punctatum*. Harrison found that beginning with the open medullary plate stage, the *anlage* of the balancer, consisting of ecto- and mesoderm, can develop into a balancer when transplanted to other parts of the body. In later stages the ectoderm of the *anlage* alone can also do this. The period

of determination of the balancer thus occurs, like that of many other organs of the head, in the stages intervening between the laying down of the medullary plate and the appearance of the balancers.

As to the problem of the *localization of the determining factors* I have carried out a number of experiments during the last year, which may be reported here. With regard to the morphological situation of the balancer region at the time of determination there are three possibilities to be kept in mind:

(1.) The factors are situated, or, rather, have originated, in the epidermis.

(2.) The factors are located in the material of the archenteron roof which underlies the *anlage* at its determination and which consists of cells destined to form the archenteron of the head and the entomesoderm of the head.

(3.) The factors are situated in the elements of the medullary plate which lie close to the balancer. These are especially the eye, behind which the balancer is laid down, the balancer, and the ganglion crest of the head which forms in the medullary ridge and the elements of which later migrate into the lateral walls of the head as ectomesoderm. There they form a large part of the visceral skeleton (Stone).

As to (1.): With regard to the ectodermal balancer *anlage* we have not arrived at any decisive result. The transplantation by Harrison in early neurula stages in regions outside of the head (Fig. 1a, b) and our own transplantation in the blastocoel of the gastrula (Fig. 1a, c) yielded negative results. Thus it appears at least quite doubtful whether the capacity for self-differentiation develops in the presumptive balancer epidermis independently of the surroundings.

As to (2.): If we lift up the anterior half of the head ectodermal plate in an early neurula, remove the underlying archenteric roof, and implant it into the blastocoel of an early gastrula, (Fig. 2a, c) it comes to lie on the ventral side of the embryo during gastrulation, either between epidermis and mesoderm or between mesoderm and endoderm, and it induces a beautiful balancer. This balancer develops at the same time as the normal one and shares the same size-relationships as the normal balancer, if the transplantations are carried out between two embryos of *Triton taeniatus.* . . . It is therefore certain that the balancer *anlage* is subjected to a very powerful induction from the archenteron roof.

As to (3.) : The experiments with the medullary plate are just as positive. In these experiments, a cephalic quarter of the head plate without the archenteron roof was transplanted into the blastocoel of a gastrula. The transplant in this case represents presumptive eye, forebrain, and a part of the midbrain. If the medullary ridge is also transplanted, it contains the material of the head ganglion crest, which as ectomesoderm gives rise later, among other things, to the mesoderm of the balancer. Such transplants primarily induce a medullary plate in the presumptive ectoderm. If one observes the further development, balancers also appear among other head organs. As I was able to report previously, only the most anterior regions of the medullary plate have the capacity for balancer induction, and not the posterior regions. Within the compass of the anterior half of the headplate more precise localization has not been possible. The anterior half contains (a) regions without medullary ridge, hence without head neural crest and presumptive balancer mesoderm, (b) regions lying anterior, lateral, and caudal of the eye *anlage* which possess inductive capacity. We must accordingly conclude that the capacity to induce a balancer lies in the rostral half of the head plate, without being committed to a specific

organ rudiment, such as head ganglion crest, eye, forebrain, or midbrain.

This conclusion becomes uncertain, however, when we consider the course of induction. As just mentioned, in general there arise as induced structures first a medullary plate, indeed a head plate, with ridges and eye rudiments, and then secondarily the balancer. It is consequently possible that the formation of the balancer is induced by the induced head-plate and thus only secondarily by the implant. Since the induced head plate abundantly contains the elements which were excluded by the experiments described above, these are not entirely conclusive. Therefore, we must carry out the experiment so that the balancer is induced without the prior development of a secondary medullary plate. This can be done by attaching a piece of the head plate to the belly epidermis of a completed gastrula, since the belly epidermis does not form a medullary plate again, as is known from the old, abundantly confirmed experiment of Spemann. This experiment has thus far produced only eye discs. In rare cases balancers are also obtained here. This, it appears to me, makes very likely the direct induction of balancers by the various portions of the rostral head plate.

The formation of the balancers by the mesoderm and the epidermis of the head is accomplished, therefore, under the determining influence of the archenteric roof and the rostral parts of the head plate. Since of these probably only the head ganglion crest participates materially in the formation of the balancer, we find that several elements in the neighborhood exert their influence on the balancer; its development is thus assured by "multiple induction." Presumptive balancer epidermis itself probably has only scant capacity to form balancer; but the essential point is that it can react to inductive factors. It is very likely that other organs of the head (nose, ear vesicles, gills, and the like) reach development according to a similar principle, which further experiments, some already under way, will show.

B. Clarification of the balancer relationships in the balancerless axolotl through combination of Axolotl and Triton material.

The axolotl is one of the urodeles which do not develop balancers. In the position of the balancers one finds only a small arch, which suggests that here the development of the balancer does not proceed to completion. We now put the question: Can axolotl induce a balancer? Three series of experiments have thus far been carried out:

(1.) The transplantation of pure rostral medullary plate of axolotl into the blastocoel of the gastrula of *Triton taeniatus* frequently gives head induction with balancers. Fig. 3 shows such a *taeniatus* embryo with a large knob (impl) on the side of the belly distal to which there sits a double balancer (H). It is considerably larger than the normal balancer of the host. The knob contains the organs of the transplant, namely eyes and brain, and those of the induction, in this case also eyes and brain.

(2.) The transplantation of rostral archenteron roof of the axolotl neurula into the blastocoel of the gastrula of *Triton taeniatus* (Fig. 2) also yielded

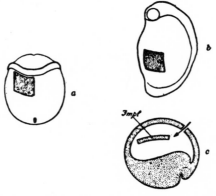

FIG. 1.—Plan of experiment to test the capacity of presumptive balancer epidermis to self-differentiate. The presumptive balancer epidermis is extirpated from a neurula with medullary ridges just raised (a) and implanted into the trunk epidermis of a somewhat older larva (b) (Harrison) or into the blastocoel of an early gastrula (c) (Mangold). Result is negative.

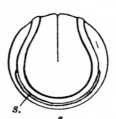
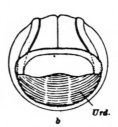
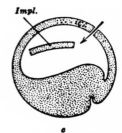

FIG. 2.—Plan of Experiment: Transplantation of the rostral archenteron roof of an early neurula (a, b) into the blastocoel of the gastrula (c).—a) Epidermis anterior to the rostral medullary ridge cut open at S.—b) Rostral medullary plate lifted up, archenteron roof (Urd) freed and excised.—c) Archenteron roof (Impl) implanted into the blastocoel through an incision in the animal region (arrow).

positive results. [In one instance,] an implantation knob appeared in the heart region, bearing a huge balancer, which probably is combined out of several balancers. More typical of this experiment is the formation of an implantation knob with a great number of balancers of various sizes. Corresponding results were also obtained in the trunk epidermis. The rostral archenteron roof has, therefore, an enormous power of induction; it induces the whole epidermis it touches. The latter usually first swells up into a vesicle and then proliferates the different balancers, the size of which is individually very variable, but generally far exceeds that of normal *T. taeniatus* balancers.

(3.) The transplantation of presumptive trunk epidermis of the early neurula of *Triton taeniatus* to the lateral facial region of the young neurula of *Axolotl* likewise yielded positive results. Fig. 4 shows an axolotl larva in ventral aspect; it has *taeniatus* epidermis on the right side of the face (left in the picture) and has formed a beautiful balancer. On the left side, in the region of the axolotl epidermis, the balancer is missing. The balancer is again considerably larger than the normal balancer of the appertaining *taeniatus* larva. As in the preceding experiment, here too abundant supernumerary structures arise.

The three experiments prove that inductive powers are present in the axolotl embryo. That in this case the induction can be a direct one, balancers being evoked immediately and not first "head," which then secondarily induces balancer formation, is shown by the last two

experiments in which no medullary plate develops in the implant.

Since the mesoderm of the axolotl, as shown by study of sections, participates in a normal manner in the formation of the balancer, the absence of the balancer in the axolotl can only lie in the *reaction capacity of the epidermis.* This is shown by the next experiment.

(4.) If presumptive epidermis from the early gastrula of axolotl is implanted into presumptive face epidermis of the gastrula of *Triton taeniatus,* the transplant readily builds lens, gills, ear vesicle, lateral line sense organs and other organs appropriate to this region which the axolotl also possesses; the balancer, foreign to the axolotl, is, however, always omitted when the transplant lies over the balancer region. . . .

Hence, in the axolotl inductive factors for balancers are present in full force in the medullary plate as well as in the archenteron roof. The absence of balancers is to be explained by the lack of reactive capacity in the epidermis.

C. General Discussion of Induction and Reaction in Inductive Development

. . . The induction of balancers by axolotl material presents a new fact for arriving at an understanding of deter-

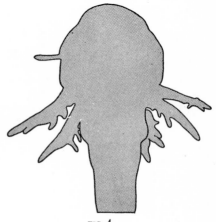

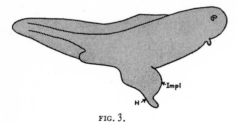

FIG. 3.

FIG. 4.

mination, since it shows that in the embryonic material of the axolotl induction factors are present for an organ which does not at all develop in the axolotl itself. Two explanations are obviously possible: (a) The action of the determination field is specific only to a limited degree and its determination factors are of so general a nature that they are the same or similar in various amphibians or even in different vertebrates; or (b) the determination fields are specific in action by virtue of the special nature of their determination factors, and the material of the axolotl is entirely or almost entirely equivalent to that of *Triton* with respect to its induction potencies. Explanation (b) is supported by the close relationship between *Axolotl* and *Triton* and the harmonious participation of axolotl mesenchyme in the balancer of a foreign species. In favor of explanation (b) is the experience obtained with numerous organs common to both species that the induction factors are not species specific. The combination of material from species as distantly related as possible would further this line of investigation. Up to now, the induction of balancers in *Triton* by frog material has led to only doubtfully positive results. Nevertheless, these and some results of other authors (Woerdeman, Spemann, and Schotté) argue for explanation (a).

As the reported experiments on the reaction capacities of the epidermis have shown, the reaction capacity of the induced material is of the greatest importance in determinative development. What then are the functions of the inducing and reacting materials in the formation of an organ? Experiments recently confirmed, especially by the systematic work of Holtfreter, have repeatedly shown that embryonic material in isolation develops into fully differentiated tissues. These findings lead to the interpretation, for the present hypothetical, that the reacting material possesses all the potencies required for the development of the organs and tissues of its species and that the inductor only determines which potencies become realized. The center of gravity of development therefore lies in the store of potencies of the reacting materials. This is, however, influenced by many different forces, namely (1.) by the hereditary constitution, which, so far as we know now, only includes actions representative of the species of the embryo; (2) by the age, in that in every stage only those potencies are immediately capable of realization which lead to the development of the next stage of the normal embryo; (3) by determination steps which have taken place before the stage of development under consideration and which have the effect that the various regions display different stores of potencies, or in other words, that the embryo represents a "model of different reaction fields." After all, one would expect that the same determinant in material of differing potency could evoke reactions under different conditions or also remain without reaction; thus in our experiment the reaction of the axolotl epidermis is lacking because obviously the balancer is not included in the store of potencies of the species. Also one must take into account the fact that the same potency in the same material can be brought to realization by various means.

And finally it is conceivable that in material not entirely equivalent in potency different inductors are necessary in order to bring the same potency to development. The specificity of action is thus a common product of the inductor on the one hand and the store of potencies of the reacting material on the other.

Part Six

~✦~

GENETICS

1884–1888   Identification of the cell nucleus as the basis for inheritance was independently reported by Hertwig, Strasburger, Kölliker, and Weismann.

1885   Rabl announced the individuality of chromosomes and Flemming observed sister chromatids passing to opposite poles of the cell during mitosis.

1886   Galton devised a new useful statistical tool, the correlation table.

1887   Weismann elaborated an all-embracing theory of chromosome behavior during cell division and fertilization and predicted the occurrence of meiosis. Roux put forth the suggestion that the linearly arranged qualities of the chromosomes were equally transmitted to daughter cells at mitosis.

1888   Boveri verified Weismann's predictions of chromosome reduction by direct observations in *Ascaris*.

1889   Galton formulated the law of ancestral inheritance, a statistical description of the relative contributions to heredity made by one's ancestors.

1890   The numerical equality of paternal and maternal chromosomes at fertilization was established by Boveri in Germany and Guignard in France.

1892   Publication of Weismann's book *Das Keimplasma* (The Germ Plasm) emphasized meiosis as an exact mechanism for chromosome distribution.

1894   Bateson foreshadowed the rediscovery of Mendel's work by calling attention to the importance of studying discontinuous variation.

1894   Karl Pearson published the first of a long series of contributions to the mathematical theory of evolution. Methods for analyzing statistical frequency distributions were developed in detail.

1898   Double fertilization in plants was described by Navoshin.

1898   Flemming determined chromosome number as 24 pairs in man.

1899   First International Congress of Genetics held in London.

1900   Mendel's principles independently discovered and verified by De Vries (Holland), Correns (Germany), and Tschermak (Austria), marking the beginning of modern genetics.

1901   Henking and others reported an "accessory chromosome" in spermatozoa, later identified as the sex chromosome.

1902   The terms F_1, F_2, allelomorphism, homozygote, and heterozygote were coined by Bateson who also listed some 26 different cases of established allelomorphism in wheat, maize, peas, snapdragon, *Datura,* Oenothera, mouse, cattle, fowl, and man.

1902–03   Sutton pointed out the mutual interrelationships between cytology and Mendelism, closing the gap between cell morphology and heredity.

1903   The concepts of phenotype, genotype, and selection were introduced and clearly defined by Johannsen.

1905   Stevens and Wilson extended the findings of cytology to the interpretation of sex determination.

1905   Bateson et al. reported the discovery of two new principles: linkage and gene interaction.

1906   Woodworth and Castle introduced *Drosophila* as new experimental material for genetic studies.

1907   Lutz proved that the *gigas* mutation in the evening primrose contained twice the usual chromosome number. This led to the analysis and artificial production of polyploidy.

1908   Nilsson-Ehle analyzed the inheritance of color in wheat and provided a useful model for the further analysis of continuously variable characters.

1909   Emerson discovered multiple allelomorphism in corn and also in beans.

1910   Epstein and Ottenberg pointed out that the human blood groups (A, B, O,) were inherited in accord with Mendelian principles. Morgan proposed a theory of sex-linked inheritance for the first mutation discovered in *Drosophila,* white eye. This was followed by the announcement of the gene theory including the principle of linkage.

1911   Richard Goldschmidt published the first edition of his *Introduction to the Science of Heredity* in which he summarized his theory of sex determination as a matter of the rate of developmental expression for sex-determining genes. This was based on his study of intersexual forms in moths.

1913   Bridges reported non-disjunction of sex chromosomes as a proof for the chromosome theory of heredity.

1915   *The Mechanism of Mendelian Heredity,* an epochal book, published by Morgan, Sturtevant, Bridges, and Muller.

1917   Emerson discovered and analyzed a highly mutable gene in maize. After thirty-five years this particular gene is still under active study.

1919   Morgan and co-workers published a summary of the rapidly growing findings in genetics on *The Physical Basis of Heredity.*

1921   Morgan estimated the gene to have a diameter of 20–70 microns. Current estimates are considerably lower.

1927   Artificial transmutation of the gene was reported by Stadler in plants and Muller in *Drosophila.*

1927   Painter found a chromosome deficiency in mice which along with genetic evidence provided the first case of localizing a specific gene to a particular chromosome in mammals.

1930   Stadler devised and perfected methods for determining spontaneous mutations rates in maize, finding that different genes mutate at widely different rates.

1931   Creighton and McClintock demonstrated a cytological proof for crossing over in maize. A similar demonstration was made by Stern in *Drosophila.*

1931   Wright presented the first unified picture of evolution in terms of Mendelism illustrating the relations between selection pressure, mutation rates, inbreeding, isolation and the like.

1932   Dobzhansky, Painter, and Muller showed that while the seriation of genes is the same for genetic and cytological maps, physical distances and crossover distances did not coincide.

1934   Painter recognized the value of giant salivary chromosomes in genetic analysis. This facilitated extensive studies on precise gene localization and chromosome structure.

Letter to Carl Nägeli. ∼

by GREGOR MENDEL

Reprinted from *The Birth of Genetics*, Supplement to *Genetics*, Vol. 35, no. 5, part 2 (1950), by permission of the editors.

Among the more important legacies of mid-twentieth century biology are the principles of segregation and independent assortment embodied in the researches of Gregor Mendel. Communicated in two relatively brief papers in 1866 and 1869, and published in a rather obscure journal, these works survey the results of nearly eight years of constant experimentation and thought. The profound generalizations derived by Mendel are perhaps too widely known to justify further elaboration here. More appropriately, one might inquire why Mendel, unlike so many serious investigators before him, succeeded in penetrating the enigma of heredity.

In no small way, Mendel's successful analysis depended upon the introduction of several methodological innovations. The most important among these was primarily the ultimate reduction and simplification of the problem to the least common term. Instead of attempting to follow the hereditary transmission of numerous character differences simultaneously, he chose to follow instead a single such difference or, at most, a limited few. Secondly, his careful choice of experimental material, over which he exerted complete control in matings, materially added to the probability of success. In addition, where others contented themselves with mere qualitative observations, Mendel insistently examined not only each generation, but also quantitatively enumerated and classified each individual. Techniques such as these, coupled with an adequate system of record-keeping, led him to uncover the regular mathematical relations which descriptively predict how the genes of contrasted parents, united in the sexual process, are segregated and then recombined in subsequent generations.

Through this kind of experimental design Mendel developed a revolutionary hypothesis which clearly depicted the materials and mode of the hereditary process. The materials of heredity were thus visualized not as a preformed picture of the organism as a whole, but rather as an organized array of unitary, discontinuous particles or genes which in the aggregate composed the potential image of the individual or species as a whole. The genotype was visualized not as a status but as a process, which determined the potencies or limits of organic development within a particular environment.

Reprinted below is a translation of one in a series of letters to Carl von Nägeli, a celebrated botanist and authority on evolution. The letter summarizes much of Mendel's original work, translations of which are easily available from many sources.

HIGHLY ESTEEMED SIR:

MY MOST CORDIAL thanks for the printed matter you have so kindly sent me! The papers "die Bastardbildung im Pflanzenreiche," "über die abgeleiteten Pflanzenbastarde," "die Theorie der Bastardbildung," "die Zwischenformen zwischen den Pflanzenarten," "die systematische Behandlung der Hieracien rücksichtlich der Mittelformen und des Umfangs der Species," especially capture my attention. This thorough revision of the theory of hybrids according to contemporary science was most welcome. Thank you again!

With respect to the essay which your honor had the kindness to accept, I think I should add the following information: the experiments which are discussed were conducted from 1856 to 1863. I knew that the results I obtained were not easily compatible with our contemporary scientific knowledge, and that under the circumstances publication of one such isolated experiment was doubly dangerous; dangerous for the experimenter and for the cause he represented. Thus I made every effort to verify, with other plants, the results obtained with Pisum. A number of hybridizations undertaken in 1863 and 1864 convinced me of the difficulty of finding plants suitable for an extended series of experiments, and that under unfavorable circumstances years might elapse without my obtaining the desired information. I attempted to inspire some control experi-

ments, and for that reason discussed the Pisum experiments at the meeting of the local society of naturalists. I encountered, as was to be expected, divided opinion; however, as far as I know, no one undertook to repeat the experiments. When, last year, I was asked to publish my lecture in the proceedings of the society, I agreed to do so, after having re-examined my records for the various years of experimentation, and not having been able to find a source of error. The paper which was submitted to you is the unchanged reprint of the draft of the lecture mentioned; thus the brevity of the exposition, as is essential for a public lecture.

I am not surprised to hear your honor speak of my experiments with mistrustful caution; I would not do otherwise in a similar case. Two points in your esteemed letter appear to be too important to be left unanswered. The first deals with the question whether one may conclude that constancy of type has been obtained if the hybrid Aa produces a plant A, and this plant in turn produces only A.

Permit me to state that, as an empirical worker, I must define constancy of type as the retention of a character during the period of observation. My statements that some of the progeny of hybrids breed true to type thus includes only those generations during which observations were made; it does not extend beyond them. For two generations all experiments were conducted with a fairly large number of plants. Starting with the third generation it became necessary to limit the numbers because of lack of space, so that, in each of the seven experiments, only a sample of those plants of the second generation (which either bred true or varied) could be observed further. The observations were extended over four to six generations. Of the varieties which bred true some plants were observed for four generations. I must further mention the case of a variety which bred true for six generations, although the parental types differed in four characters. In 1859 I obtained a very fertile descendant with large, tasty, seeds from a first generation hybrid. Since, in the following year, its progeny retained the desirable characteristics and were uniform, the variety was cultivated in our vegetable garden, and many plants were raised every year up to 1865. The parental plants were $bcDg$ and $BCdG$:

$B.$ albumen yellow $b.$ albumen green
$C.$ seed-coat grayish $c.$ seed-coat white
   brown
$D.$ pod inflated $d.$ pod constricted
$G.$ axis long $g.$ axis short

The hybrid just mentioned was $BcDG$.

The color of the albumen could be determined only in the plants saved for seed production, for the other pods were harvested in an immature condition. Never was green albumen observed in these plants, reddish-purple flower color (an indication of brown seed-coat), constriction of the pod, nor short axis.

This is the extent of my experience. I cannot judge whether these findings would permit a decision as to constancy of type; however, I am inclined to regard the separation of parental characteristics in the progeny of hybrids in Pisum as complete, and thus permanent. The progeny of hybrids carries one or the other of the parental characteristics, or the hybrid form of the two; I have never observed gradual transitions between the parental characters or a progressive approach toward one of them. The course of development consists simply in this; that in each generation the two parental characteristics appear, separated and unchanged, and there is nothing to indicate that one of them has either inherited or taken over anything from the other. For an example, permit me to point to the packets, numbers 1035–1088, which I sent you. All the seeds originated in the first generation of a hybrid in which brown and white seed-coats were combined. Out of the brown seed of this hybrid, some plants were obtained with seed-coats of a pure white color, without any admixture of brown. I expect those to retain the same constancy of character as found in the parental plant.

The second point, on which I wish to elaborate briefly, contains the following statement: "You should regard the numerical expressions as being only empirical, because they can not be proved rational."

My experiments with single characters all lead to the same result: that from the seeds of the hybrids, plants are obtained half of which in turn carry the hybrid character (Aa), the other half, however, receive the parental characters A and a in equal amounts. Thus, on the average, among four plants two have the hybrid character Aa, one the parental character A, and the other the parental character a. Therefore $2Aa + A + a$ or $A + 2Aa + a$ is the empirical simple, developmental series for two differentiating characters. Likewise it was shown in an empirical manner that, if two or three differentiating characters are combined in the hybrid, the developmental series is a combination of two or three simple series. Up to this point I don't believe I can be accused of having left the realm of experimentation. If then I extend this combination of simple series to any number of differences between the two parental plants, I have indeed entered the rational domain. This seems permissible, however, because I have proved by previous experiments that the development of any two differentiating characteristics proceeds independently of any other differences. Finally, regarding my statements on the differences among the ovules and pollen cells of the hybrids; they also are based on experiments. These and similar experiments on the germ cells appear to be important, for I believe that their results furnish the explanation for the development of hybrids as observed in Pisum. These experiments should be repeated and verified.

I regret very much not being able to send your honor the varieties you desire. As I mentioned above, the experiments were conducted up to and including 1863; at that time they were terminated in order to obtain space and time for the growing of other experimental plants. Therefore seeds from those experiments are no longer available. Only one experiment on differences in the time of flowering was continued; and seeds are available from the 1864 harvest of this experiment. These are the last I collected, since I had to abandon the experiment in the following year because of devastation by the pea beetle, *Bruchus pisi*. In the early years of experimentation this insect was only rarely found on the plants, in 1864 it caused considerable damage, and appeared in such numbers in the following summer that hardly a 4th or 5th of the seeds was spared. In the last few years it has been necessary to discontinue cultivation of peas in the vicinity of Brünn. The seeds remaining can still be useful, among them are some varieties which I expect to remain constant; they are derived from hybrids in which two, three, and four differentiating characters are combined. All the seeds were obtained from members of the first generation, i.e., of such plants

as were grown directly from the seeds of the original hybrids.

I should have scruples against complying with your honor's request to send these seeds for experimentation, were it not in such complete agreement with my own wishes. I fear that there has been partial loss of viability. Furthermore the seeds were obtained at a time when *Bruchus pisi* was already rampant, and I cannot acquit this beetle of possibly transferring pollen; also, I must mention again that the plants were destined for a study of differences in flowering time. The other differences were also taken into account at the harvest, but with less care than in the major experiment. The legend which I have added to the packet numbers on a separate sheet is a copy of the notes I made for each individual plant, with pencil, on its envelope at the time of harvest. The dominant characters are designated as *A, B, C, D, E, F, G* and as concerns their dual meaning please refer to p. 11. The recessive characters are designated *a, b, c, d, e, f, g;* these should remain constant in the next generation, Therefore, from those seeds which stem from plants with recessive characters only, identical plants are expected (as regards the characters studied).

Please compare the numbers of the seed packets with those in my record, to detect any possible error in the designations—each packet contains the seeds of a single plant only.

Some of the varieties represented are suitable for experiments on the germ cells; their results can be obtained during the current summer. The round yellow seeds of packets 715, 730, 736, 741, 742, 745, 756, 757, and on the other hand, the green angular seeds of packets 712, 719, 734, 737, 749, and 750 can be recommended for this purpose. By repeated experiments it was proved that, if plants with green seeds are fertilized by those with yellow seeds, the albumen of the resulting seeds has lost the green color and has taken up the yellow color. The same is true for the shape of the seed. Plants with angular seeds, if fertilized by those with round or rounded seeds, produce round or rounded seeds. Thus, due to the changes induced in the color and shape of the seeds by fertilization with foreign pollen, it is possible to recognize the constitution of the fertilizing pollen.

Let B designate yellow color; b, green color of the albumen.

Let A designate round shape; a, angular shape of the seeds.

If flowers of such plants as produce green and angular seeds by self-fertilization are fertilized with foreign pollen, and if the seeds remain green and angular, then the pollen of the donor plant was, as regards the two characters .... ab

If the shape of the seeds is changed, the pollen was taken from .... Ab

If the color of the seeds is changed, the pollen was taken from .... aB

If both shape and color is changed, the pollen was taken from .... AB

The packets enumerated above contain round and yellow, round and green, angular and yellow, and angular and green seeds from the hybrids $ab + AB$. The round and yellow seeds would be best suited for the experiment. Among them (see experiment p. 15) the varieties AB, ABb, Aab, and $AaBb$ may occur; thus four cases are possible when plants, grown from green and angular seeds, are fertilized by the pollen of those grown from the above mentioned round and yellow seeds, i.e.

$$\text{I. } ab + AB$$
$$\text{II. } ab + ABb$$
$$\text{III. } ab + AaB$$
$$\text{IV. } ab + AaBb$$

If the hypothesis that hybrids form as many types of pollen cells as there are possible constant combination types is correct, plants of the makeup

AB	produce pollen of the type AB
ABb	" " " " " AB and Ab
AaB	" " " " " AB and aB
$AaBb$	" " " " " $AB, Ab, aB,$ and ab

Fertilization of ovules occurs:

	I. Ovules ab with pollen AB
II.	" ab " " $AB,$ and Ab
III.	" ab " " $AB,$ and aB
IV.	" ab " " $AB, Ab, aB,$ and ab

The following varieties may be obtained from this fertilization:

I. $AaBb$
II. $AaBb$ and Aab
III. $AaBb$ and aBb
IV. $AaBb, Aab, aBb,$ and ab

If the different types of pollen are produced in equal numbers, there should be in

I. All seeds round and yellow

II. one half round and yellow
one half round and green

III. one half round and yellow
one half angular and yellow

IV. one quarter round and yellow
one quarter round and green
one quarter angular and yellow
one quarter angular and green

Furthermore, since the numerical relations between AB, ABb, AaB, $AaBb$ are 1:2:2:4, among any nine plants grown from round yellow seed there should be found on the average $AaBb$ four times, ABb and AaB twice each, and AB once; thus the IVth case should occur four times as frequently as the 1st and twice as frequently as the IInd or IIIrd.

If on the other hand, plants grown from the round yellow seeds mentioned are fertilized by pollen from green angular plants, the results should be exactly the same, provided that the ovules are of the same types, and formed in the same proportions, as was reported for the pollen.

I have not performed this experiment myself, but I believe, on the basis of similar experiments, that one can depend on the result indicated.

In the same fashion individual experiments may be performed for each of the two seed characters separately, all those round seeds which occurred together with angular ones, and all the yellow ones which occurred with green seeds on

the same plant are suitable. If, for instance, a plant with green seeds was fertilized by one with yellow seeds, the seeds obtained should be either 1) all yellow, or 2) half yellow and half green, since the plants originating from yellow seeds are of the varieties B and Bb. Since, furthermore, B and Bb occur in the ratio of 1:2, the 2nd fertilization will occur twice as frequently as the 1st.

Regarding the other characters, the experiments may be conducted in the same way; results, however, will not be obtained until next year. . . .

As must be expected, the experiments proceed slowly. At first beginning, some patience is required, but later, when several experiments are progressing concurrently, matters are improved. Every day, from spring to fall, one's interest is refreshed daily, and the care which must be given to one's wards is thus amply repaid. In addition, if I should, by my experiments, succeed in hastening the solution of these problems, I should be doubly happy.

Accept, highly esteemed Sir, the expression of most sincere respect from

Your devoted,
G. MENDEL
(Altbrünn, Monastery of St. Thomas)
Brünn, 18 April, 1867

On the Chemical Composition of Pus Cells.

by F. MIESCHER

From *Hoppe-Seyler's medizinische-chemische Untersuchungen*, Vol. 4, pp. 441–460 (1871). Abridged and translated by M. L. Gabriel for this volume.

In his reflections on the growing unity of modern biology C. D. Darlington, an eminent contemporary British cytologist, has aptly noted that as Darwin had attained a satisfactory overview concerning evolu-

tion, Mendel was busily engaged in a formulation of particulate inheritance, and Hertwig had just witnessed the fusion of pronuclei at fertilization. This is also the period during which F. Miescher conducted his pioneer investigations concerned with the chemical analysis of the cell nucleus.

Miescher's major contributions in this field were, first, the demonstration that normal, formed cellular elements, such as the nucleus, could be isolated relatively free of the omnipresent contaminating cytoplasm, and, second, that isolated as well as intact nuclei contained as a principal constituent the hitherto unknown, phosphorus-rich nucleoprotein. The central importance of nucleic acid compounds cannot be overemphasized. Most current investigators believe that they will surely provide a basis for understanding the processes of self-reproduction, growth, heredity, sexuality, and evolution.

One particular class of nucleic acid compounds, frequently designated as DNA or desoxypentose nucleic acid, is entirely localized within the cell nucleus, intimately associated with the chromosome structure itself. Furthermore, the distribution of DNA along the longitudinally differentiated chromosome corresponds closely to the distribution of active gene loci.

Although considerable effort has been expended in uncovering the chemical and biological nature of the nucleic acids, their precise metabolic functions are still unclear. However, it is known that for a variety of biological materials the DNA concentration per cell is constant. The concentration varies in an entirely predictable fashion. Somatic cells contain twice the concentration present in the reduced gametes; in polyploid species the concentration is directly proportional to the number of chromosome sets. Further clues to the biological function of the nucleic acids stem from investigations concerned with virus infection and also from the discovery of DNA-induced bacterial transformations. The latter topic is discussed elsewhere in this volume.

Nucleic acids, as they normally occur within the cell, are chemically linked or bound to proteins in a fashion that is not altogether clear at the present time. However, lest the impression be gained that nucleic acids are themselves simple substances, since upon enzymatic or chemical hydrolysis they yield a low number of simple chemical fragments, it should be recalled that modern molecular weight estimates for nucleic acids give approximate values of one to several million. Among the megamolecules known to modern science the nucleic acids certainly pose a fascinating challenge in their size and complexity.

THE CHEMISTRY OF pus has until recently been studied almost entirely from the point of view of pathology. In recent times pus has also been utilized in the study of the properties of protoplasm. This material is not perfect, and must be used with caution, but it is the only one easily obtainable and for this reason suitable as a preliminary starting point.

The material for investigation was supplied by the Tübingen surgical clinic. The dressings, mostly obtained from surgical wounds, were collected and brought to the laboratory daily and immediately used. Material that in appearance and odor showed indications of advanced decomposition was discarded. The material at my disposal was very variable in quantity, seldom as much as a couple of ounces, often minims.

It is obvious that I have not been dealing with physiologically fresh, i.e., living, pus cells. Consequently my results will require correction through special observations.

The first desideratum in this investigation is the separation of the cells from the serum. Filtration often yields a somewhat clear serum, but this is nearly always only a part of that present. Sedimentation by means of salt solutions, which has been applied with good success to blood corpuscles, fails here, as the entire mass swells to a slimy consistency even at the most varied concentrations. For this reason, I turned to other salt solutions. After trying a variety of salts of alkalies and alkaline earths, I finally settled upon a mixture of one part of cold saturated solution of Glauber's salts [sodium sulfate] with nine parts of water. The dressings, containing cotton soaked with pus, were washed out with this solution, which does not produce any turbidity in clear filtered pus serum. The liquid was strained through linen cloth to remove the cotton fibers. Most of the cells settled out from this liquid so rapidly that usually after one or two hours a turbid fluid could be decanted from a pulpy sediment. The washing could usually be repeated two or three times during the course of a day. Most of the wash liquid could be removed from the paste of pus cells by means of filtration. The cells so obtained appeared under the microscope as spherical, slightly swollen, opaque rather than pale, and in good material, without any trace of decomposition.

THE NUCLEI AND NUCLEIN

A material consisting of pure cells like the present one must especially invite an attack upon the problem of the chemical constitution of the cell nucleus. I have elsewhere mentioned that by extracting cells with very dilute soda [sodium carbonate] solutions, one obtains, among other things, a substance in solution which is precipitated by acid, and is insoluble both in excess of acid and in salts, but which dissolves with a trace of caustic or carbonic alkali. In accordance with well-known histo-chemical facts, this material was most likely to be attributed to the nuclei. I was not, however, able to succeed in separating these substances satisfactorily from the associated protein by means of dilute acids. An unfilterable turbidity, hard to handle, remained. I therefore attempted to isolate the nuclei themselves.

For this purpose I first used very dilute hydrochloric acid, the prolonged action of which is to dissolve the protoplasm, leaving behind the naked nuclei. But the results were incomplete. After several days of treatment, some nuclei were nearly always isolated, sometimes a fair number; but in the majority of cases some of the protoplasm stubbornly adhered even when the liquid was changed six to ten times and the acid took up only traces of further protein. On this account the precipitation of the undissolved remnants of protoplasm was incomplete and the filtration was protracted and tedious. Acetic acid gave even poorer results.

In a more mechanical way I obtained small amounts of nuclei from cells treated for weeks (in the cold of winter) with dilute hydrochloric acid. I shook the undissolved residue long and vigorously with ether and water. The mass of cells still containing protoplasmic residues collected in the interface between the two liquids. At the bottom of the aqueous layer, however, a fine powdery sediment was visible after a time. This could be collected on a filter. It consisted of completely pure nuclei, with smooth contours, homogeneous content, and sharply demarcated nucleoli. Compared with their original volume, they were somewhat smaller. By shaking with fresh water, nuclei could be obtained anew from the remaining cells, but always in very small numbers. A higher specific gravity of the nuclei, as compared with the protoplasm, may well be the basis for this method of separation.

The nuclei so obtained remain entirely unaltered in pure water, but in very dilute alkaline fluids they become much swollen and pale. The nucleoli too become pale and invisible. The addition of acid restores the previous structural conditions. The nuclei also swell somewhat in NaCl solutions. Iodine stains them strongly yellow. The dilute soda solution mentioned extracts from the nuclei a yellowish solution of a substance that, when treated with dilute acetic acid or HCl, yields a flocculent precipitate insoluble in an excess of acid. This precipitate did not swell at all in pure water, but dissolved in the least trace of caustic or carbonic alkali as well as in ordinary acid sodium phosphate—but not in NaCl—to a liquid which remained clear on boiling. It gave a xanthoprotein reaction with nitric acid even when carefully washed; with sodium hydroxide and copper sulfate it formed a blue-violet solution. It dissolved in fuming hydrochloric acid; the precipitate which formed on dilution did not dissolve even in a large volume of water. This substance therefore showed itself to be related to, but not a member of, the proteins. The reactions, except for the entire lack of swelling or solubility in neutral water, agreed in general with those of Eichwald's mucin.

A substance, insoluble even in concentrated soda solutions, was retained on the filter. After drying with alcohol and ether this could be lifted off the filter as a collodion-like film. Under the microscope this still clearly displayed the contours of the nuclei and their nucleoli.

This film was soluble, though not instantaneously, in concentrated HCl and in caustic alkalies, but on the other hand it remained unchanged even after being heated for hours with glacial acetic acid at 140° in a sealed glass tube (in contrast to keratinous substances). According to these solubility characteristics, a certain similarity to the elastic substance is presumable. The minute amounts of nuclei obtained in the manner described barely sufficed for the few reactions mentioned; elementary analysis was out of the question.

I therefore seized upon a means whose effectiveness in dissolving protein had already been applied previously to the chemistry of albumin, i.e., to fluid containing pepsin. I used an extract of pigs' stomach filtered to clarity with 10 cc of fuming HCl to a liter of water. The direct treatment of freshly-washed pus cells with this fluid at 40° did not give satisfactory results. The bulk of the material dissolved, but a quantity of oily droplets was liberated, probably as a partial result of the decomposition of lecithin, and these kept the undissolved residue suspended as a barely filterable turbidity. I therefore preceded a longer —usually three to four times as long— digestion period with a treatment with warm alcohol and then subjected the residue, now quite free of lecithin, to digestion at 37°-45°. Within a few hours a finely powdered gray sediment separated from a clear yellowish fluid. To be sure of a complete action, I allowed the digestion to proceed for 18–24 hours, during which the fluid was twice decanted and changed. After the second extraction, the sediment underwent no further visible change with respect to quantity or microscopic characteristics. The sediment consisted exclusively of isolated nuclei without any trace of protoplasmic residue. Sometimes a few fine, moderately refractile granules were intermingled, but these for the most part passed through the filter on washing. If the extraction with alcohol was not exhaustive, some oil droplets were noticeable. The sediment was repeatedly shaken up with fresh ether, in order to remove fats. After the last decantation of the ether, the nuclei could be readily collected on the filter as a clay-like gray mass and washed at will with water without producing any alteration. Washing was continued until tannin failed to make the filtrate turbid.

By means of the method here given I was able with full assurance to obtain the nuclei out of pus cells in the desired quantities once I was clear as to the necessary precautions. The nuclei so obtained are completely naked but at least the majority are not as smooth as those isolated solely by means of hydrochloric acid. Although these nuclei do not differ markedly in size from those prepared by the method mentioned above, they usually have a somewhat shrunken, distinctly refringent appearance, some looking as though they had an unequally thickened membrane, or presenting the appearance of a granular cloudiness. It is uncertain whether this is due to an alteration of the contents or to wrinkling and roughness of the surface. The contours are smooth in some, and in others appear to be corroded. In nuclei in which the granulation is less pronounced, the nucleoli are clearly visible. The washed mass obtained in this manner was then treated several times with warm alcohol. The alcohol extracted small amounts of a substance which on evaporation was oily and light brown. It dissolved slowly in ether leaving behind a somewhat crumbly residue. According to these properties it is most similar to lecithin; unfortunately, I neglected to analyse it with phosphorus. With the third extraction, no further trace worth mentioning of this substance was taken up.

The mass of nuclei thus purified behaved, except for its microscopic condition, like the nuclei isolated with dilute HCl. With dilute soda solution it gave a yellow liquid, from which a precipitate that was insoluble in an excess of acid could be precipitated with acetic acid or HCl. The acid filtrate did not become cloudy either on neutralization or with potassium ferrocyanide. The major part of the substance remained undissolved, but was slowly soluble in caustic alkali. That it was not the alcohol or the heat of boiling that was responsible for the insolubility is clear from the quite similar behavior of nuclei isolated with HCl alone. The changes in microscopic appearance, on the contrary, may be the result of the extraction by alcohol of a substance—lecithin, I believe. Some of the nuclei were unequally cloudy; the quantity of extractable material may therefore be variable—perhaps according to the stage of development of the nucleus.

The material soluble in soda solution displayed the mucin-like reactions, as described above for the nuclei isolated with HCl. I have, however, been unable to produce any larger quantities of it; the filters became clogged with the swollen residues, and when the process was protracted, the material in solution became altered; products were formed which could be precipitated by tannin, but not by acetic acid. I used the small amount of material obtained for a nitrogen determination. I therefore used only whole nuclei for my later experiments, leaving for more favorable material the separation of the constituents which for the present I shall refer to provisionally as *soluble* and *insoluble nuclein.*

The purified nuclei are completely soluble, though not instantaneously so, in concentrated HCl. If the reagent has acted only a short time, then upon dilution with water nearly all the material is thrown down again as a flocculent precipitate, insoluble in large amounts of water; however, the filtrate gives a slight precipitate on treatment with potassium ferrocyanide solution, as well as on neutralization, and the latter filtrate is made somewhat turbid by tannin. With more prolonged action these transformation products increase in quantity, and finally one obtains no precipitate at all either on dilution or with potassium ferrocyanide. At most a precipitate may still be formed by treatment with tannin. At times the solution then has a purple-red color.

Similar is the effect of caustic alkalies, which completely dissolve the nuclei. At first, upon acidifying with HCl or acetic acid, nearly everything reprecipitates; the precipitate is however very easily soluble in the most dilute soda solution. From this I draw the supposition that soluble and insoluble nuclein are not essentially different, but may be only modifications, easily convertible one into the other; this, of course, requires further proof. Here, too, the acid filtrate yields a turbidity on neutralization or with potassium ferrocyanide. After treatment with fairly dilute sodium hydroxide for several days, the neutralized solution formed an abundant precipitate that was almost completely soluble in $\frac{1}{1000}$ HCl and dilute acetic acid; but also the neutral filtrate of this was made turbid by tannin. I regard this as a proof that the albumin-like reaction mentioned above need not necessarily be ascribed to contamination by albumin. It seems much more likely that albumin-like or syntonin-like substances may be formed as intermediates in the transformations of nuclein; lastly, however, products usually lumped together as peptone-like are formed. Which stage in the transformation I obtained, I could not determine for individual cases; under apparently similar conditions I obtained different results from time to time. It is obvious that only elementary analysis and precise investigation of the products formed will afford a definitive conclusion as to whether the two reactions are not deceptive. Boiling glacial acetic acid

does not dissolve either soluble or insoluble nuclein but appears also to produce quite gradually a transformation of a similar type. I have not performed any reactions with metallic salts since I know only of alkaline solutions of nuclein. On the other hand I have attempted to determine the essential characteristics of the elementary composition, as far as my very scanty material would allow. I have preferred to repeat the analyses for a few of the most important constituents, rather than to perform a single complete elementary analysis, as this procedure gives a better preliminary decision as to whether one is dealing with a chemical entity or a mixture. As soon as I find it possible, I shall complete my data. The substance contains N, S, and is especially rich in phosphorus. The old tradition of phosphorus-containing proteins thus has a real basis.

I. 0.1915 gr. of soluble nuclein give 1811 Pt. = 13.47 N. The nuclei were not extracted with alcohol after isolation. The following determinations were made with whole nuclei extracted with hot alcohol.

II. 0.2278 gr. gave 0.2378 Pt. = 14.60 N. A small amount of platinum chloride was accidentally decomposed during evaporation.

III. 0.2545 gr. gave 0.2518 Pt. = 13.99 N.

IV. 0.1862 gr. gave 0.1840 Pt. = 13.97% N.

V. 0.3882 gr., burned with potassium hydroxide and saltpeter, gave 0.0494 $BaSO_4$ = 2.005% S.

VI. 0.4611 gr. gave 0.0598 $BaSO_4$ = 1.78% S.

VII. 0.2453 gr. gave 0.0318 $BaSO_4$ = 1.77% S.

VIII. 0.3882 gr. gave 0.0350 $Mg_2P_2O_7$ = 5.76% P_2O_5.

IX. 0.4611 gr. gave 0.0430 $Mg_2P_2O_7$ = 5.96% P_2O_5.

Analyses number V and VIII, as well as VI and IX, were performed on the same sample; the two aliquots, however, came from different preparations. The N determinations were carried out according to the method of Will and Varrentrapp; the combustions, with the exception of V (and VIII), with soda and saltpeter.

I believe that from the analysis, incomplete though it be, the conclusion may well be drawn that we are not dealing with a fortuitous mixture, but with a chemical entity or a mixture of very closely related substances, aside from the presence of small amounts of impurities. Also favoring this conclusion is the close correspondence in N content between the soluble nuclein and the whole nuclei, despite a considerable difference in the preparation which must have reduced the N content. On the ground merely of qualitative analysis, one might think of a compound of lecithin with a protein or protein derivative, as has been advanced for vitellin or ichthin. But the presence of 5.8% P_2O_5 and 14% N in one and the same substance refutes this assumption. It is more likely that we here have a substance *sui generis,* not comparable with any other group at present known. . . .

According to experiments with other tissues, to be reported on shortly, it seems likely to me that a whole family of such phosphorus-containing substances, differing somewhat from each other, will emerge, as a group of nuclein substances, which perhaps will deserve equal consideration with the proteins.

I cannot help thinking that here lies the most essential physiological role of phosphorus in the organism. I have in mind specifically the well-known remarkable fact that in plants phosphorus is principally or almost exclusively accumulated at the growing points; surely the appearance of nuclei is restricted to the growing parts, i.e., to the cells in the course of multiplication. . . .

Thus far I have progressed on the basis of the available material. It is clear that, aside from elementary analyses, a number of simpler and more obvious experiments are lacking, from which essential disclosures concerning the relation of the nuclein substance to the hitherto known groups may be expected. I myself will publish further communications as soon as possible. I think, however, that the results obtained, though fragmentary, are sufficiently significant to invite the investigations of others, especially professional chemists. A knowledge of the relationships between nuclear materials, proteins, and their immediate products of metabolism will gradually help to raise the curtain which at present so completely veils the inner process of cellular growth.

Contributions to the Knowledge of the Cell and its Life Phenomena. ~

by WALTHER FLEMMING

From *Archiv für Mikroskopische Anatomie*, Vol. 16, pp. 302–406 (1879). Abridged and translated by M. L. Gabriel for this volume.

In this important paper Flemming describes mitosis in living and fixed cells of the salamander. An essential contribution was Flemming's development of improved fixing and staining methods to make visible the cytological details. This monograph, portions of which follow, includes a remarkably foresighted treatment of the problems of cell division, some of which are still active research problems today. Of major significance was Flemming's discovery of the longitudinal reduplication of the chromosome and his tentative proposal that the daughter halves separate and are distributed to the anaphase nuclei, later confirmed by van Beneden and Heuser. The present-day terminology of this subject did not come until later: "mitosis" was coined by Flemming in 1882, "prophase," "metaphase," and so forth by Strasburger in 1884, and "chromosome" in 1888 by Waldeyer—hence the somewhat cumbersome descriptive phrases used in this paper.

IN THE LARVA of the salamander the unpigmented regions of the tail-fin are the best object for observation of the living cell-divisions in the epithelium. The wonderfully transparent gill filaments do not show the living epithelium, and although they show the dividing nuclei, these are, however, too pale to be sufficiently visible. . . .

On the other hand, the gill filaments are as though made to order for obtaining fixed and stained preparations of cell divisions, since no further sectioning or preparation is required. As fixatives I have tried out a number of reagents, but have always come back to the same three which give the best results: picric acid, chromic acid, and less satisfactory, gold chloride.

A chief advantage of the picric acid treatment is that it subsequently provides very beautiful nuclear staining with haematoxylin or (less good) carmine. The acid must be well washed out before the staining; the haematoxylin solution is best when much diluted.

Description of Cell Division in Salamandra (after the living object) in Comparison with Stained Preparations

In the description I shall restrict myself chiefly to the epithelium of the fins and the gill filaments.

In a well-fed larva one need not search long to find various stages of division, which one encounters in the superficial cell layers as well as in the deep layers, among the resting nuclei of the tail fin. The earliest stages that can be recognized in the living tissue show the following:

1st. Phase: Appearance of a fine basketwork of tightly wound threads

Instead of the pale but sharply marked-off resting nucleus, the middle of the epithelial cell is occupied by a pale body, not sharply delimited, which is often slightly or markedly larger than a resting nucleus, and which in the living condition appears to be densely and finely granular. This granulation is, however, only apparent: stained preparations of this phase show with great clarity that this is a coherent, dense, and regular framework of delicately spiraled threads, which in the living condition are too pale to be entirely visible, so that the optical cross and oblique sections of their gyres give the impression of granulations. In lightly stained preparations one can ascertain that the nucleolus is no longer present. On the other hand there still exists a sharp differentiation of the nuclear figure from the plasma visible in stained objects as a fine but sharp contour. . . .

The coiled thread structure is much more dense, more regularly distributed in the nucleus, and much more considerable in mass than the structure in the resting nucleus; the threads of the former are quite or almost uniformly thick, which is not the case in the latter. . . .

In its resting condition the ground substance is stainable like the network and the nucleoli, but in lesser degree. In the well-marked coil stage ·[prophase], on the other hand, a stainable ground substance is no longer present. We now assume that this substance is taken over into the formed part of the nucleus, into the network, in preparation for the division (in connection with which the nucleoli at this time lose their form and disappear and presumably divide). Where this transition of the stainable substance into the network has not yet been completely accomplished, the ground substance takes a pale stain and unchanged remnants of it may be present. The reagents show these up as granules just as in the resting nucleus. Later these two remnants disappear also, and there is no longer present in the nucleus any substance which can coagulate as granules; everything stainable has been taken up into the structural elements. The latter have therefore grown in size and simultaneously divided into nearly equal spirals through the nucleus. All this occurs first at the periphery of the nucleus.

That an actual transformation of this kind of the substance in the nucleus must take place is immediately evident. It is only necessary to recall that the ground substance of the reticulum was stainable in the resting stage, whereas the stainability disappears during the division. It is on the face of it impossible that the coiled thread of the developing nucleus is only a morphological rearrangement of the resting network including the nucleoli. This is obvious from the fact that the mass of the coiled thread is clearly larger than that of the resting nuclear structure, and that—if I may thus express it—the quantity of stain which the basket accumulates may be estimated to be as large as that which the entire nucleus including the ground substance takes up in the resting condition. . . .

2d Phase: Loose coil or basket form of the mother nucleus

If one observes a metamorphosed nucleus for some time, the visible granules gradually become thicker and more isolated, and soon one clearly recognizes coiled threads which, however, on account of their paleness cannot clearly be seen to be connected. The staining of such an object shows plainly that this connection is actually present. The nucleus has the form of a very delicate extensively interconnected basket-work of winding threads of uniform thickness which are distinctly stainable. The ground substance, on the other hand, no longer takes up any trace of stain, and there are no longer present in the nucleus any finely granular masses (coagulations). The nucleoli have already disappeared prior to this. The threads loosen out more and more, and their direction becomes for the most part perpendicular or nearly so to the long axis of the nucleus, a condition that quite typically recurs (even more markedly) at the formation of the young nuclei after division.

If one comparatively estimates the mass of the basket structure of this form with the mass of the stainable substance in the earlier phases, both appear to be equal. If one, however, compares the thickness of the threads, it has appreciably increased in phase 2 as compared with phase 1; and at the same time the compactness of the windings has lessened. The idea that this thickening of the threads might take place by the fusion of adjacent threads is ruled out. In the first place one entirely fails to find figures in which the threads are partly of the thickness of phase 1 and partly of approximately double thickness; and on the other hand, one finds every transitional stage from the fine-threaded compactly wound coils to the coarse-threaded loosely wound stage. From this the following emerges as the most likely conception of the manner in which this transformation takes place: the threads of the fine-threaded dense basket shorten in length and at the same time grow in thickness, somewhat comparably—but much slower—to the way in which a muscle fiber contracts or a rubber band shortens from its stretched

condition; and at the same time they slowly become displaced in such a manner that they always remain an equal distance apart to the greatest extent possible. . . .

3d Phase: Astral form of the mother nucleus

In living divisions during the transition to this phase, the thread network is seen to become somewhat looser, and loops spread out peripherally to the clear space. The center remains indistinct. Stained preparations of the transition to this condition show a stratification of the threads in which the order is often difficult to discern; soon, however, there follow groupings in which a typical stratification of the threads is apparent, although it is not equally distinct in all cases. That is to say, there occur central and peripheral bendings of the threads— I will briefly call them loops. . . .

Up to now I have passed over another very remarkable phenomenon: *the threads divide themselves in half lengthwise*. This process can already occur at the end of the coiled stage, or in the course of the third phase now being described: accordingly one encounters both single and double threads in all these conditions. The threads may remain single during the stage of the transformation of the star. But that the lengthwise splitting of the threads is a typical process is proven without any doubt in *Salamandra* by the great number of such figures.

The thread halves lie almost exactly parallel in epithelial nuclei and red blood-cell nuclei, slightly diverging in endothelial cells, and often are turned back in the same direction for a short distance in connective tissue cells.

Later the threads move apart from one another along their entire length, and in this way there arises a fine threaded star, the rays of which are double in number and half as thick as previously.

That this longitudinal division of the threads (in *Salamandra,* at least) is an essential and constant stage, is indicated by the simple fact that also in the following stage (equatorial plate) the threads are always of approximately half the thickness as compared with the single-threaded star.

No investigator of nuclear division has hitherto reported anything of such a splitting of the threads; I therefore immediately asked myself whether the action of the reagents might perhaps be involved, unlikely as this might appear, since the phenomenon was always encountered in a similar manner in picric acid and chromic acid preparations. I can rule out every such idea, since I have been fortunate enough in several cases to see the double threads in the living condition as well. . . .

4th Phase: Equatorial Plate

This stage sets in quickly and passes quickly, and is therefore fixed by reagents relatively infrequently; in the investigation of every living epithelial cell division, however, one sees it typically recurring, and because of its characteristic form it deserved to be denoted as a separate phase.

Instead of the flattened star extending toward the poles in the form of two cones, as is characteristic of the previous stage, a grouping of the threads occurs in such a way that all the elements, at first somewhat coiled, but later stretched out more and more parallel to the division axis, fill up the space of a thick plate comprising about one-fifth to one-fourth and sometimes as much as one-third of the entire cell length. The plate always lies in the equator and is oriented at right angles to the division axis. . . .

With reference to this stage one might point out the following possibilities, without being able to present proofs for any of them:

(1.) Materials of the two future nuclei have already been preformed and grouped during the star stage. In this case, in the stage of the equatorial plate there would follow only the rearrangement of the elements. . . .

(2.) It is [also] possible that the separation of the two nuclear halves might have taken place earlier than in the stage of the equatorial plate. In this case one phenomenon is especially noteworthy: the longitudinal splitting of the threads. What does this signify in general? When I discovered this, I immediately thought that perhaps it represents a homology, though in very different form, of the division in two which the elements of the "nuclear plate" undergo according to Strasburger's, Bütschli's, and O. Hertwig's findings: that one longitudinal half of each thread might move into one half of the nuclear figure, and the other half thread into the other nuclear half, in other words, each into a future daughter nucleus.

If we assume that one longitudinal half of a double strand is predestined for one young nucleus and the other longitudinal half for the other young nucleus, and that this obtains for all the strands, and if we further assume—as indeed cannot be proven—that before the onset of phase 4 all the central loops have separated so that each double thread has come apart into four quarters, then no further division is necessary, but the four quarters need only to move in such a way that two come to lie in each nuclear half, and this could take place in the phase of the equatorial plate. Each thread extending from the polar side of the nuclear figure to the equatorial level would represent such a quarter strand.

This would presuppose that the connection in the equator between threads of the two sides which are observed at this stage must be only secondary contacts or temporary fusions of the thread ends having no special significance.

I have presented this hypothesis here

because the longitudinal splitting of the threads appears to me to be too remarkable not to be worthy of some attempt at explanation. At the same time I throw this out purely as a possibility without insisting upon it. . . .

5th Phase: Separation of the Nuclear Figure

This expression is meant to signify only the moving apart of the two halves since the actual separation of the two nuclear halves has already taken place.

Each half of the figure has somewhat the form of a broad fish-basket but with outwardly slightly convex rods. If this stage is seen in polar view, it has the appearance of a star. This, however, is not very distinctly observed in the epithelium since the cells, as mentioned, always divide in the horizontal plane. . . .

6th Phase: Star form of the daughter nuclei

The threads of the two nuclear halves * up to now having their free ends directed opposite those of the other side, move further and further apart so that some of those situated in the periphery often attain an orientation towards the poles of the cell. In this way the figure acquires the form of a flattened star, sometimes very regular and sometimes less so. . . .

At this time the constriction furrow frequently makes its appearance in one side of the cell body.

7th Phase: Wreath and Coil Form of the Daughter Nuclei

In the living cell each daughter nucleus has somewhat the appearance that the mother nucleus had earlier in the second phase. A characteristic feature

---

* I use the expression nuclear halves for convenience; it remains an open question whether during or before the separation any part of the old nucleus might remain in the plasma or whether anything might be acquired from the plasma.

is the constant deepening of the polar side, so that the two baskets, each with the shape of a convex-concave plate, turn their convex sides to one another. In the later course of this phase the windings move so close together that the living young nucleus gives the impression of a lumpy, internally homogeneous clump; staining shows very clearly, however, that this is a false impression and that an entirely homogeneous phase does not at all occur here. It is only necessary to add acetic acid to the apparently homogeneous form to see immediately a clear picture of a structure of irregular rods.

In this phase the cell divides. The first sign of this was already present in the previous phase; the furrow gradually affects also the other side, the equator becomes progressively narrower, and the cell body constricts in two; in the epithelial cells this happens quite gradually without interruptions and pauses (in other cells I was not able to observe this directly). No differentiation is noticeable in the equatorial plane in the interior of the cell. . . .

8th Phase (if one wishes to distinguish this as such): Reticular form of the daughter nuclei, reversion to resting condition

Pairs of young nuclei in all stages of transition from the seventh phase to the resting form are everywhere abundantly found; hence this transition lasts a fairly long time. It is quite clear that after the division of the cell the threads are at first coiled, and then become so arranged that the majority lie extended transversely to the longitudinal axis of the nucleus. As a result, such young, transversely barred nuclear pairs are at first glance like resting stages, except for the fact that they are smaller. From this condition the filamentous structure passes into the condition of a uniform reticulum; however, the threads are no longer coiled. The reticulum becomes progressively more dense but ever paler, while the nucleus slowly enlarges. Simultaneously, the nucleus has acquired a sharp demarcation from the cell body, and the interstitial substance between the threads is now stainable. But an actual, substantial membrane cannot yet be demonstrated in nuclei. In the following, still paler stage, a more distinct contour appears, whereupon the form reverts to that of the resting stage. The reticulum of such young nuclei, though pale, is clearer and more regular than in old nuclei in the living as well as in the preserved condition.

I have the impression that the nuclear membrane does not arise as a continuous layer which solidifies or is secreted, but rather that the peripheral parts of the reticulum coalesce into a thin layer at the boundary of the cytoplasm.

I have not been able to make direct observations upon the appearance of nucleoli. In young nuclei and also in still paler larger ones they are not yet visible; this very essential question therefore still remains to be determined.

From all this it is clear that the daughter nuclei at first have the form of a flattened star. This transforms into a star or wreath having coiled threads, which become peripheral, and central loops from which a convoluted skein arises. From this a reticulum with interstitial substance is formed. It is likewise clear that this whole process, with the exception of the double-stranded stars, is a reversed sequence of the changes which the mother nucleus underwent.

Researches on the Maturation of the Egg and Fertilization.

by EDOUARD VAN BENEDEN

Excerpted from *Archives de Biologie*, Vol. 4, pp. 265–640, (1883). Translated by M. L. Gabriel for this volume.

Basic for the clarification of the role of the chromosomes as the physical agents of Mendelian phenomena was the discovery of their behavior in meiosis. Van Beneden, in an elaborate and detailed monograph, portions of which appear below, traced the spermatogenesis and oögenesis of Ascaris megalocephala, and showed that during the process the chromosome number was reduced to one-half that of the somatic cells. He called attention to the important fact that fertilization brings about a restoration of the diploid chromosome complement. Confirmation of these discoveries soon followed, but the exact mechanism of reduction by synapsis and the formation of bivalent pairs of chromosomes was not understood until the 1890's.

I WISH TO CALL attention to the numerical composition, if I may thus express myself, of the chromatic elements of the egg at successive moments in the history of its maturation.

At all stages of development we find

the chromatic mass of the egg nucleus divided into two portions, each composed of four elements. At times the latter are aggregated two by two.

In the germinative corpuscle there exist two nuclear plates each composed of four chromatic globules. . . .

In the first polar body we find two chromatic bodies, each composed of two and perhaps of four parts more or less clearly separated.

In the deuthyalosome [secondary oöcyte] we find two chromatic residues which are separated into two groups of elements.

In the second polar body there exist two chromatic bodies, each composed of two parts and each of these again consisting of two agglutinated elements.

In the female pronucleus there are two chromatic aggregations. Each of these consists of two small chromatic masses each composed of two deeply stained rods. . . .

As for the phenomena of maturation in the male pronucleus, they are identical with those I have described with regard to the female pronucleus: when they have reached their complete development the two elements are similarly constituted. . . . Then the two pronuclei approach one another toward the center of the egg. In order to join its mate, the female pronucleus, which always arises in the neighborhood of the superior pole of the egg, travels a much greater distance than the male pronucleus; the latter is displaced relatively little.

The segmentation of the egg takes place by indirect means [by mitosis]; the two pronuclei, without fusing, both participate in the formation of a single dicentric figure. Both undergo simultaneously, and while they are still perfectly distinct, the same changes which occur in a nucleus of an ordinary cell in the course of karyokinetic division. Each pronucleus furnishes two loops to the chromatic star of the equatorial disc; the star is comprised of two male loops

and two female loops. Each of these divides longitudinally into two halves one of which goes to one daughter nucleus and the other to the second daughter nucleus. There does not occur at the outset any fusion between the male and female chromatic elements. If such a fusion ever does occur, it cannot take place except in the nuclei of the first two embryonic cells. The chromatic star of the equatorial plate supplied in part by the female pronucleus and in part by the male pronucleus, is identical with those which form in the blastomeres when they divide. On both sides the star consists of four chromatic loops. If the chromatic stars which are seen during the division of the first two blastomeres represent a nucleus in the course of division, it also follows that the first star, which develops out of the pronuclei, is the equivalent of a single cellular nucleus.

But since this manner of expression is also quite applicable to earlier stages, we are thus led to consider the two pronuclei, though they are distant one from another and entirely separated, as together representing a single nucleus of a cell: each pronucleus is the equivalent of half a nucleus. But this conclusion should not cause us to forget that neither before nor during karyokinesis, does there occur any fusion whatever, at least as far as the chromatic elements of the pronuclei are concerned.

Neither does the achromatic substance of the two pronuclei mingle into a single mass; in short, though the two pronuclei behave as though together they constituted a single nucleus, at none of the first stages of the division do they cease to be distinct. The conjugation of the two pronuclei into a morphologically single embryonic nucleus does not take place. Before embarking upon a description of the phenomena which lead to the division of the egg into the first two blastomeres, we must ask ourselves at what moment the egg should be considered as fertilized and in what fertilization essentially consists.

It emerges clearly from the facts which I have just summarized that the egg, provided with its two pronuclei, behaves like a single cell and that the sum of the two nuclear elements which it contains are equivalent to an ordinary nucleus. The first cell of the embryo is fully constituted from the moment when the two pronuclei are formed; fertilization therefore coincides with the genesis of these pronuclei.

I have shown above that, as long as the second polar globule has not been eliminated, the elements of the spermatozoon which are destined to give birth to the male pronucleus do not undergo any kind of change. But, from the moment when the egg has rid itself of its second polar globule and of its second perivitelline layer, the spermatozoon engenders the pronucleus, and at this same moment the female pronucleus is constituted. It seems therefore that the egg only exerts its influence upon the spermatozoon, that it only determines it to play its role which consists in the formation of half a cellular nucleus (male pronucleus), after it has cleared itself of these products. Only afterwards does its sexual character manifest itself; of the primitive egg cell there remains only a reduced vitellus, provided with half a cellular nucleus.

The male pronucleus proceeds to complete this reduced cell which I call the female gonocyte and to make of it a new complete cell; fertilization apparently consists essentially in this reconstitution of the first embryonic cell, revivified and provided with all the energy necessary to transform itself, while passing through a series of more and more complex stages, into an individual resembling the parent. This singular phenomenon of the origin of the cell out of two different elements appears to be intimately linked with the rejection by the egg cell on the one hand, and by the spermatocyte on the other, of certain products: of the polar globules and the perivitelline layers in the case of the egg, and of the cytophoral portions in the spermatocyte. . . . In this regard the egg cell and the spermatocyte are distinguished from all other cells. Just as the egg supplied with its female pronucleus is no more than a portion of a cell which I call a female gonocyte, similarly a spermatozoon is a reduced cell, a spermatocyte less a cyttophoral portion; I call it a male gonocyte. It seems to me difficult not to connect together these phenomena of reduction or elimination and of reconstitution or fertilization, not to see in the latter phenomenon a replacement or a substitution. . . .

The achromatic contours of the two pronuclei become less and less distinct; these bodies, pressed one against the other, now form together a clear mass which . . . encloses four chromatic loops; they come to be oriented in one and the same plane, the equatorial plane of the cell in the course of division. . . . The number of loops is constant: one regularly finds four of them; they are approximately of the same length. It emerges from the latest evidence of the study of the previous stages of development that two of these loops are derived from the male pronucleus, the other two from the female pronucleus.

I must now call attention to another phenomenon encountered in a great number of eggs which have arrived at the stage under consideration and which sometimes has already appeared in the preceding stage; I refer to the doubling of the chromatic loops. The fact of the longitudinal division of the chromatic cords was discovered by Flemming in dividing cells of the tissues of the salamander and confirmed by Retzius and by Pfitzner. This is, in my opinion, one of the most important facts of karyokinesis. . . .

If we recall that of the four loops

constituting the equatorial disc two were supplied by the male pronucleus and the other two derived from the female pronucleus, we arrive at the conclusion that each daughter nucleus receives half of its chromatic substance from the spermatozoon, the other from the egg. If the pronuclei have a sexual character, if one is male, the other female, it is clear that the nuclei of the first few blastomeres are hermaphrodites.

The reason for the doubling of the chromatic cords at the time of the division of the nuclei was suspected by Flemming: he wondered whether each primary loop does not furnish a secondary loop to each of the daughter nuclei. Probable as this hypothesis appeared to him as it made understandable the *why* of the· doubling, he was not able to support it by any factual observation; the large number of loops which one sees in the nuclei of the salamander do not allow one to follow each loop to see what it becomes. Such difficulty is not encountered in the typical figures of the egg or the blastomeres of the *Ascaris* of the horse. It was this relative simplicity which allowed me to settle positively this point, so important for the description of the indirect division of cells, and to establish the descent of the chromatic substance of cellular nuclei from the male and female gonocytes, the spermatozoon on the one hand and the mature egg on the other. . . .

The Chromosomes in Heredity. ❧

by WALTER S. SUTTON

Reprinted from the *Biological Bulletin* of the Marine Biological Laboratory of Woods Hole, Massachusetts, Vol. 4, (1903), pp. 231-51, by permission of the Managing Editor.

The closing years of the nineteenth century provide the background for the foundations of our modern chromosomal theory of inheritance. This point in the development of biological theory is marked by a convergence of findings from somewhat unrelated fields. In particular, it involved the rapidly expanding knowledge of nuclear cytology, embryonic development, Mendelism, and biometry. The chromosome theory of heredity rests solidly on the widely demonstrated parallelism between the behavior of the hypothetical Mendelian factor, or gene, and the directly observable nuclear components, the chromosomes.

The first general synthesis correlating the regularities of Mendelizing variations with those of overt chromosome mechanics was contributed in the 1903 essay by Sutton which is reprinted here in abridged form. It must be pointed out that while credit for the penetrating insight is freely accorded to Sutton his remarkable synthesis was foreshadowed by the work of many previous investigators. What were some of the develop-

ments that paved the way for Sutton's achievement? By 1883 van Beneden, in his studies on Ascaris, had demonstrated that in the zygote and
its derivatives, the chromosome group is double, or diploid, while in the
gametes it is single, or haploid. Shortly thereafter, Weismann postulated
from theoretical arguments, and Strasburger observationally demonstrated the reduction of chromosome numbers as a consequence of
meiosis. In 1891 Henking noted that the reductive process was initiated
by the onset of chromosomal pairing. A few years later, in 1901, Montgomery urged, from purely cytological considerations, that the chrom-
somes of the diploid group exhibited a constancy in size differences,
occurred in pairs, and that each member of a given pair had a different
ancestry. That is, the synaptic mates, or conjugant members of a
chromosomal pair, are respectively of maternal and paternal origin. He
further concluded that it was through the mechanism of meiosis that
disjunction or separation of the material and paternal homologues was
achieved. Despite these significant findings, Montgomery did not attempt to bring these facts into harmony with the advances in Mendelian theory.

To this background it is necessary to add the conclusions derived from
experimental embryology, for these played a significant role in providing
added substance to Sutton's work. Experiments and observations reported by Fol, O. Hertwig, Boveri, and others deal with the results
following the fertilization of ova by more than a single sperm. Such eggs
contain abnormal chromosome numbers and develop into abnormal
monstrous embryos. From Boveri's extended studies, 1887–1902, sound
quantitative proof was obtained which led to an important generalization: mere number of chromosomes does not determine development, but
rather each chromosome plays a definite role in normal development and
is therefore differentiated from other such units in the normal chromosome complement.

IN A RECENT announcement of some results of a critical study of the chromosomes in the various cell-generations of *Brachystola* the author briefly called attention to a possible relation between the phenomena there described and certain conclusions first drawn from observations on plant hybrids by Gregor Mendel in 1865, and recently confirmed by a number of able investigators. Further attention has already been called to the theoretical aspects of the subject in a brief communication by Professor E. B. Wilson. The present paper is devoted to a more detailed discussion of these aspects, the speculative character of which may be justified by the attempt to indicate certain lines of work calculated to test the validity of the conclusions drawn. The general conceptions here advanced were evolved purely from cytological data, before the author had knowledge of the Mendelian principles, and are now presented as the contribution of a cytologist who can make no pretensions to complete familiarity with the results of experimental studies on heredity. As will appear hereafter, they completely satisfy the conditions in typical Mendelian cases, and it seems that many of the known deviations from the Mendelian type may be explained by easily conceivable variations from the normal chromosomic processes.

It has long been admitted that we must look to the organization of the germ-cells for the ultimate determination of hereditary phenomena. Mendel fully appreciated this fact and even instituted special experiments to determine the nature of that organization. From them he drew the brilliant conclusion that, while, in the organism, maternal and paternal potentialities are present in the field of each character, *the germ-cells in respect to each character are pure.* Little was then known of the nature of cell-division, and Mendel attempted no comparisons in that direction; but to those who in recent years have revived and extended his results the probability of a relation between cell-organization and cell-division has repeatedly occurred. Bateson clearly states his impression in this regard in the following words: "It is impossible to be presented with the fact that in Mendelian cases the cross-bred produces on an average *equal* numbers of gametes of each kind, that is to say, a symmetrical result, without suspecting that this fact must correspond with some symmetrical figure of distribution of the gametes in the cell divisions by which they are produced."

Nearly a year ago it became apparent to the author that the high degree of organization in the chromosome-group of the germ-cells as shown in *Brachystola* could scarcely be without definite significance in inheritance, for, as shown in the paper already referred to, it had appeared that:

1. The chromosome group of the presynaptic germ-cells is made up of two equivalent chromosome-series, and that strong ground exists for the conclusion that one of these is paternal and the other maternal.

2. The process of synapsis (pseudo-reduction) consists in the union in pairs of the homologous members (*i. e.*, those that correspond in size) of the two series.*

3. The first post-synaptic or matura-

tion mitosis is equational and hence results in no chromosomic differentiation.[1]

4. The second post-synaptic division is a reducing division, resulting in the separation of the chromosomes which have conjugated in synapsis, and their relegation to different germ-cells.

5. The chromosomes retain a morphological individuality throughout the various cell-divisions.

It is well known that in the eggs of many forms the maternal and paternal chromosome groups remain distinctly independent of each other for a considerable number of cleavage-mitoses, and with this fact in mind the author was at first inclined to conclude that in the reducing divisions all the maternal chromosomes must pass to one pole and all the paternal ones to the other, and that the germ-cells are thus divided into two categories which might be described as maternal and paternal respectively. But this conception, which is identical with that recently brought forward by Cannon, was soon seen to be at variance with many well-known facts of breeding; thus:

1. If the germ-cells of hybrids are of pure descent, no amount of cross-breeding could accomplish more than the condition of a first-cross.

2. If any animal or plant has but two categories of germ-cells, there can be only four different combinations in the offspring of a single pair.

3. If either maternal or paternal chromosomes are entirely excluded from every ripe germ-cell, an individual cannot receive chromosomes (qualities) from more than one ancestor in each generation of each of the parental lines of descent, e. g., could not inherit chromosomes (qualities) from both paternal or both maternal grandparents.

Moved by these considerations a more careful study was made of the whole

---

* The conclusion that synapsis involves a union of paternal and maternal chromosomes in pairs was first reached by Montgomery in 1901.

[1] This is not true of many organisms.—*Editors.*

division-process, including the positions of the chromosomes in the nucleus before division, the origin and formation of the spindle, the relative positions of the chromosomes and the diverging centrosomes, and the point of attachment of the spindle fibers to the chromosomes. The results gave no evidence in favor of parental purity of the gametic chromatin as a whole. On the contrary, many points were discovered which strongly indicate * that the position of the bivalent chromosomes in the equatorial plate of the reducing division is purely a matter of chance—that is, that any chromosome pair may lie with maternal or paternal chromatid indifferently toward either pole irrespective of the positions of other pairs—and hence that a large number of different combinations of maternal and paternal chromosomes are possible in the mature germ-products of an individual. To illustrate this, we may consider a form having eight chromosomes in the somatic and presynaptic germ-cells and consequently four in the ripe germ-products. The germ-cell series of the species in general may be designated by the letters A, B, C, D, and any cleavage nucleus may be considered as containing chromosomes A, B, C, D from the father and a, b, c, d, from the mother. Synapsis being the union of homologues would result in the formation of the bivalent chromosomes Aa, Bb, Cc, Dd, which would again be resolved into their components by the reducing division. Each

of the ripe germ-cells arising from the reduction divisions must receive one member from each of the synaptic pairs, but there are sixteen possible combinations of maternal and paternal chromosomes that will form a complete series, to wit: a, B, C, D; A, b, C, D; A, B, c, D; A, B, C, d; a, b, C, D; a, B, c, D; a, B, C, d; a, b, c, d; and their conjugates A, b, c, d; a, B, c, d; a, b, C, d; a, b, c, D; A, B, c, d; A, b, C, d; A, b, c, D; A, B, C, D. Hence instead of two kinds of gametes an organism with four chromosomes in its reduced series may give rise to 16 different kinds; and the offspring of two unrelated individuals may present 16 × 16 or 256 combinations, instead of the four to which it would be limited by a hypothesis of parental purity of gametes. Few organisms, moreover, have so few as 8 chromosomes, and since each additional pair doubles the number of possible combinations in the germ-products * and quadruples that of the zygotes it is plain that in the ordinary form having from 24 to 36 chromosomes, the possibilities are immense. The table below shows the number of possible combinations in forms having from 2 to 36 chromosomes in the presynaptic cells.

Thus if Bardeleben's estimate of sixteen chromosomes for man (the lowest estimate that has been made) be correct, each individual is capable of producing 256 different kinds of germ-products with reference to their chromosome combinations, and the numbers of combinations possible in the offspring of a single pair is 256 × 256 or 65,536; while *Toxopneustes*, with 36 chromosomes, has a possibility of 262,144 and 68,719,476,736 different combinations in the gametes of a single individual and the zygotes of a pair respectively. It is this

---

* Absolute proof is impossible in a pure-bred form on account of the impossibility of distinguishing between maternal and paternal members of any synaptic pair. If, however, such hybrids as those obtained by Moenkhaus with fishes can be reared to sexual maturity absolute proof of this point may be expected. This observer was able in the early cells of certain fish hybrids to distinguish the maternal from the paternal chromosomes by differences in form, and if the same can be done in the maturation-divisions the question of the distribution of chromosomes in reduction becomes a very simple matter of observation.

* The number of possible combinations in the germ-products of a single individual of any species is represented by the simple formula 2^n in which n represents the number of chromosomes in the reduced series.

Chromosomes.		Combinations in Gametes.	Combinations in Zygotes.
Somatic Series.	Reduced Series.		
2	1	2	4
4	2	4	16
6	3	8	64
8	4	16	256
10	5	32	1,024
12	6	64	4,096
14	7	128	16,384
16	8	256	65,536
18	9	512	262,144
20	10	1,024	1,048,576
22	11	2,048	4,194,304
24	12	4,096	16,777,216
26	13	8,192	67,108,864
28	14	16,384	268,435,456
30	15	32,768	1,073,741,824
32	16	65,536	4,294,967,296
34	17	131,072	17,179,869,184
36	18	262,144	68,719,476,736

possibility of so great a number of combinations of maternal and paternal chromosomes in the gametes which serves to bring the chromosome-theory into final relation with the known facts of heredity; for Mendel himself followed out the actual combinations of two and three distinctive characters and found them to be inherited independently of one another and to present a great variety of combinations in the second generation.

The constant size-differences observed in the chromosomes of *Brachystola* early led me to the suspicion, which, however, a study of spermatogenesis alone could not confirm, that the individual chromosomes of the reduced series play different *rôles* in development. The confirmation of this surmise appeared later in the results obtained by Boveri in a study of larvæ actually lacking in certain chromosomes of the normal series, which seem to leave no alternative to the conclusion that the chromosomes differ qualitatively and as individuals represent distinct potentialities. Accepting this conclusion we should be able to find an

exact correspondence between the behavior in inheritance of any chromosome and that of the characters associated with it in the organism.

In regard to the characters, Mendel found that, if a hybrid produced by crossing two individuals differing in a particular character be self-fertilized, the offspring, in most cases, conform to a perfectly definite rule as regards the differential character. Representing the character as seen in one of the original parents by the letter A and that of the other by a, then all the offspring arising by self-fertilization of the hybrid are represented from the standpoint of the given character by the formula AA: 2Aa: aa.—that is, one fourth receive only the character of one of the original pure-bred parents, one fourth only that of the other; while one half the number receive the characters of both original parents and hence present the condition of the hybrid from which they sprang.

We have not heretofore possessed graphic formulæ to express the combinations of chromosomes in similar breeding experiments, but it is clear from the data already given that such formulæ may now be constructed. The reduced chromosome series in *Brachystola* is made up of eleven members, no two of which are exactly of the same size. These I distinguished in my previous paper by the letters A, B, C, . . . K. In the unreduced series there are twenty-two elements * which can be seen to make up two series like that of the mature germ-cells, and hence may be designated as A, B, C . . . K + A, B, C . . . K. Synapsis results in the union of homologues and the production of a single series of double-elements thus: AA, BB, CC . . . KK, and the reducing division effects the separation of these pairs so that one member of each passes to each of the resulting germ-products.

* Disregarding the accessory chromosome which takes no part in synapsis.

There is reason to believe that the division-products of a given chromosome in *Brachystola* maintain in their respective series the same size relation as did the parent element; and this, taken together with the evidence that the various chromosomes of the series represent distinctive potentialities, make it probable that a given size-relation is characteristic of the physical basis of a definite set of characters. But each chromosome of any reduced series in the species has a homologue in any other series, and from the above consideration it should follow that these homologues cover the same field in development. If this be the case chromosome *A* from the father and its homologue, chromosome *a,* from the mother in the presynaptic cells of the offspring may be regarded as the physical bases of the antagonistic [2] unit-characters A and a of father and mother respectively. In synapsis, copulation of the homologues gives rise to the bivalent chromosome *Aa,* which as is indicated above would, in the reducing division, be separated into the components *A* and *a.* These would in all cases pass to different germ-products and hence in a monœcious form we should have four sorts of gametes,

$$A \; \male \qquad a \; \male$$
$$A \; \female \qquad a \; \female$$

which would yield four combinations,

$$A \; \male \; + \; A \; \female = AA$$
$$A \; \male \; + \; a \; \female = Aa$$
$$a \; \male \; + \; A \; \female = aA$$
$$a \; \male \; + \; a \; \female = aa$$

Since the second and third of these are alike the result would be expressed by the formula *AA* : *2Aa* : *aa* which is the same as that given for any character in a Mendelian case. *Thus the phenomena of germ-cell division and of heredity are seen to have the same essential features, viz., purity of units (chromosomes, char-*

acters) and the independent transmission of the same; while as a corollary, it follows in each case that each of the two antagonistic units (chromosomes, characters) is contained by exactly half the gametes produced. . . .

We have seen reason, in the foregoing considerations, to believe that there is a definite relation between chromosomes and allelomorphs [*] or unit characters but we have not before inquired whether an entire chromosome or only a part of one is to be regarded as the basis of a single allelomorph. The answer must unquestionably be in favor of the latter possibility, for otherwise the number of distinct characters possessed by an individual could not exceed the number of chromosomes in the germ-products; which is undoubtedly contrary to fact. We must, therefore, assume that some chromosomes at least are related to a number of different allelomorphs. If then, the chromosomes permanently retain their individuality, it follows that all the allelomorphs represented by any one chromosome must be inherited together. On the other hand, it is not necessary to assume that all must be apparent in the organism, for here the question of dominance enters and it is not yet known that dominance is a function of an entire chromosome. It is conceivable that the chromosome may be divisible into smaller entities (somewhat as Weismann assumes), which represent the allelomorphs and may be dominant or recessive independently. In this way the same chromosome might at one time represent both dominant and recessive allelomorphs.

Such a conception infinitely increases the number of possible combinations of characters *as actually seen* in the individuals and unfortunately at the same time increases the difficulty of determining what characters are inherited together, since usually recessive chro-

---

[2] Differential.—*Editors.*

[*] Bateson's term.

matin entities (allelomorphs?) constantly associated in the same chromosome with usually dominant ones would evade detection for generations and then becoming dominant might appear as reversions in a very confusing manner.

The Chromosomes in Relation to the Determination of Sex in Insects. ‿

by EDMUND B. WILSON

Reprinted from *Science*, Vol. 22, pp. 500–502 (1905), by permission of the editors.

In the opening years of the twentieth century the essentials of Mendelian heredity and its chromosomal basis had been abundantly elucidated. However, the general problem concerning the relationship of genetic phenomena to that of sex determinations remained wholly unexplored. Progress in this area lagged, since, for the most part, investigations on the nature of sex were dominated by the preconceived notion that it was determined by conditions wholly external to the organism. The inadequacy of this thesis has long since been demonstrated, though it is hardly possible to overemphasize the importance of environmental conditions in the development of any character complex or feature of organic differentiation.

Mendel himself first suggested that sex determination might be a manifestation of segregation. Later, this view was incorporated into the writings of such leaders in biological thought as Correns, De Vries, Strasburger, Bateson, and Castle. Direct evidence for the correctness of this interpretation came first, however, from the studies of Correns published in 1907. He showed that in species crosses between monoecious and dioecious plants, sex was determined by the pollen grains. All eggs were of a single type, while pollen grains were of two equal classes. One of them was female-producing; the other was male-producing. This finding led Correns to compare the results of the sexual cross to those obtained in the typical Mendelian backcross of the heterozygote to the corresponding homozygote. Subsequent genetic studies by other investigators using different materials, showed that either sex might be heterogametic. Thus, in birds and butterflies the female is the heterogametic sex, while in the Diptera and mammals the female is homogametic.

The fundamental contribution toward solving the sex determination problem arose from the field of cytology in independent publications by McClung in 1902 and by Wilson and Stevens in 1905. In essence, their evidence disclosed a remarkably perfect correlation between the sexuality of an organism and its nuclear morphology with respect to a distinctive chromosome pair. The details of the findings are reported in Wilson's paper which follows.

Four years after the publication of this classical paper Wilson summarized the status of the problem as follows:

"The cytological evidence has revealed a visible mechanical basis for the production of males and females in equal numbers and irrespective of external conditions. Phenomena of this kind seem likely to throw further light on the mechanism of Mendelian heredity as well as of sex production, for they demonstrate a disjunction of different elements in the formation of the gametes; and this is a fact, not a theory."

MATERIAL PROCURED during the past summer demonstrates with great clearness that the sexes of Hemiptera show constant and characteristic differences in the chromosome groups, which are of such a nature as to leave no doubt that a definite connection of some kind between the chromosomes and the determination of sex exists in these animals. These differences are of two types. In one of these, the cells of the female possess one more chromosome than those of the male; in the other, both sexes possess the same number of chromosomes, but one of the chromosomes in the male is much smaller than the corresponding one in the female (which is in agreement with the observations of Stevens on the beetle *Tenebrio*). These types may conveniently be designated as *A* and *B*, respectively. The essential facts have been determined in three genera of each type, namely, (type *A*) *Protenor belfragei, Anasa tristis* and *Alydus pilosulus,* and (type *B*) *Lygæus turcicus, Euschistus fissilis* and *Cœnus delius.* The chromosome groups have been examined in the dividing oogonia and ovarian follicle cells of the female and in the dividing spermatogonia and investing cells of the testis in case of the male.

Type *A* includes those forms in which (as has been known since Henking's paper of 1890 on *Pyrrochoris*) the spermatozoa are of two classes, one of which contains one more chromosome (the so-called 'accessory' or heterotropic chromosome) than the other. In this type the somatic number of chromosomes in the female is an even one, while the somatic number in the male is one less (hence an odd number) the actual numbers being in *Protenor* and *Alydus* ♀ 14, ♂ 13, and in *Anasa* ♀ 22, ♂ 21. A study of the chromosome groups in the two sexes brings out the following additional facts. In the cells of the female all the chromosomes may be arranged two by two to form pairs, each consisting of two chromosomes of equal size, as is most obvious in the beautiful chromosome groups of *Protenor,* where the size differences of the chromosomes are very marked. In the male all the chromosomes may be thus symmetrically paired with the exception of one which is without a mate. This chromosome is the 'accessory' or heterotropic one; and it is a consequence of its unpaired character that it passes into only one half of the spermatozoa.[1]

In type *B* all of the spermatozoa contain the same number of chromosomes (half the somatic number in both sexes), but they are, nevertheless, of two classes, one of which contains a large

---

[1] The terms accessory chromosome, heterotropic chromosome, or idiochromosome may be considered as equivalent to sex chromosome.— *Editors.*

and one a small 'idiochromosome.' Both sexes have the same somatic number of chromosomes (fourteen in the three examples mentioned above), but differ as follows: In the cells of the female (oogonia and follicle-cells) all of the chromosomes may, as in type A, be arranged two by two in equal pairs, and a small idiochromosome is not present. In the cells of the male all but two may be thus equally paired. These two are the unequal idiochromosomes, and during the maturation process they are so distributed that the small one passes into one half of the spermatozoa, the large one into the other half.

These facts admit, I believe, of but one interpretation. Since all of the chromosomes in the female (oogonia) may be symmetrically paired, there can be no doubt that synapsis in this sex gives rise to the reduced number of symmetrical bivalents, and that consequently all of the eggs receive the same number of chromosomes. This number (eleven in $Anasa$, seven in $Protenor$ or $Alydus$) is the same as that present in those spermatozoa that contain the 'accessory' chromosome. It is evident that both forms of spermatozoa are functional, and that in type A females are produced from eggs fertilized by spermatozoa that contain the 'accessory' chromosome, while males are produced from eggs fertilized by spermatozoa that lack this chromosome (the reverse of the conjecture made by McClung). Thus if n be the somatic number in the female $n/2$ is the number in all of the matured eggs, $n/2$ the number in one half of the spermatozoa (namely, those that contain the 'accessory'), and $n/2—1$ the number in the other half. Accordingly:

In fertilization

$$\text{Egg } \frac{n}{2} + \text{spermatozoon } \frac{n}{2} = n \text{ (female).}$$

$$\text{Egg } \frac{n}{2} + \text{spermatozoon } \frac{n}{2} - 1 = n - 1 \text{ (male).}$$

The validity of this interpretation is completely established by the case of $Protenor$, where, as was first shown by Montgomery, the 'accessory' is at every period unmistakably recognizable by its great size. The spermatogonial divisions invariably show but one such large chromosome, while an equal pair of exactly similar chromosomes appear in the oogonial divisions. One of these in the female must have been derived in fertilization from the egg-nucleus, the other (obviously the 'accessory') from the sperm-nucleus. It is evident, therefore, that all of the matured eggs must before fertilization contain a chromosome that is the maternal mate of the 'accessory' of the male, and that females are produced from eggs fertilized by spermatozoa that contain a similar group (i. e., those containing the 'accessory'). The presence of but one large chromosome (the 'accessory') in the somatic nuclei of the male can only mean that males arise from eggs fertilized by spermatozoa that lack such a chromosome, and that the single 'accessory' of the male is derived in fertilization from the egg nucleus.

In type B all of the eggs must contain a chromosome corresponding to the large idiochromosome of the male. Upon fertilization by a spermatozoon containing the large idiochromosome a female is produced, while fertilization by a spermatozoon containing the small one produces a male.

The two types distinguished above may readily be reduced to one; for if the small idiochromosome of type B be supposed to disappear, the phenomena become identical with those in type A. There can be little doubt that such has been the actual origin of the latter type, and that the 'accessory' chromosome was originally a large idiochromosome, its smaller mate having vanished. The unpaired character of the 'accessory' chromosome thus finds a complete explanation, and its behavior loses its apparently anomalous character.

The foregoing facts irresistibly lead to the conclusion that a causal connection of some kind exists between the chromosomes and the determination of sex; and at first thought they naturally suggest the conclusion that the idiochromosomes and heterotropic chromosomes are actually sex determinants, as was conjectured by McClung in case of the 'accessory' chromosome. Analysis will show, however, that great, if not insuperable, difficulties are encountered by any form of the assumption that these chromosomes are specifically male or female sex determinants. It is more probable, for reasons that will be set forth hereafter, that the difference between eggs and spermatozoa is primarily due to differences of degree or intensity, rather than of kind, in the activity of the chromosome groups in the two sexes; and we may here find a clue to a general theory of sex determination that will accord with the facts observed in hemiptera.[2] A significant fact that bears on

this question is that in both types the two sexes differ in respect to the behavior of the idiochromosomes or 'accessory' chromosomes during the synaptic and growth periods, these chromosomes assuming in the male the form of condensed chromosome nucleoli, while in the female they remain, like the other chromosomes, in a diffused condition. This indicates that during these periods these chromosomes play a more active part in the metabolism of the cell in the female than in the male. The primary factor in the differentiation of the germ cells may, therefore, be a matter of metabolism, perhaps one of growth.

---

[2] This prophetic statement was not verified until 1932 when C. Bridges published an extensive analysis supporting the hypothesis that sexuality might properly be regarded as a quantitative continuum on which male and female represent but two modal points. The actual degree of sexuality of a given organism was found to depend upon the ratio of autosomes to sex chromosomes in a wholly predictable fashion. The autosomes of *Drosophila* contribute a net tendency toward maleness, while the X chromosomes contribute a net tendency toward femaleness. Ordinary females, i.e., those containing the regular diploid set of autosomes and sex chromosomes, are no way distinguishable by their appearance from similar females carrying an additional Y chromosome. —*Editors*.

Random Segregation Versus Coupling in Mendelian Inheritance. ✍

by T. H. MORGAN

Reprinted from *Science*, Vol. 34, p. 384 (1911), by permission of the editors.

Mendel's first law, the segregation principle, concerns the distribution of an allelic gene pair, and corresponds with the directly observable behavior of homologous chromosomes during meiosis. However, his second principle, the law of random assortment, implies that an organ-

ism cannot possess more gene pairs than the number of chromosomes in a haploid set, if it is granted that the genes are borne by chromosomes. Within the first decade or so after the rediscovery of Mendelism this logical consequence of the theory was sharply contradicted by experience. Obviously, some extension or revision of Mendelian theory was required.

Data significantly affecting the generality of the second law were advanced first by Bateson and Punnett in 1906. In their pioneer genetical studies of certain pollen characters in sweet peas they found that gene combinations entering the F_1 hybrid together tended to remain associated during gamete formation. The F_2 ratios which they observed were significantly different from the classical 9:3:3:1 and could be explained only if the gametic series involved in their formation corresponded to a 7:1:1:7 ratio. Classical Mendelian independent assortment required a gametic ratio of 1:1:1:1. In an attempt to account for these departures Bateson and Punnett hypothesized that following segregation certain gametic classes reproduced more rapidly than others. While additional cases verifying the qualitative fact of gene association continued to accumulate in scientific literature, the numerical data could not be explained in any satisfactory fashion by the Bateson-Punnett scheme. Because of these inadequacies and also because it soon became clear that segregation occurred during meiosis the theory of differential gametic reproduction was abandoned.

The resolution of this impasse in the advancement of modern gene theory is unquestionably credited to T. H. Morgan, Nobel laureate in 1933. Morgan's alternative linkage theory supposes that genes are organized in a definite linear order within the chromosome. Thus, genes are expected to exhibit linkage if they lie within the same chromosome, but, should they lie in nonhomologous chromosomes, they would be transmitted according to the principle of independent assortment. The possibilities of recombination for linked genes were thus envisioned to depend on the breakage of chromosomes and their rejoining in such a way as to result in the exchange of equal segments without disturbance of the basic linear sequence. On this theory all the genes of a given organism should fall into a finite series of linkage groups equal in number to the chromosomes comprising a haploid set. It must be recalled at this point that Morgan's theory, unlike the purely formalistic approach of Bateson and Punnett, rested solidly upon a body of accumulated cytological evidence concerning the intimate details of chromosome behavior during the prophase of the first meiotic division.

The first test of the validity of these assumptions was provided by Morgan (1911) himself when he showed that several sex-linked mutants in Drosophila were associated with the behavior of the heteromorphic sex chromosomes. During the ensuing forty years thousands of experiments, in a wealth of diverse biological forms, have confirmed the universality of Morgan's interpretation of linkage.

MENDEL'S LAW OF inheritance rests on the assumption of random segregation of the factors for unit characters. The typi-cal proportions for two or more characters, such as 9:3:3:1, etc., that characterize Mendelian inheritance, depend on an assumption of this kind. In recent years a number of cases have come to light in which when two or more characters are involved the proportions do not accord with Mendel's assumption of random segregation. The most notable cases of this sort are found in sex-limited inheritance in *Abraxas* and *Drosophila,* and in several breeds of poultry, in which a coupling between the factors for femaleness and one other factor must be assumed to take place, and in the case of peas where color and shape of pollen are involved. In addition to these cases Bateson and his collaborators (Punnett, DeVilmorin and Gregory) have recently published a number of new ones.

In order to account for the results Bateson assumes not only coupling, but also repulsions in the germ cells. The facts appear to be exactly comparable to those that I have discovered in *Drosophila,* and since these results have led me to a very simple interpretation, I venture to contrast Bateson's hypothesis with the one that I have to offer.

The facts on which Bateson bases his interpretation may be briefly stated in his own words, namely: "that if *A, a* and *B, b,* are two allelomorphic pairs subject to coupling and repulsion, the factors *A* and *B* will repel each other in the gametogenesis of the double heterozygote resulting from the union *Ab × aB,* but will be coupled in the gametogenesis of the double heterozygote resulting from the union *AB × ab,*" and further, "We have as yet no probable surmise to offer as to the essential nature of this distinction, and all that can yet be said is that in these special cases the distribution of the characters in the heterozygote is affected by the distribution in the original pure parents." Bateson further points out that since "sex in the fowls acts as a repeller of at least three other factors, . . . some of them may be found able to take precedence of the others in such a way as to annul

the present repulsion with subsequent coupling as a consequence."

In place of attractions, repulsions and orders of precedence, and the elaborate systems of coupling, I venture to suggest a comparatively simple explanation based on results of inheritance of eye color, body color, wing mutations and the sex factor for femaleness in *Drosophila.* If the materials that represent these factors are contained in the chromosomes, and if those factors that "couple" be near together in a linear series, then when the parental pairs (in the heterozygote) conjugate like regions will stand opposed. There is good evidence to support the view that during the strepsinema stage homologous chromosomes twist around each other, but when the chromosomes separate (split) the split is in a single plane, as maintained by Janssens. In consequence, the original materials will, for short distances, be more likely to fall on the same side of the split, while remoter regions will be as likely to fall on the same side as the last, as on the opposite side. In consequence, we find coupling in certain characters, and little or no evidence at all of coupling in other characters; the difference depending on the linear distance apart of the chromosomal materials that represent the factors. Such an explanation will account for all of the many phenomena that I have observed and will explain equally, I think, the other cases so far described. The results are a simple mechanical result of the location of the materials in the chromosomes and of the method of union of homologous chromosomes, and the proportions that result are not so much the expression of a numerical system as of the relative location of the factors in the chromosomes. *Instead of random segregation in Mendel's sense we find "associations of factors" that are located near together in the chromosomes. Cytology furnishes the mechanism that the experimental evidence demands.*

Artificial Transmutation of the Gene. ❧

by H. J. MULLER

Reprinted from *Science*, Vol. 66, pp. 84–87 (1927), by permission of the editors and author.

Originally defined as the unit of hereditary transmission, the gene was thought to possess the few simple properties required by the Mendelian principles. Beyond this, it was further recognized that substituting the mutant gene for the normal allele led, in unspecified ways, to an alteration in development, culminating in the appearance of a recognizable phenotypic difference relative to the wild type standard. This definition was equally applicable to large chromosome segments or to entire chromosomes. However, the discovery of crossing over and the elucidation of its cytological basis necessarily occasioned a major revision of the gene concept which was to include still another fundamental property. In crossing over genes behaved as units between which, and not through which, exchanges occurred.

Once a mutant is detected it is a relatively simple matter to discover both the chromosome with which it is associated as well as its specific genetic or cytological locus on that chromosome. With this information at hand the hereditary transmission of the mutated gene is qualitatively and quantitatively predictable in all future crosses. But such considerations, although they are fundamental to any gene study, shed little or no light on problems concerned with the processes or mechanisms that must be involved in the origination of new gene forms. Thus, our conception of the gene as the unit particle of segregation, physiological reaction, and crossing over must be extended to embrace the knowledge that the gene is also the basic unit of biological change or mutation. In this more inclusive sense, the gene, through its seemingly inherent capacity for change, provides the essential raw materials for the phenomena of variation, adaptation, and evolution. The deeper understanding of these biological processes, characteristic of all life, directly depends therefore on our insight into the nature of the gene and its capacity for mutational alteration.

The study of gene mutation is seriously hampered by the low rate of spontaneous mutations. Most genes display spontaneous mutation rates varying from 500 to less than one per one million tested gametes. From this single datum it is a simple matter to understand why it is extremely difficult to formulate an effective experimental attack on the problem of gene mutation. This serious limitation to direct study of the gene *was removed by the epochal discovery that the mutation rate could be increased several thousand per cent through the action of X-rays. This finding, reported in 1927 by Muller and based on his studies with* Drosophila, *was independently verified by Stadler through his investigations with barley. The new finding seemed to offer a readily available tool by means of which the gene could be altered at the will of the investigator.*

From the thousands of investigations which followed in the next 25 years, it has become increasingly clear that many of the Mendelizing variations produced with ionizing radiations are associated with chromosomal rearrangements. These include deficiencies, duplications, translocations, inversions, and the like. In fact, experience with the maize plant seems to suggest that all radiation-induced mutations represent physical loss of gene material or gene inactivations. However, this conclusion is not supported by the accumulated data gained from experience with Drosophila, *where the opportunities for critical cytological analysis far exceed those in maize. Although the radiological attack has yielded a massive body of information relating to chromosome and gene structure our ignorance in this area far exceeds our understanding. This will doubtless remain a fertile field for investigation for a considerable time in the future.*

MOST MODERN GENETICISTS will agree that gene mutations form the chief basis of organic evolution, and therefore of most of the complexities of living things. Unfortunately for the geneticists, however, the study of these mutations, and, through them, of the genes themselves, has heretofore been very seriously hampered by the extreme infrequency of their occurrence under ordinary conditions, and by the general unsuccessfulness of attempts to modify decidedly, and in a sure and detectable way, this sluggish "natural" mutation rate. Modification of the innate nature of organisms, for more directly utilitarian purposes, has of course been subject to these same restrictions, and the practical breeder has hence been compelled to remain content with the mere making of recombinations of the material already at hand; providentially supplemented, on rare and isolated occasions, by an unexpected mutational windfall. To these circumstances are due the wide-spread desire on the part of biologists to gain some measure of control over the hereditary changes within the genes.

It has been repeatedly reported that germinal changes, presumably mutational, could be induced by X or radium rays, but, as in the case of the similar published claims involving other agents (alcohol, lead, antibodies, etc.), the work has been done in such a way that the meaning of the data, as analyzed from a modern genetic standpoint, has been highly disputatious at best; moreover, what were apparently the clearest cases have given negative or contrary results on repetition. Nevertheless, on theoretical grounds, it has appeared to the present writer that radiations of short wave length should be especially promising for the production of mutational changes, and for this and other reasons a series of experiments concerned with this problem has been undertaken during the past year on the fruit fly, *Drosophila melanogaster,* in an attempt to provide critical data. The well-known favorableness of this species for genetic study, and the special methods evolved during the writer's eight years' intensive work on its mutation rate (including the work on temperature, to be referred to later), have finally made possible the finding of some decisive effects, consequent upon the application of X-rays. The effects here referred to are truly mutational, and not to be confused with the well-known effects of X-rays upon the distribution of the chromatin, expressed by non-disjunction, non-inherited crossover modifications, etc. In the present condensed digest of the work, only the broad facts and conclusions therefrom, and some of the problems raised, can be presented, without any details of the genetic methods employed, or of the individual results obtained.

It has been found quite conclusively that treatment of the sperm with relatively heavy doses of X-rays induces the occurrence of true "gene mutations" in a high proportion of the treated germ cells. Several hundred mutants have been obtained in this way in a short time and considerably more than a hundred of the mutant genes have been followed through these four or more generations. They are (nearly all of them, at any rate) stable in their inheritance, and most of them behave in the manner typical of the Mendelian chromosomal mutant genes found in organisms generally. The nature of the crosses was such as to be much more favorable for the detection of mutations in the X-chromosomes than in the other chromosomes, so that most of the mutant genes dealt with were sex-linked; there was, however, ample proof that mutations were occurring similarly throughout the chromatin. When the heaviest treatment was given to the sperm, about a seventh of the offspring that hatched from them and bred contained individually detectable mutations in their treated X-chromosome. Since the X forms about one fourth of the haploid chromatin, then, if we assume an equal rate of mutation in all the chromosomes (per unit of their length), it follows that almost "every other one" of the sperm cells capable of producing a fertile adult contained an "individually detectable" mutation in some chromosome or other. Thousands of untreated parent flies were bred as controls in the same way as the treated ones. Comparison of the mutation rates under the two sets of conditions showed that the heavy treatment had caused a rise of about fifteen thousand per cent. in the mutation rate over that in the untreated germ cells.

Regarding the types of mutations produced, it was found that, as was to have been expected, both on theoretical grounds and on the basis of the previous mutation studies of Altenburg and the writer, the lethals (recessive for the lethal effect, though some were dominant for visible effects) greatly outnumbered the non-lethals producing a visible morphological abnormality. There were some "semi-lethals" also (defining these as mutants having a viability ordinarily between about 0.5 per cent. and 10 per cent. of the normal), but, fortunately for the use of lethals as an index of mutation rate, these were not nearly so numerous as the lethals. The elusive class of "invisible" mutations that caused an even lesser reduction of viability, not readily confusable with lethals, appeared larger than that of the semi-lethals, but they were not subjected to study. In addition, it was also possible to obtain evidence in these experiments for the first time, of the occurrence of dominant lethal genetic changes, both in the X and in the other chromosomes. Since the zygotes receiving these never developed to maturity, such lethals could not be detected individually, but their number was so great that through egg counts and effects on the sex ratio evidence could be obtained of them *en masse*. It was found that their numbers are of the same order of magnitude as those of the recessive lethals. The "partial sterility" of treated males is, to an appreciable extent at least, caused by these dominant lethals. Another abundant class of mutations not previously recognized was found to be those which, when heterozygous, cause sterility but produce no detectable change in appearance; these too occur in numbers rather similar to those of the recessive lethals, and they may hereafter afford one of the readiest indices of the general mutation rate, when this is high. The sterility thus caused, occurring as it does in the offspring of the treated individuals, is of course a separate phenomenon from the "partial sterility" of the treated individuals themselves, caused by the dominant lethals.

In the statement that the proportion of "individually detectable mutations" was about one seventh for the X, and therefore nearly one half for all the chromatin, only the recessive lethals and semi-lethals and the "visible" mutants were referred to. If the dominant lethals, the dominant and recessive sterility genes and the "invisible" genes that merely reduce (or otherwise affect) viability or fertility had been taken into account, the percentage of mutants given would have been far higher, and it is accordingly evident that in reality the great majority of the treated sperm cells contained mutations of some kind or other. It appears that the rate of gene mutation after X-ray treatment is high enough, in proportion to the total number of genes, so that it will be practicable to study it even in the case of individual loci, in an attack on problems of allelomorphism, etc.

Returning to a consideration of the induced mutations that produced visible effects, it is to be noted that the conditions of the present experiment allowed the detection of many which approached or overlapped the normal type to such an extent that ordinarily they would have escaped observation, and definite evidence was thus obtained of the relatively high frequency of such changes here, as compared with the more conspicuous

ones. The belief has several times been expressed in the *Drosophila* literature that this holds true in the case of "natural" mutations in this organism, but it has been founded only on "general impressions"; Baur, however, has demonstrated the truth of it in *Antirrhinum*. On the whole, the visible mutations caused by raying were found to be similar, in their general characteristics, to those previously detected in non-rayed material in the extensive observations on visible mutations in *Drosophila* carried out by Bridges and others. A considerable proportion of the induced visible mutations were, it is true, in loci in which mutation apparently had never been observed before, and some of these involved morphological effects of a sort not exactly like any seen previously (*e.g.,* "splotched wing," "sex-combless," etc.), but, on the other hand, there were also numerous repetitions of mutations previously known. In fact, the majority of the well-known mutations in the X-chromosome of *Drosophila melanogaster,* such as "white eye," "miniature wing," "forked bristles," etc., were reobtained, some of them several times. Among the visible mutations found, the great majority were recessive, yet there was a considerable "sprinkling" of dominants, just as in other work. All in all, then, there can be no doubt that many, at least, of the changes produced by X-rays are of just the same kind as the "gene mutations" which are obtained, with so much greater rarity, without such treatment, and which we believe furnish the building blocks of evolution.

In addition to the gene mutations, it was found that there is also caused by X-ray treatment a high proportion of rearrangements in the linear order of the genes. This was evidenced in general by the frequent inherited disturbances in crossover frequency (at least 3 per cent. were detected in the X-chromosome alone, many accompanied but some unaccompanied by lethal effects), and evidenced specifically by various cases that were proved in other ways to involve inversions, "deficiencies," fragmentations, translocations, etc., of portions of a chromosome. These cases are making possible attacks on a number of genetic problems otherwise difficult of approach.

The transmuting action of X-rays on the genes is not confined to the sperm cells, for treatment of the unfertilized females causes mutations about as readily as treatment of the males. The effect is produced both on oöcytes and early oögonia. It should be noted especially that, as in mammals, X-rays (in the doses used) cause a period of extreme infertility, which commences soon after treatment and later is partially recovered from. It can be stated positively that the return of fertility does not mean that the new crop of eggs is unaffected, for these, like those mature eggs that managed to survive, were found in the present experiments to contain a high proportion of mutant genes (chiefly lethals, as usual). The practice, common in current X-ray therapy, of giving treatments that do not certainly result in permanent sterilization, has been defended chiefly on the ground of a purely theoretical conception that eggs produced after the return of fertility must necessarily represent "uninjured" tissue. As this presumption is hereby demonstrated to be faulty it would seem incumbent for medical practice to be modified accordingly, at least until genetically sound experimentation upon mammals can be shown to yield results of a decisively negative character. Such work upon mammals would involve a highly elaborate undertaking, as compared with the above experiments on flies.

From the standpoint of biological theory, the chief interest of the present experiments lies in their bearing on the problems of the composition and behavior of chromosomes and genes. Through special genetic methods it has been possible to obtain some information concerning the manner of distribution of the transmuted genes amongst the cells of the first and later zygote generations following treatment. It is found that the mutation does not usually involve a permanent alteration of all of the gene substance present at a given chromosome locus at the time of treatment, but either affects in this way only a portion of that substance, or else occurs subsequently, as an after-effect, in only one of two or more descendant genes derived from the treated gene. An extensive series of experiments, now in project, will be necessary for deciding conclusively between these two possibilities, but such evidence as is already at hand speaks rather in favor of the former. This would imply a somewhat compound structure for the gene (or chromosome as a whole) in the sperm cell. On the other hand, the mutated tissue is distributed in a manner that seems inconsistent with a general applicability of the theory of "gene elements" first suggested by Anderson in connection with variegated pericarp in maize, then taken up by Eyster, and recently reenforced by Demerec in *Drosophila virilis*.

A precociously doubled (or further multiplied) condition of the chromosomes (in "preparation" for later mitoses) is all that is necessary to account for the above-mentioned *fractional effect* of X-rays on a given locus; but the theory of a divided condition of each gene, into a number of (originally identical) "elements" that can become separated somewhat indeterminately at mitosis, would lead to expectations different from the results that have been obtained in the present work. It should, on that theory, often have been found here, as in the variegated corn and the eversporting races of *D. virilis,* that mutated tissue gives rise to normal by frequent "reverse mutation"; moreover, treated tissues not at first showing a mutation might frequently give rise to one, through a "sorting out" of diverse elements, several generations after treatment. Neither of these effects was found. As has been mentioned, the mutants were found to be stable through several generations, in the great majority of cases at least. Hundreds of non-mutated descendants of treated germ cells, also, were carried through several generations, without evidence appearing of the production of mutations in generations subsequent to the first. Larger numbers will be desirable here, however, and further experiments of a different type have also been planned in the attack on this problem of gene structure, which probably can be answered definitely.

Certain of the above points which have already been determined, especially that of the fractional effect of X-rays, taken in conjunction with that of the production of dominant lethals, seem to give a clue to the especially destructive action of X-rays on tissues in which, as in cancer, embryonic and epidermal tissues, the cells undergo repeated divisions (though the operation of additional factors, e.g., abnormal mitoses, tending towards the same result, is not thereby precluded); moreover, the converse effect of X-rays, in occasionally producing cancer, may also be associated with their action in producing mutations. It would be premature, however, at this time to consider in detail the various X-ray effects previously considered as "physiological," which may now receive a possible interpretation in terms of the gene-transmuting property of X-rays; we may more appropriately confine ourselves here to matters which can more strictly be demonstrated to be genetic.

Further facts concerning the nature of the gene may emerge from a study of the comparative effects of varied dosages of X-rays, and of X-rays administered at different points in the life cycle and under varied conditions. In the experiments herein reported, several different dosages were made use of, and while the figures are not yet quite conclusive they make it probable that, within the limits used, the number of recessive lethals does not vary directly with the X-ray energy absorbed, but more nearly with the square root of the latter. Should this lack of exact proportionality be confirmed, then, as Dr. Irving Langmuir has pointed out to me, we should have to conclude that these mutations are not caused directly by single quanta of X-ray energy that happen to be absorbed at some critical spot. If the transmuting effect were thus relatively indirect there would be a greater likelihood of its being influenceable by other physico-chemical agencies as well, but our problems would tend to become more complicated. There is, however, some danger in using the total of lethal mutations produced by X-rays as an index of gene mutations occurring in single loci, for some lethals, involving changes in crossover frequency, are probably associated with rearrangements of chromosome regions, and such changes would be much less likely than "point mutations" to depend on single quanta. A reexamination of the effect of different dosages must therefore be carried out, in which the different types of mutations are clearly distinguished from one another. When this question is settled, for a wide range of dosages and developmental stages, we shall also be in a position to decide whether or not the minute amounts of gamma radiation present in nature cause the ordinary mutations which occur in wild and in cultivated organisms in the absence of artificially administered X-ray treatment.

As a beginning in the study of the effect of varying other conditions, upon the frequency of the mutations produced by X-rays, a comparison has been made between the mutation frequencies following the raying of sperm in the male and in the female receptacles, and from germ cells that were in different portions of the male genital system at the time of raying. No decisive differences have been observed. It is found, in addition, that aging the sperm after treatment, before fertilization, causes no noticeable alteration in the frequency of detectable mutations. Therefore the death rate of the mutant sperm is no higher than that of the unaffected ones; moreover, the mutations can not be regarded as secondary effects of any semi-lethal physiological changes which might be supposed to have occurred more intensely in some ("more highly susceptible") spermatozoa than in others.

Despite the "negative results" just mentioned, however, it is already certain that differences in X-ray influences, by themselves, are not sufficient to account for all variations in mutation frequency, for the present X-ray work comes on the heels of the determination of mutation rate being dependent upon temperature (work as yet unpublished). This relation had first been made probable by work of Altenburg and the writer in 1918, but was not finally established until the completion of some experiments in 1926. These gave the first definite evidence that gene mutation may be to any extent controllable, but the magnitude of the heat effect, being similar to that found for chemical reactions in general, is too small, in connection with the almost imperceptible "natural" mutation rate, for it, by itself, to provide a powerful tool in the mutation study. The result, however, is enough to indicate that various factors besides X-rays probably do affect the composition of the gene, and that the measurement of their effects, at least when in combination with X-rays, will be practicable. Thus we may hope that problems of the composition and behavior of the gene can shortly be approached from various new angles, and new handles found for their investigation, so that it will be legitimate to speak of the subject of "gene physiology," at least, if not of gene physics and chemistry.

In conclusion, the attention of those working along classical genetic lines may be drawn to the opportunity, afforded them by the use of X-rays, of creating in their chosen organisms a series of artificial races for use in the study of genetic and "phaenogenetic" phenomena. If, as seems likely on general considerations, the effect is common to most organisms, it should be possible to produce, "to order," enough mutations to furnish respectable genetic maps, in their selected species, and, by the use of the mapped genes, to analyze the aberrant chromosome phenomena simultaneously obtained. Similarly, for the practical breeder, it is hoped that the method will ultimately prove useful. The time is not ripe to discuss here such possibilities with reference to the human species.

The writer takes pleasure in acknowledging his sincere appreciation of the cooperation of Dr. Dalton Richardson, Roentgenologist, of Austin, Texas, in the work of administering the X-ray treatments.

A Correlation of Cytological and Genetical Crossing-over in Zea mays. ∾

by HARRIET B. CREIGHTON
and BARBARA McCLINTOCK

Reprinted from the *Proceedings of the National Academy of Sciences*, Vol. 17, pp. 492–497 (1931), by permission of the authors and editors.

The relationship between genetic recombination and the occurrence of chromatin exchange between equivalent segments of homologous chromosomes at the cytological level was first suggested by Morgan in 1911 as an explanation for the genetic phenomenon of linkage. At an earlier date, and at a time when the details of meiosis were almost wholly unknown, DeVries had speculatively developed a similar view. Morgan ingeniously emphasized that if the genes were arranged in a linear fashion on the chromosomes, equivalent blocks of maternal and paternal genes could be exchanged during the period of meiotic synapsis through the formation of chiasmata. These had been described previously by Janssens. While the utility of this outlook was abundantly verified in thousands of varied experiments, and no disagreements between theory and observation were reported in the twenty-year period following its introduction, direct proof conclusively validating the theory was notably lacking. That no such proof was obtained for nearly twenty years is more easily appreciated if it is recalled that two homologous chromosomes are identical even in favorable cytological material under ideal conditions. Thus, while chiasmata are directly observable, and while they might be interpreted as due to an exchange between homologous chromosomes, there is no simple way to visually differentiate the maternal and paternal elements participating in an exchange.

Direct proof that cytological and genetic crossing over was correlated with a physically visible exchange between homologous chromosomes was not achieved until 1931. At this time, Creighton and McClintock in maize, and independently Stern in Drosophila, developed the techniques and special stocks essential to the demonstration. The crucial requirement for both methods, which are alike in principle, is the finding or synthesizing of new strains in which the two ends of a particular homologous chromosome pair can be distinguished by readily detectable cytological differences.

In the case analyzed by Creighton and McClintock the two ends of chromosome number IX were marked by constant, heritable cytological features. One end of chromosome IX carried a large deeply staining, heterochromatic knob; the other end was marked by an additional length of chromatin due to a previous reciprocal interchange or translocation with chromosome VIII of the regular genome.

Thus, in plants doubly heterozygous for both the knob and the translocation, it was possible to show, via direct cytological examination, that recombinations for both the knob and the translocation were regularly produced during meiosis. In addition to the two original parental types for chromosome IX, two new types were observed. These could arise only by the occurrence of a physical exchange between the homologous segments. Moreover, this behavior was directly correlated with genetic crossing over for several genes known to be located in the segment between the translocation point and the knob. The populations investigated by Creighton and McClintock were admittedly small, but the correlation between genetic and cytological crossing over was direct, decisive, and unequivocal. The parallel, independent demonstration by Stern, which involved the sex chromosomes, provided considerably larger populations in which genetic crossing over is more precisely localized.

Beyond any question, this is one of the truly great experiments of modern biology, and the conclusion—that pairing chromosomes heteromorphic for two or more regions exchange parts at the same time that they exchange genes assigned to these regions—will doubtless continue to stimulate as much research during the next 25 years as they have during the 25 years following its publication.

A REQUIREMENT FOR the genetical study of crossing-over is the heterozygous condition of two allelomorphic factors in the same linkage group. The analysis of the behavior of homologous or partially homologous chromosomes, which are morphologically distinguishable at two points, should show evidence of cytological crossing-over. It is the aim of the present paper to show that cytological crossing-over occurs and that it is accompanied by genetical crossing-over.

In a certain strain of maize the second-smallest chromosome (chromosome 9) possesses a conspicuous knob at the end of the short arm. Its distribution through successive generations is similar to that of a gene. If a plant possessing knobs at the ends of both of its 2nd-smallest chromosomes is crossed to a plant with no knobs, cytological observations show that in the resulting F_1 individuals only one member of the homologous pair possesses a knob. When such

an individual is back-crossed to one having no knob on either chromosome, half of the offspring are heterozygous for the knob and half possess no knob at all. The knob, therefore, is a constant feature of the chromosome possessing it. When present on one chromosome and not on its homologue, the knob renders the chromosome pair visibly heteromorphic.

In a previous report it was shown that in a certain strain of maize an interchange had taken place between chromosome 8 and 9. The interchanged pieces were unequal in size; the long arm of chromosome 9 was increased in relative length, whereas the long arm of chromosome 8 was correspondingly shortened. When a gamete possessing these two interchanged chromosomes meets a gamete containing a normal chromosome set, meiosis in the resulting individual is characterized by a side-by-side synapsis of homologous parts. Therefore, it should be possible to have crossing-over between the knob and the interchange point.

In the previous report it was also shown that in such an individual the only functioning gametes are those which possess either the two normal chromosomes (N, n) or the two interchanged chromosomes (I, i), i.e., the full genom in one or the other arrangement. The functional gametes therefore possess either the shorter, normal, knobbed chromosome (n) or the longer, interchanged, knobbed chromosome (I). Hence, when such a plant is crossed to a plant possess-

ing the normal chromosome complement, the presence of the normal chromosome in functioning gametes of the former will be indicated by the appearance of ten bivalents in the prophase of meiosis of the resulting individuals. The presence of the interchanged chromosome in other gametes will be indicated in other F_1 individuals by the appearance of eight bivalents plus a ring of four chromosomes in the late prophase of meiosis.

If a gamete possessing a normal chromosome number 9 with no knob, meets a gamete possessing an interchanged chromosome with a knob, it is

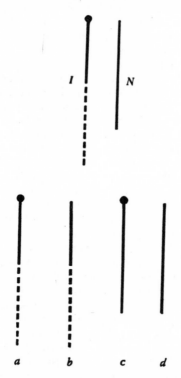

FIG. 1.—Above—Diagram of the chromosomes in which crossing-over was studied.
Below—Diagram of chromosome types found in gametes of a plant with the constitution shown above.
  a—Knobbed, interchanged chromosome.
  b—Knobless, interchanged chromosome.
  c—Knobbed, normal chromosome.
  d—Knobless, normal chromosome.
   a and d are non-crossover types.
   b and c are crossover types.

TABLE 1

KNOB-INTERCHANGED / KNOBLESS-NORMAL	×	KNOBLESS-NORMAL, CULTURE 337 AND KNOBBED-NORMAL CULTURES A125 AND 340			
		PLANTS POSSESSING 2 NORMAL CHROMOSOMES		PLANTS POSSESSING AN INTERCHANGED CHROMOSOME	
CULTURE		NON-CROSSOVERS	CROSSOVERS	NON-CROSSOVERS	CROSSOVERS
337		8	3	6	2
A125		39	31	36	23
340		5	3	5	3
Totals		52	37	47	28

clear that these two chromosomes which synapse along their homologous parts during prophase of meiosis in the resulting individual are visibly different at each of their two ends. If no crossing-over occurs, the gametes formed by such an individual will contain either the knobbed, interchanged chromosome (*a*, Fig. 1) or the normal chromosome without a knob (*d*, Fig. 1). Gametes containing either a knobbed, normal chromosome (*c*, Fig. 1) or a knobless, interchanged chromosome (*b*, Fig. 1) will be formed as a result of crossing-over. If such an individual is crossed to a plant possessing two normal knobless chromosomes, the resulting individuals will be of four kinds. The non-crossover gametes would give rise to individuals which show either (1) ten bivalents at prophase of meiosis and no knob on chromosome 9, indicating that a gamete with a chromosome of type *d* has functioned or (2) a ring of four chromosomes with a single conspicuous knob, indicating that a gamete of type *a* has functioned. The crossover types will be recognizable as individuals which possess either (1) ten bivalents and a single knob associated with bivalent chromosome 9 or (2) a ring of four chromosomes with no knob, indicating that

crossover gametes of types *c* and *b*, respectively, have functioned. The results of such a cross are given in culture 337, table 1. Similarly, if such a plant is crossed to a normal plant possessing knobs at the ends of both number 9 chromosomes and if crossing-over occurs, the resulting individuals should be of four kinds. The non-crossover types would be represented by (1) plants homozygous for the knob and possessing the interchanged chromosome and (2) plants heterozygous for the knob and possessing two normal chromosomes. The functioning of gametes which had been produced as the result of crossing-over between the knob and the interchange would give rise to (1) individuals heterozygous for the knob and possessing the interchanged chromosome and (2) those homozygous for the knob and possessing two normal chromosomes. The results of such crosses are given in cultures A125 and 340, table 1. Although the data are few, they are consistent. The amount of crossing-over between the knob and the interchange, as measured from these data, is approximately 39%.

In the preceding paper it was shown that the knobbed chromosome carries the genes for colored aleurone (*C*), shrunken

TABLE 2

KNOB-*C*-*wx* / KNOBLESS-*c*-*Wx*	×	KNOBLESS-*c*-*wx*					
C-*wx*		*c*-*Wx*		*C*-*Wx*		*c*-*wx*	
Knob	Knobless	Knob	Knobless	Knob	Knobless	Knob	Knobless
12	5	5	34	4	0	0	3

endosperm (*sh*) and waxy endosperm (*wx*). Furthermore, it was shown that the order of these genes, beginning at the interchange point is *wx-sh-c*. It is possible, also, that these genes all lie in the short arm of the knobbed chromosome. Therefore, a linkage between the knob and these genes is to be expected.

One chromosome number 9 in a plant possessing the normal complement had a knob and carried the genes *C* and *wx*. Its homologue was knobless and carried the genes *c* and *Wx*. The non-crossover gametes should contain a knobbed-*C-wx* or a knobless-*c-Wx* chromosome. Crossing-over in region 1 (between the knob and *C*) would give rise to knobless *C-wx* and knobbed-*c-Wx* chromosomes. Crossing-over in region 2 (between *C* and *wx*) would give rise to knobbed-*C-Wx* and knobless-*c-wx* chromosomes. The results of crossing such a plant to a knobless-*c-wx* type are given in table 2. It would be expected on the basis of interference that the knob and *C* would

remain together when a crossover occurred between *C* and *wx;* hence, the individuals arising from colored starchy (*C-Wx*) kernels should possess a knob, whereas those coming from colorless, waxy (*c-wx*) kernels should be knobless. Although the data are few they are convincing. It is obvious that there is a fairly close association between the knob and *C*.

To obtain a correlation between cytological and genetic crossing-over it is necessary to have a plant heteromorphic for the knob, the genes *c* and *wx* and the interchange. Plant 338 (17) possessed in one chromosome the knob, the genes *C* and *wx* and the interchanged piece of chromosome 8. The other chromosome was normal, knobless and contained the genes *c* and *Wx*. This plant was crossed to an individual possessing two normal, knobless chromosomes with the genes *c-Wx* and *c-wx,* respectively. This cross is diagrammed as follows:

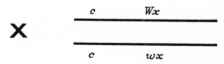

The results of the cross are given in table 3. In this case all the colored kernels gave rise to individuals possessing a knob, whereas all the colorless kernels gave rise to individuals showing no knob.

The amount of crossing-over between the knob and the interchange point is approximately 39% (Table 1), between *c* and the interchange approximately 33%, between *wx* and the interchange, 13% (preceding paper). With this information in mind it is possible to analyze the data given in table 3. The data are necessarily few since the ear contained but few kernels. The three individuals in class I are clearly non-crossover types. In class II the individuals have resulted from a crossover

in region 2, i.e., between *c* and *wx*. In this case a crossover in region 2 has not been accompanied by a crossover in region 1 (between the knob and *C*) or region 3 (between *wx* and the interchange). All the individuals in class III had normal chromosomes. Unfortunately, pollen was obtained from only 1 of the 6 individuals examined for the presence of the knob. This one individual was clearly of the type expected to come from a gamete produced through crossing-over in region 2. Class IV is more difficult to analyze. Plants 6, 9, 10, 13, and 14 are normal and *WxWx;* they therefore represent non-crossover types. An equal number of non-crossover types are expected among the normal *Wxwx* class. Plants 1, 2, 4, 11 and 12 may be of

TABLE 3

PLANT NUMBER	KNOB-C-wx-INTERCHANGED / KNOBLESS-c-$W$$x$-NORMAL × KNOBLESS-$c$-$W$$x$-NORMAL / KNOBLESS-$c$-$wx$-NORMAL		
	KNOBBED OR KNOBLESS	INTERCHANGED OR NORMAL	
Class I, C-wx kernels			
1	Knob	Interchanged	
2	Knob	Interchanged	
3	Knob	Interchanged	
Class II, c-wx kernels			
1	Knobless	Interchanged	
2	Knobless	Interchanged	
Class III, C-$W$$x$ kernels			*Pollen*
1	Knob	Normal	$WxWx$
2	Knob	Normal	....
3	....	Normal	$WxWx$
5	Knob	Normal	....
6	Knob	......	....
7	Knob	Normal	....
8	Knob	Normal	....
Class IV, c-$W$$x$ kernels			
1	Knobless	Normal	$Wxwx$
2	Knobless	Normal	$Wxwx$
3	Knobless	Interchanged	$Wxwx$
4	Knobless	Normal	$Wxwx$
5	Knobless	Interchanged	$WxWx$
6	Knobless	Normal	$WxWx$
7	Knobless	Interchanged	$Wxwx$
8	Knobless	Interchanged	$WxWx$
9	Knobless	Normal	$WxWx$
10	Knobless	Normal	$WxWx$
11	Knobless	Normal	$Wxwx$
12	Knobless	Normal	$Wxwx$
13	Knobless	Normal	$WxWx$
14	Knobless	Normal	$WxWx$
15	Knobless	Normal	$Wx—$

this type. It is possible but improbable that they have arisen through the union of a c-Wx gamete with a gamete resulting from a double crossover in region 2 and 3. Plants 5 and 8 are single crossovers in region 3, whereas plants 3 and 7 probably represent single crossovers in region 2 or 3.

The foregoing evidence points to the fact that cytological crossing-over occurs and is accompanied by the expected types of genetic crossing-over.

Conclusions.—Pairing chromosomes, heteromorphic in two regions, have been shown to exchange parts at the same time they exchange genes assigned to these regions.

Genetic Control of Biochemical Reactions in Neurospora.

by G. W. BEADLE and E. L. TATUM

Reprinted from the *Proceedings of the National Academy of Sciences*, Vol. 27, pp. 499–506 (1941), by permission of the editors and authors.

From the viewpoint of modern biology development is conceived as an orderly series of integrated biochemical events that is somehow associated with, or determined by the appearance of specific enzyme patterns. And, since a wealth of genetic experience had revealed that a given gene substitution, other conditions remaining constant, provoked a specific developmental alteration, it was not unreasonable to suppose that the specificity of gene action might be traced to its effects on the specific regulators of biological activity, the enzymes. The possibility that genes may act through the mediation of enzymes is a proposal repeatedly encountered in scientific literature. It appears for the first time in the 1917 publication of L. T. Troland. For the most part, these proposals are based on theoretical or speculative considerations and, at best, they are accompanied by a scarcity of direct supporting data.

The 1941 publication by Beadle and Tatum, reprinted here, marks a significant turning point in analyzing the general problem of genetic control in metabolism and development. Instead of attempting to work out the chemical basis for known genetic characters, these workers deliberately reversed the procedure and set out to determine if and how the gene controlled known biochemical reactions. The pink bread mold, Neurospora crassa, an ascomycete, provides ample opportunities for biochemical study and is, moreover, well adapted to genetic analysis. Therefore, it is not surprising to find that a long range program has centered about this organism.

The rationale behind the experimental design that characterizes most modern work in biochemical genetics might be outlined as follows: Neurospora wild type, or normal, stocks can be grown on a wholly defined chemical medium. This is composed of water, inorganic salts, a carbon source such as sucrose, and a single growth factor, biotin. Neurospora is virtually autotrophic; i.e., it can synthesize or reproduce all the complex components of its protoplasm from these simple, stable, low energy content molecules. Wild type stocks are irradiated or treated with mutagenic chemicals and from this material strains are isolated which will no longer grow on the simple minimal medium described above. It may be inferred that these derived strains cannot carry out all *of the transformations and syntheses achieved by the wild type. For such metabolically blocked strains it is generally found that the addition of a single specific substance, such as a particular amino acid, vitamin, purine, or pyrimidine, will enable growth to occur, and that the growth attained is directly proportional to the concentration of the specific metabolite added. Several hundred strains of this kind have been fully tested both genetically and biochemically. Most of them are typically representative of single gene mutations and the lethal phenotype, or metabolic block, can be overcome by supplying a single metabolite to the minimal medium. Within recent years a number of mutants have been found to possess multiple requirements, and some mutants are temperature sensitive, i.e., the nutritional requirements depend on the temperature at which the stock is maintained.*

The simplest, most economical hypothesis that can account for the impressive body of data accumulated in the study of this and related organisms, is the assumption that the gene produces its effects by regulating the activity, concentration, or specificity of particular enzymes. This view does not necessarily imply the existence of any simple one-to-one relationship between the gene and the enzyme. Actually, recent studies, in which the extracted, purified enzymes of wild and mutant stocks were compared, have demonstrated that a single enzyme can be affected by a considerable number of different genes.

FROM THE STANDPOINT of physiological genetics the development and functioning of an organism consist essentially of an integrated system of chemical reactions controlled in some manner by genes. It is entirely tenable to suppose that these genes which are themselves a part of the system, control or regulate specific reactions in the system either by acting directly as enzymes or by determining the specificities of enzymes. Since the components of such a system are likely to be interrelated in complex ways, and since the synthesis of the parts of individual genes are presumably dependent on the functioning of other genes, it would appear that there must exist orders of directness of gene control ranging from simple one-to-one relations to relations of great complexity. In investigating the rôles of genes, the physiological geneticist usually attempts to determine the physiological and biochemical bases of already known hereditary traits. This approach, as made in the study of anthocyanin pigments in plants, the fermentation of sugars by yeasts and a number of other instances, has established that many biochemical reactions are in fact controlled in specific ways by specific genes. Furthermore, investigations of this type tend to support the assumption that gene and enzyme specificities are of the same order. There are, however, a number of limitations inherent in this approach. Perhaps the most serious of these is that the investigator must in general confine himself to a study of non-lethal heritable characters. Such characters are likely to involve more or less non-essential so-called "terminal" reactions. The selection of these for genetic study was perhaps responsible for the now rapidly disappearing belief that genes are concerned only with the control of "superficial" characters. A second difficulty, not unrelated to the first, is that the standard approach to the problem implies the use of characters with visible manifestations. Many such characters involve morphological variations, and these are likely to be based on systems of biochemical reactions so complex as to make analysis exceedingly difficult.

Considerations such as those just outlined have led us to investigate the general problem of the genetic control of developmental and metabolic reactions by reversing the ordinary procedure and, instead of attempting to work out the chemical bases of known genetic characters, to set out to determine if and how genes control known biochemical reactions. The ascomycete *Neurospora* offers many advantages for such an approach and is well suited to genetic studies. Accordingly, our program has been built around this organism. The procedure is based on the assumption that x-ray treatment will induce mutations in genes concerned with the control of known specific chemical reactions. If the organism must be able to carry out a certain chemical reaction to survive on a given medium, a mutant unable to do this will obviously be lethal on this medium. Such a mutant can be maintained and studied, however, if it will grow on a medium to which has been added the essential product of the genetically blocked reaction. The experimental procedure based on this reasoning can best be illustrated by considering a hypothetical example. Normal strains of *Neurospora crassa* are able to use sucrose as a carbon source, and are therefore able to carry out the specific and enzymatically controlled reaction involved in the hydrolysis of this sugar. Assuming this reaction to be genetically controlled, it should be possible to induce a gene to mutate to a condition such that the organism could no longer carry out sucrose hydrolysis. A strain carrying this mutant would then be unable to grow on a medium containing sucrose as a sole carbon source but should be able to grow on a medium containing some other normally utilizable carbon source. In other words, it should be possible to

establish and maintain such a mutant strain on a medium containing glucose and detect its inability to utilize sucrose by transferring it to a sucrose medium.

Essentially similar procedures can be developed for a great many metabolic processes. For example, ability to synthesize growth factors (vitamins), amino acids and other essential substances should be lost through gene mutation if our assumptions are correct. Theoretically, any such metabolic deficiency can be "by-passed" if the substance lacking can be supplied in the medium and can pass cell walls and protoplasmic membranes.

In terms of specific experimental practice, we have devised a procedure in which x-rayed single-spore cultures are established on a so-called "complete" medium, i.e., one containing as many of the normally synthesized constituents of the organism as is practicable. Subsequently these are tested by transferring them to a "minimal" medium, i.e., one requiring the organism to carry on all the essential syntheses of which it is capable. In practice the complete medium is made up of agar, inorganic salts, malt extract, yeast extract and glucose. The minimal medium contains agar (optional), inorganic salts * and biotin, and a disaccharide, fat or more complex carbon source. Biotin, the one growth factor that wild type *Neurospora* strains cannot synthesize, is supplied in the form of a commercial concentrate containing 100 micrograms of biotin per cc. Any loss of ability to synthesize an essential substance present in the complete medium and absent in the minimal medium

---

* Throughout our work with *Neurospora*, we have used as a salt mixture the one designated number 3 by Fries, N., *Symbolae Bot. Upsalienses*, Vol. 3, No. 2, 1–188 (1938). This has the following composition: NH_4 tartrate, 5 g.; NH_4NO_3, 1 g.; KH_2PO_4, 1 g.; $MgSO_4 \cdot 7H_2O$, 0.5 g.; NaCl, 0.1 g.; $CaCl_2$, 0.1 g.; $FeCl_3$, 10 drops 1% solution; H_2O, 1 l. The tartrate cannot be used as a carbon source by *Neurospora*.

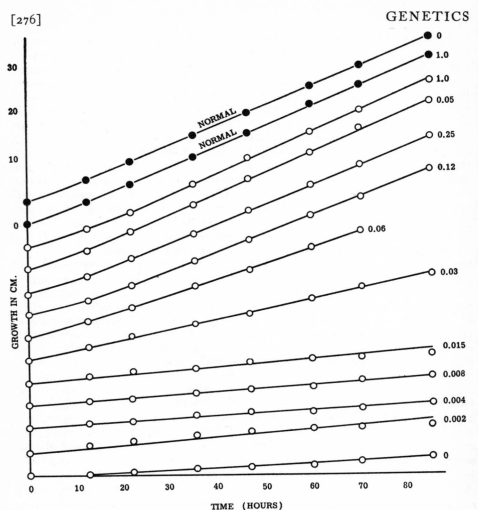

FIG. 1.—Growth of normal (top two curves) and pyridoxinless (remaining curves) strains of *Neurospora sitophila* in horizontal tubes. The scale on the ordinate is shifted a fixed amount for each successive curve in the series. The figures at the right of each curve indicate concentration of pyridoxine (B₆) in micrograms per 25 cc. medium.

is indicated by a strain growing on the first and failing to grow on the second medium. Such strains are then tested in a systematic manner to determine what substance or substances they are unable to synthesize. These subsequent tests include attempts to grow mutant strains on the minimal medium with (1) known vitamins added, (2) amino acids added or (3) glucose substituted for the more complex carbon source of the minimal medium.

Single ascospore strains are individually derived from perithecia of *N. crassa* and *N. sitophila* x-rayed prior to meiosis. Among approximately 2000 such strains, three mutants have been found that grow essentially normally on the complete medium and scarcely at all on the minimal medium with sucrose as the carbon source. One of these strains (*N. sitophila*) proved to be unable to synthesize vitamin B₆ (pyridoxine). A second strain (*N. sitophila*) turned out

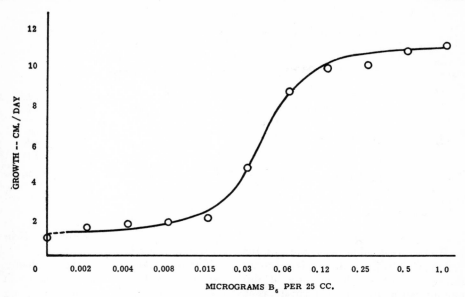

FIG. 2.—The relation between growth rate (cm./day) and vitamin B₆ concentration.

to be unable to synthesize vitamin B_1 (thiamine). Additional tests show that this strain is able to synthesize the pyrimidine half of the B_1 molecule but not the thiazole half. If thiazole alone is added to the minimal medium, the strain grows essentially normally. A third strain (*N. crassa*) has been found to be unable to synthesize para-aminobenzoic acid. This mutant strain appears to be entirely normal when grown on the minimal medium to which *p*-aminobenzoic acid has been added. Only in the case of the "pyridoxinless" strain has an analysis of the inheritance of the induced metabolic defect been investigated. For this reason detailed accounts of the thiamine-deficient and *p*-aminobenzoic acid-deficient strains will be deferred.

Qualitative studies indicate clearly that the pyridoxinless mutant, grown on a medium containing one microgram or more of synthetic vitamin B_6 hydrochloride per 25 cc. of medium, closely approaches in rate and characteristics of growth normal strains grown on a

similar medium with no B_6. Lower concentrations of B_6 give intermediate growth rates. A preliminary investigation of the quantitative dependence of growth of the mutant on vitamin B_6 in the medium gave the results summarized in table 1. Additional experiments have given results essentially similar but in only approximate quanti-

TABLE 1

GROWTH OF PYRIDOXINLESS STRAIN OF *N. sitophila* ON LIQUID MEDIUM CONTAINING INORGANIC SALTS, 1% SUCROSE, AND 0.004 MICROGRAM BIOTIN PER CC. TEMPERATURE 25° C. GROWTH PERIOD, 6 DAYS FROM INOCULATION WITH CONIDIA

MICROGRAMS B₆ PER 25 CC. MEDIUM	STRAIN	DRY WEIGHT MYCELIA, MG.
0	Normal	76.7
0	Pyridoxinless	1.0
0.01	"	4.2
0.03	"	5.7
0.1	"	13.7
0.3	"	25.5
1.0	"	81.1
3.0	"	81.1
10.0	"	65.4
30.0	"	82.4

TABLE 2

RESULTS OF CLASSIFYING SINGLE ASCOSPORE CULTURES FROM THE CROSS OF
PYRIDOXINLESS AND NORMAL *N. sitophila*

ASCUS NUMBER	1	2	3	4	5	6	7	8
17	—	*pdx*	*pdx*	*pdx*	*N*	*N*	*N*	—
18	—	—	*N*	*N*	—	—	*pdx*	*pdx*
19	—	*pdx*	—	—	—	—	—	*N*
20	—	—	*N*	—	—	—	—	*pdx*
22	—	—	*N*	—	—	—	—	—
23	—	*	*	*	*N*	*N*	*pdx*	*pdx*
24	*N*	*N*	*N*	*N*	*pdx*	*pdx*	*pdx*	*pdx*

N, normal growth on B_6-free medium, *pdx*, slight growth on B_6-free medium. Failure of ascospore germination indicated by dash.

* Spores 2, 3 and 4 isolated but positions confused. Of these, two germinated and both proved to be mutants.

tative agreement with those of table 1. It is clear that additional study of the details of culture conditions is necessary before rate of weight increase of this mutant can be used as an accurate assay for vitamin B_6.

It has been found that the progression of the frontier of mycelia of *Neurospora* along a horizontal glass culture tube half filled with an agar medium provides a convenient method of investigating the quantitative effects of growth factors. Tubes of about 13 mm. inside diameter and about 40 cm. in length are used. Segments of about 5 cm. at the two ends are turned up at an angle of about 45°. Agar medium is poured in so as to fill the tube about half full and is allowed to set with the main segment of the tube in a horizontal position. The turned up ends of the tube are stoppered with cotton plugs. Inoculations are made at one end of the agar surface and the position of the advancing front recorded at convenient intervals. The frontier formed by the advancing mycelia is remarkably well defined, and there is no difficulty in determining its position to within a millimeter or less. Progression along such tubes is strictly linear with time and the rate is independent of tube length (up to 1.5 meters). The rate is not changed by reducing the inside tube diameter to 9 mm., or by sealing one or both ends. It

therefore appears that gas diffusion is in no way limiting in such tubes.

The results of growing the pyridoxinless strain in horizontal tubes in which the agar medium contained varying amounts of B_6 are shown graphically in figures 1 and 2. Rate of progression is clearly a function of vitamin B_6 concentration in the medium.* It is likewise evident that there is no significant difference in rate between the mutant supplied with B_6 and the normal strain growing on a medium without this vitamin. These results are consistent with the assumption that the primary physiological difference between pyridoxinless and normal strains is the inability of the former to carry out the synthesis of vitamin B_6. There is certainly more than one step in this synthesis and accordingly the gene differential involved is presumably concerned with only one specific step in the biosynthesis of vitamin B_6.

In order to ascertain the inheritance of the pyridoxinless character, crosses between normal and mutant strains were made. The techniques for hybridization

* It is planned to investigate further the possibility of using the growth of *Neurospora* strains in the described tubes as a basis of vitamin assay, but it should be emphasized that such additional investigation is essential in order to determine the reproducibility and reliability of the method.

and ascospore isolation have been worked out and described by Dodge, and by Lindegren. The ascospores from 24 asci of the cross were isolated and their positions in the asci recorded. For some unknown reason, most of these failed to germinate. From seven asci, however, one or more spores germinated. These were grown on a medium containing glucose, malt-extract and yeast extract, and in this they all grew normally. The normal and mutant cultures were differentiated by growing them on a B_6 deficient medium. On this medium the mutant cultures grew very little, while the non-mutant ones grew normally. The results are summarized in table 2. It is clear from these rather limited data that this inability to synthesize vitamins B_6 is transmitted as it should be if it were differentiated from normal by a single gene.

The preliminary results summarized above appear to us to indicate that the approach outlined may offer considerable promise as a method of learning more about how genes regulate development and function. For example, it should be possible, by finding a number of mutants unable to carry out a particular step in a given synthesis, to determine whether only one gene is ordinarily concerned with the immediate regulation of a given specific chemical reaction.

It is evident, from the standpoints of biochemistry and physiology, that the method outlined is of value as a technique for discovering additional substances of physiological significance. Since the complete medium used can be made up with yeast extract or with an extract of normal *Neurospora,* it is evident that if, through mutation, there is lost the ability to synthesize an essential substance, a test strain is thereby made available for use in isolating the substance. It may, of course, be a substance not previously known to be essential for the growth of any organism.

Thus we may expect to discover new vitamins, and in the same way, it should be possible to discover additional essential amino acids if such exist. We have, in fact, found a mutant strain that is able to grow on a medium containing Difco yeast extract but unable to grow on any of the synthetic media we have so far tested. Evidently some growth factor present in yeast and as yet unknown to us is essential for *Neurospora.*

Summary.—A procedure is outlined by which, using *Neurospora,* one can discover and maintain x-ray induced mutant strains which are characterized by their inability to carry out specific biochemical processes.

Following this method, three mutant strains have been established. In one of these the ability to synthesize vitamin B_6 has been wholly or largely lost. In a second the ability to synthesize the thiazole half of the vitamin B_1 molecule is absent, and in the third para-aminobenzoic acid is not synthesized. It is therefore clear that all of these substances are essential growth factors for *Neurospora.**

Growth of the pyridoxinless mutant (a mutant unable to synthesize vitamin B_6) is a function of the B_6 content of the medium on which it is grown. A method is described for measuring the growth by following linear progression of the mycelia along a horizontal tube half filled with an agar medium.

Inability to synthesize vitamin B_6 is apparently differentiated by a single gene from the ability of the organism to elaborate this essential growth substance.

NOTE: Since the manuscript of this paper was sent to press it has been established that inability to synthesize both thiazole and *p*-aminobenzoic acid are also inherited as though differentiated from normal by single genes.

* The inference that the three vitamins mentioned are essential for the growth of normal strains is supported by the fact that an extract of the normal strain will serve as a source of vitamin for each of the mutant strains.

Part Seven

~~

EVOLUTION

CHRONOLOGY

1749–1804   Buffon's *Histoire Naturelle* asserted that species were mutable; drew attention to vestigial organs.

1794–1796   Erasmus Darwin's *Zoönomia* published; advanced the idea that environmental influences transformed species.

1795   James Hutton's *Theory of the Earth* published, interpreting certain geological strata as former sea beds.

1798   Publication of Malthus' *Essay on Population.*

1809   Lamarck's *Philosophie Zoologique* emphasized the fundamental unity of life and the capacity of species to vary; environmental influences stressed.

1817   William Smith's *Stratigraphical System of Organized Fossils* showed that certain strata have characteristic series of fossils.

1830–1833   Charles Lyell's *Principles of Geology* advanced the theory of uniformitarianism, i.e., the view that geological formations were explainable in terms of forces and conditions observable at present.

1837   The voyage of the *Beagle* with Darwin aboard as naturalist.

1844   Darwin's first sketch of the theory of natural selection.

1856   Discovery of the first Neanderthal remains.

1856   Lord Kelvin computed the age of the solar system as 25 million years (later 40 million years).

1858   Joint announcement by Darwin and Wallace of the theory of natural selection.

1859   Publication of Darwin's *Origin of Species.*

1871   Publication of Darwin's *Descent of Man.*

1894   Bateson's *Materials for the Study of Variation* emphasized the importance of discontinuous variations.

1900   Rediscovery of Mendelian phenomena.

1901–1903   De Vries' *Mutationslehre* advanced the thesis that species are not continuously connected but arise through sudden large changes.

1901–1904   Nuttall investigated biological relationships by the precipitin reaction.

[281]

1907   Boltwood first proposed the use of radioactivity data to determine the age of minerals.

1916   Crampton described geographical races of the snail *Partula* in Tahiti.

1927   Karpechenko obtained a tetraploid hybrid between the cabbage and the radish, thus creating the new species *Raphanobrassica*.

1930 ff.   Sewall Wright's studies on the mathematics of evolutionary changes in populations were published.

1930   Publication of R. A. Fisher's *The Genetical Theory of Natural Selection*.

1931 ca.   On the basis of radioactivity and geological data, the age of the earth was shown to be at least two billion years.

1932 ff.   Goldschmidt's studies of adaptation in geographical races of the gypsy moth.

1933   Timofeeff-Ressovsky experimentally measured the viability of strains of *Drosophila funebris* of different geographical origin.

1934   L'Héritier and Teissier devised the "population cage" method for the experimental study of natural selection.

1935   Sumner experimentally showed the selective value of protective coloration in fishes.

1937   Publication of Dobzhansky's *Genetics and the Origin of Species*.

1941 ff.   Gustafsson and co-workers produced agriculturally superior new strains of cereals by selection from mutants produced by X-rays.

1954   Revised estimates put the age of the earth at five to six billion years.

On the Tendency of Species to Form Varieties: and on the Perpetuation of Varieties and Species by Natural Means of Selection.

by CHARLES DARWIN and ALFRED WALLACE

Reprinted from the *Journal of the Linnaean Society of London*, Vol. 3, pp. 45–62 (1859).

Despite the persistent urging of his friend Sir Charles Lyell, Darwin was reluctant to publish his views on natural selection before he had gathered all the available evidence into a complete work. But on June 18, 1858 he received a letter from Alfred Russel Wallace, then in Malaya, enclosing an essay in which was set forth the theory of natural selection almost in Darwin's own terms, and requesting Darwin to forward it to Lyell. "I never saw a more striking coincidence;" wrote Darwin, "if Wallace had had my MS sketch written out in 1842, he could not have made a better short abstract." Darwin sent the paper to Lyell. He did not believe he could now honorably publish his own views and he was ready to yield to Wallace the honor of priority. But his friend Sir Joseph Hooker took matters out of Darwin's hands by arranging a joint presentation of papers by both Darwin and Wallace before the Linnaean Society on July 1, 1858. Darwin himself was not present at the meeting. Lyell and Hooker introduced the papers to an audience that listened with respectful interest, but volunteered no discussion. A year and a half later The Origin of Species *was published.*

On the Tendency of Species to form Varieties; and on the Perpetuation of Varieties and Species by Natural Means of Selection. By CHARLES DARWIN, Esq., F.R.S., F.L.S., & F.G.S., and ALFRED WALLACE, Esq. Communicated by Sir CHARLES LYELL, F.R.S., F.L.S., and J. D. HOOKER, Esq., M.D., V.P. R.S., F.L.S., &c.

[Read July 1st, 1858.]

London, June 30th, 1858.

MY DEAR SIR,—The accompanying papers, which we have the honour of communicating to the Linnean Society, and which all relate to the same subject, viz. the Laws which affect the Production of Varieties, Races, and Species, contain the results of the investigations of two indefatigable naturalists, Mr. Charles Darwin and Mr. Alfred Wallace.

These gentlemen having, independently and unknown to one another, conceived the same very ingenious theory to account for the appearance and perpetuation of varieties and of specific forms on our planet, may both fairly claim the merit of being original thinkers in this important line of inquiry; but neither of them having published his views, though Mr. Darwin has for many years past been repeatedly urged by us to do so, and both authors having now unreservedly placed their papers in our hands, we think it would best promote the interests

of science that a selection from them should be laid before the Linnean Society.

Taken in the order of their dates, they consist of:—

1. Extracts from a MS. work on Species,* by Mr. Darwin, which was sketched in 1839, and copied in 1844, when the copy was read by Dr. Hooker, and its contents afterwards communicated to Sir Charles Lyell. The first Part is devoted to "The Variation of Organic Beings under Domestication and in their Natural State;" and the second chapter of that Part, from which we propose to read to the Society the extracts referred to, is headed, "On the Variation of Organic Beings in a state of Nature; on the Natural Means of Selection; on the Comparison of Domestic Races and true Species."

2. An abstract of a private letter addressed to Professor Asa Gray, of Boston, U.S., in October 1857, by Mr. Darwin, in which he repeats his views, and which shows that these remained unaltered from 1839 to 1857.

3. An Essay by Mr. Wallace, entitled "On the Tendency of Varieties to depart indefinitely from the Original Type." This was written at Ternate in February 1858, for the perusal of his friend and correspondent Mr. Darwin,

---

* This MS. work was never intended for publication, and therefore was not written with care.—C. D. 1858.

and sent to him with the expressed wish that it should be forwarded to Sir Charles Lyell, if Mr. Darwin thought it sufficiently novel and interesting. So highly did Mr. Darwin appreciate the value of the views therein set forth, that he proposed, in a letter to Sir Charles Lyell, to obtain Mr. Wallace's consent to allow the Essay to be published as soon as possible. Of this step we highly approved, provided Mr. Darwin did not withhold from the public, as he was strongly inclined to do (in favour of Mr. Wallace), the memoir which he had himself written on the same subject, and which, as before stated, one of us had perused in 1844, and the contents of which we had both of us been privy to for many years. On representing this to Mr. Darwin, he gave us permission to make what use we thought proper of his memoir, &c.; and in adopting our present course, of presenting it to the Linnean Society, we have explained to him that we are not solely considering the relative claims to priority of himself and his friend, but the interests of science generally; for we feel it to be desirable that views founded on a wide deduction from facts, and matured by years of reflection, should constitute at once a goal from which others may start, and that, while the scientific world is waiting for the appearance of Mr. Darwin's complete work, some of the leading results of his labours, as well as those of his able correspondent, should together be laid before the public.

We have the honour to be yours very obediently,

CHARLES LYELL.
JOS. D. HOOKER.

J. J. Bennett, Esq.,
Secretary of the Linnean Society.

1. *Extract from an unpublished Work on Species, by* C. DARWIN, *Esq., consisting of a portion of a Chapter entitled,* "On the Variation of Organic Beings in a state of Na-ture; on the Natural Means of Selection; on the Comparison of Domestic Races and true Species."

De Candolle, in an eloquent passage, has declared that all nature is at war, one organism with another, or with external nature. Seeing the contented face of nature, this may at first well be doubted; but reflection will inevitably prove it to be true. The war, however, is not constant, but recurrent in a slight degree at short periods, and more severely at occasional more distant periods; and hence its effects are easily overlooked. It is the doctrine of Malthus applied in most cases with tenfold force. As in every climate there are seasons, for each of its inhabitants, of greater and less abundance, so all annually breed; and the moral restraint which in some small degree checks the increase of mankind is entirely lost. Even slow-breeding mankind has doubled in twenty-five years; and if he could increase his food with greater ease, he would double in less time. But for animals without artificial means, the amount of food for each species must, *on an average,* be constant, whereas the increase of all organisms tends to be geometrical, and in a vast majority of cases at an enormous ratio. Suppose in a certain spot there are eight pairs of birds, and that *only* four pairs of them annually (including double hatches) rear only four young, and that these go on rearing their young at the same rate, then at the end of seven years (a short life, excluding violent deaths, for any bird) there will be 2048 birds, instead of the original sixteen. As this increase is quite impossible, we must conclude either that birds do not rear nearly half their young, or that the average life of a bird is, from accident, not nearly seven years. Both checks probably concur. The same kind of calculation applied to all plants and animals affords results more or less striking, but in very few instances more striking than in man.

Many practical illustrations of this rapid tendency to increase are on record, among which, during peculiar seasons, are the extraordinary numbers of certain animals; for instance, during the years 1826 to 1828, in La Plata, when from drought some millions of cattle perished, the whole country actually *swarmed* with mice. Now I think it cannot be doubted that during the breeding-season all the mice (with the exception of a few males or females in excess) ordinarily pair, and therefore that this astounding increase during three years must be attributed to a greater number than usual surviving the first year, and then breeding, and so on till the third year, when their numbers were brought down to their usual limits on the return of wet weather. Where man has introduced plants and animals into a new and favourable country, there are many accounts in how surprisingly few years the whole country has become stocked with them. This increase would necessarily stop as soon as the country was fully stocked; and yet we have every reason to believe, from what is known of wild animals, that *all* would pair in the spring. In the majority of cases it is most difficult to imagine where the checks fall—though generally, no doubt, on the seeds, eggs, and young; but when we remember how impossible, even in mankind (so much better known than any other animal), it is to infer from repeated casual observations what the average duration of life is, or to discover the different percentage of deaths to births in different countries, we ought to feel no surprise at our being unable to discover where the check falls in any animal or plant. It should always be remembered, that in most cases the checks are recurrent yearly in a small, regular degree, and in an extreme degree during unusually cold, hot, dry, or wet years, according to the constitution of

the being in question. Lighten any check in the least degree, and the geometrical powers of increase in every organism will almost instantly increase the average number of the favoured species. Nature may be compared to a surface on which rest ten thousand sharp wedges touching each other and driven inwards by incessant blows. Fully to realize these views much reflection is requisite. Malthus on man should be studied; and all such cases as those of the mice in La Plata, of the cattle and horses when first turned out in South America, of the birds by our calculation, &c., should be well considered. Reflect on the enormous multiplying power *inherent and annually in action* in all animals; reflect on the countless seeds scattered by a hundred ingenious contrivances, year after year, over the whole face of the land; and yet we have every reason to suppose that the average percentage of each of the inhabitants of a country usually remains constant. Finally, let it be borne in mind that this average number of individuals (the external conditions remaining the same) in each country is kept up by recurrent struggles against other species or against external nature (as on the borders of the Arctic regions, where the cold checks life), and that ordinarily each individual of every species holds its place, either by its own struggle and capacity of acquiring nourishment in some period of its life, from the egg upwards; or by the struggle of its parents (in short-lived organisms, when the main check occurs at longer intervals) with other individuals of the *same* or *different* species.

But let the external conditions of a country alter. If in a small degree, the relative proportions of the inhabitants will in most cases simply be slightly changed; but let the number of inhabitants be small, as on an island, and free access to it from other countries be circumscribed, and let the change of conditions continue progressing (forming new stations), in such a case the original inhabitants must cease to be as perfectly adapted to the changed conditions as they were originally. It has been shown in a former part of this work, that such changes of external conditions would, from their acting on the reproductive system, probably cause the organization of those beings which were most affected to become, as under domestication, plastic. Now, can it be doubted, from the struggle each individual has to obtain subsistence, that any minute variation in structure, habits, or instincts, adapting that individual better to the new conditions, would tell upon its vigour and health? In the struggle it would have a better *chance* of surviving; and those of its offspring which inherited the variation, be it ever so slight, would also have a better *chance*. Yearly more are bred than can survive; the smallest grain in the balance, in the long run, must tell on which death shall fall, and which shall survive. Let this work of selection on the one hand, and death on the other, go on for a thousand generations, who will pretend to affirm that it would produce no effect, when we remember what, in a few years, Blakewell effected in cattle, and Western in sheep, by this identical principle of selection?

To give an imaginary example from changes in progress on an island:—let the organization of a canine animal which preyed chiefly on rabbits, but sometimes on hares, become slightly plastic; let these same changes cause the number of rabbits very slowly to decrease, and the number of hares to increase; the effect of this would be that the fox or dog would be driven to try to catch more hares: his organization, however, being slightly plastic, those individuals with the lightest forms, longest limbs, and best eyesight, let the difference be ever so small, would be slightly favoured, and would tend to live longer, and to survive during that time of the

year when food was scarcest; they would also rear more young, which would tend to inherit these slight peculiarities. The less fleet ones would be rigidly destroyed. I can see no more reason to doubt that these causes in a thousand generations would produce a marked effect, and adapt the form of the fox or dog to the catching of hares instead of rabbits, than that greyhounds can be improved by selection and careful breeding. So would it be with plants under similar circumstances. If the number of individuals of a species with plumed seeds could be increased by greater powers of dissemination within its own area (that is, if the check to increase fell chiefly on the seeds), those seeds which were provided with ever so little more down, would in the long run be most disseminated; hence a greater number of seeds thus formed would germinate, and would tend to produce plants inheriting the slightly better-adapted down.*

Besides this natural means of selection, by which those individuals are preserved, whether in their egg, or larval, or mature state, which are best adapted to the place they fill in nature, there is a second agency at work in most unisexual animals, tending to produce the same effect, namely, the struggle of the males for the females. These struggles are generally decided by the law of battle, but in the case of birds, apparently, by the charms of their song, by their beauty or their power of courtship, as in the dancing rock-thrush of Guiana. The most vigorous and healthy males, implying perfect adaptation, must generally gain the victory in their contests. This kind of selection, however, is less rigorous than the other; it does not require the death of the less successful, but gives to them fewer descendants. The struggle falls, moreover, at a time of year when food is generally abundant,

* I can see no more difficulty in this, than in the planter improving his varieties of the cotton-plant.—C. D. 1858.

and perhaps the effect chiefly produced would be the modification of the secondary sexual characters, which are not related to the power of obtaining food, or to defence from enemies, but to fighting with or rivalling other males. The result of this struggle amongst the males may be compared in some respects to that produced by those agriculturists who pay less attention to the careful selection of all their young animals, and more to the occasional use of a choice mate.

II. *Abstract of a Letter from* C. DARWIN, Esq., *to* Prof. ASA GRAY, *Boston, U.S., dated Down, September 5th,* 1857.

1. It is wonderful what the principle of selection by man, that is the picking out of individuals with any desired quality, and breeding from them, and again picking out, can do. Even breeders have been astounded at their own results. They can act on differences inappreciable to an uneducated eye. Selection has been *methodically* followed in *Europe* for only the last half century; but it was occasionally, and even in some degree methodically, followed in the most ancient times. There must have been also a kind of unconscious selection from a remote period, namely in the preservation of the individual animals (without any thought of their offspring) most useful to each race of man in his particular circumstances. The "roguing," as nurserymen call the destroying of varieties which depart from their type, is a kind of selection. I am convinced that intentional and occasional selection has been the main agent in the production of our domestic races; but however this may be, its great power of modification has been indisputably shown in later times. Selection acts only by the accumulation of slight or greater variations, caused by external conditions, or by the mere fact that in generation the child is not absolutely similar to its parent. Man, by this power of accumulating variations, adapts living beings to his wants—may be said to make the wool of one sheep good for carpets, of another for cloth, &c.

2. Now suppose there were a being who did not judge by mere external appearances, but who could study the whole internal organization, who was never capricious, and should go on selecting for one object during millions of generations; who will say what he might not effect? In nature we have some *slight* variation occasionally in all parts; and I think it can be shown that changed conditions of existence is the main cause of the child not exactly resembling its parents; and in nature geology shows us what changes have taken place, and are taking place. We have almost unlimited time; no one but a practical geologist can fully appreciate this. Think of the Glacial period, during the whole of which the same species at least of shells have existed; there must have been during this period millions on millions of generations.

3. I think it can be shown that there is such an unerring power at work in *Natural Selection* (the title of my book), which selects exclusively for the good of each organic being. The elder De Candolle, W. Herbert, and Lyell have written excellently on the struggle for life; but even they have not written strongly enough. Reflect that every being (even the elephant) breeds at such a rate, that in a few years, or at most a few centuries, the surface of the earth would not hold the progeny of one pair. I have found it hard constantly to bear in mind that the increase of every single species is checked during some part of its life, or during some shortly recurrent generation. Only a few of those annually born can live to propagate their kind. What a trifling difference must often determine which shall survive, and which perish!

4. Now take the case of a country

undergoing some change. This will tend to cause some of its inhabitants to vary slightly—not but that I believe most beings vary at all times enough for selection to act on them. Some of its inhabitants will be exterminated; and the remainder will be exposed to the mutual action of a different set of inhabitants, which I believe to be far more important to the life of each being than mere climate. Considering the infinitely various methods which living beings follow to obtain food by struggling with other organisms, to escape danger at various times of life, to have their eggs or seeds disseminated, &c. &c., I cannot doubt that during millions of generations individuals of a species will be occasionally born with some slight variation, profitable to some part of their economy. Such individuals will have a better chance of surviving, and of propagating their new and slightly different structure; and the modification may be slowly increased by the accumulative action of natural selection to any profitable extent. The variety thus formed will either coexist with, or, more commonly, will exterminate its parent form. An organic being, like the woodpecker or misseltoe, may thus come to be adapted to a score of contingences —natural selection accumulating those slight variations in all parts of its structure, which are in any way useful to it during any part of its life.

5. Multiform difficulties will occur to every one, with respect to this theory. Many can, I think, be satisfactorily answered. *Natura non facit saltum* answers some of the most obvious. The slowness of the change, and only a very few individuals undergoing change at any one time, answers others. The extreme imperfection of our geological records answers others.

6. Another principle, which may be called the principle of divergence, plays, I believe, an important part in the origin of species. The same spot will support more life if occupied by very diverse forms. We see this in the many generic forms in a square yard of turf, and in the plants or insects on any little uniform islet, belonging almost invariably to as many genera and families as species. We can understand the meaning of this fact amongst the higher animals, whose habits we understand. We know that it has been experimentally shown that a plot of land will yield a greater weight if sown with several species and genera of grasses, than if sown with only two or three species. Now, every organic being, by propagating so rapidly, may be said to be striving its utmost to increase in numbers. So it will be with the offspring of any species after it has become diversified into varieties, or sub-species, or true species. And it follows, I think, from the foregoing facts, that the varying offspring of each species will try (only few will succeed) to seize on as many and as diverse places in the economy of nature as possible. Each new variety or species, when formed, will generally take the place of, and thus exterminate its less well-fitted parent. This I believe to be the origin of the classification and affinities of organic beings at all times; for organic beings always *seem* to branch and sub-branch like the limbs of a tree from a common trunk, the flourishing and diverging twigs destroying the less vigorous—the dead and lost branches rudely representing extinct genera and families.

This sketch is *most* imperfect; but in so short a space I cannot make it better. Your imagination must fill up very wide blanks.

C. DARWIN.

III. *On the Tendency of Varieties to depart indefinitely from the Original Type.* By ALFRED RUSSEL WALLACE.

One of the strongest arguments which have been adduced to prove the original and permanent distinctness of species is, that *varieties* produced in a state of domesticity are more or less unstable, and often have a tendency, if left to themselves, to return to the normal form of the parent species; and this instability is considered to be a distinctive peculiarity of all varieties, even of those occurring among wild animals in a state of nature, and to constitute a provision for preserving unchanged the originally created distinct species.

In the absence or scarcity of facts and observations as to *varieties* occurring among wild animals, this argument has had great weight with naturalists, and has led to a very general and somewhat prejudiced belief in the stability of species. Equally general, however, is the belief in what are called "permanent or true varieties,"—races of animals which continually propagate their like, but which differ so slightly (although constantly) from some other race, that the one is considered to be a *variety* of the other. Which is the *variety* and which the original *species,* there is generally no means of determining, except in those rare cases in which the one race has been known to produce an offspring unlike itself and resembling the other. This, however, would seem quite incompatible with the "permanent invariability of species," but the difficulty is overcome by assuming that such varieties have strict limits, and can never again vary further from the original type, although they may return to it, which, from the analogy of the domesticated animals, is considered to be highly probable, if not certainly proved.

It will be observed that this argument rests entirely on the assumption, that *varieties* occurring in a state of nature are in all respects analogous to or even identical with those of domestic animals, and are governed by the same laws as regards their permanence or further variation. But it is the object of the present paper to show that this assumption is altogether false, that there is a general principle in nature which will cause many *varieties* to survive the parent species, and to give rise to successive variations departing further and further from the original type, and which also produces, in domesticated animals, the tendency of varieties to return to the parent form.

The life of wild animals is a struggle for existence. The full exertion of all their faculties and all their energies is required to preserve their own existence and provide for that of their infant offspring. The possibility of procuring food during the least favourable seasons, and of escaping the attacks of their most dangerous enemies, are the primary conditions which determine the existence both of individuals and of entire species. These conditions will also determine the population of a species; and by a careful consideration of all the circumstances we may be enabled to comprehend, and in some degree to explain, what at first sight appears so inexplicable—the excessive abundance of some species, while others closely allied to them are very rare.

The general proportion that must obtain between certain groups of animals is readily seen. Large animals cannot be so abundant as small ones; the carnivora must be less numerous than the herbivora; eagles and lions can never be so plentiful as pigeons and antelopes; the wild asses of the Tartarian deserts cannot equal in numbers the horses of the more luxuriant prairies and pampas of America. The greater or less fecundity of an animal is often considered to be one of the chief causes of its abundance or scarcity; but a consideration of the facts will show us that it really has little or nothing to do with the matter. Even the least prolific of animals would increase rapidly if unchecked, whereas it is evident that the animal population of the globe must be stationary, or perhaps, through the influence of man, decreasing. Fluctuations there may be; but permanent increase, except in restricted localities, is almost impossible. For example, our own observation must convince us that birds do not go on increasing every year in a geometrical ratio, as they would do, were there not some powerful check to their natural increase. Very few birds produce less than two young ones each year, while many have six, eight, or ten; four will certainly be below the average; and if we suppose that each pair produce young only four times in their life, that will also be below the average, supposing them not to die either by violence or want of food. Yet at this rate how tremendous would be the increase in a few years from a single pair! A simple calculation will show that in fifteen years each pair of birds would have increased to nearly ten millions! whereas we have no reason to believe that the number of the birds of any country increases at all in fifteen or in one hundred and fifty years. With such powers of increase the population must have reached its limits, and have become stationary, in a very few years after the origin of each species. It is evident, therefore, that each year an immense number of birds must perish—as many in fact as are born; and as on the lowest calculation the progeny are each year twice as numerous as their parents, it follows that, whatever be the average number of individuals existing in any given country, *twice that number must perish annually,* —a striking result, but one which seems at least highly probable, and is perhaps under rather than over the truth. It would therefore appear that, as far as the continuance of the species and the keeping up the average number of individuals are concerned, large broods are superfluous. On the average all above *one* become food for hawks and kites, wild cats and weasels, or perish of cold and hunger as winter comes on. This is strikingly proved by the case of particular species; for we find that their abundance in individuals bears no relation whatever to their fertility in producing

offspring. Perhaps the most remarkable instance of an immense bird population is that of the passenger pigeon of the United States, which lays only one, or at most two eggs, and is said to rear generally but one young one. Why is this bird so extraordinarily abundant,[1] while others producing two or three times as many young are much less plentiful? The explanation is not difficult. The food most congenial to this species, and on which it thrives best, is abundantly distributed over a very extensive region, offering such differences of soil and climate, that in one part or another of the area the supply never fails. The bird is capable of a very rapid and long-continued flight, so that it can pass without fatigue over the whole of the district it inhabits, and as soon as the supply of food begins to fail in one place is able to discover a fresh feeding-ground. This example strikingly shows us that the procuring a constant supply of wholesome food is almost the sole condition requisite for ensuring the rapid increase of a given species, since neither the limited fecundity, nor the unrestrained attacks of birds of prey and of man are here sufficient to check it. In no other birds are these peculiar circumstances so strikingly combined. Either their food is more liable to failure, or they have not sufficient power of wing to search for it over an extensive area, or during some season of the year it becomes very scarce, and less wholesome substitutes have to be found; and thus, though more fertile in offspring, they can never increase beyond the supply of food in the least favourable seasons. Many birds can only exist by migrating, when their food becomes scarce, to regions possessing a milder, or at least a different climate, though, as these migrating birds are seldom excessively abundant, it is evident that the countries they visit are

[1] The passenger pigeon is now extinct. The last known survivor died in the Cincinnati zoo in 1914.—*Editors.*

still deficient in a constant and abundant supply of wholesome food. Those whose organization does not permit them to migrate when their food becomes periodically scarce, can never attain a large population. This is probably the reason why woodpeckers are scarce with us, while in the tropics they are among the most abundant of solitary birds. Thus the house sparrow is more abundant than the redbreast, because its food is more constant and plentiful,—seeds of grasses being preserved during the winter, and our farm-yards and stubble-fields furnishing an almost inexhaustible supply. Why, as a general rule, are aquatic, and especially sea birds, very numerous in individuals? Not because they are more prolific than others, generally the contrary; but because their food never fails, the sea-shores and river-banks daily swarming with a fresh supply of small mollusca and crustacea. Exactly the same laws will apply to mammals. Wild cats are prolific and have few enemies; why then are they never as abundant as rabbits? The only intelligible answer is, that their supply of food is more precarious. It appears evident, therefore, that so long as a country remains physically unchanged, the numbers of its animal population cannot materially increase. If one species does so, some others requiring the same kind of food must diminish in proportion. The numbers that die annually must be immense; and as the individual existence of each animal depends upon itself, those that die must be the weakest—the very young, the aged, and the diseased,—while those that prolong their existence can only be the most perfect in health and vigour—those who are best able to obtain food regularly, and avoid their numerous enemies. It is, as we commenced by remarking, "a struggle for existence," in which the weakest and least perfectly organized must always succumb.

Now it is clear that what takes place among the individuals of a species must also occur among the several allied species of a group,—viz. that those which are best adapted to obtain a regular supply of food, and to defend themselves against the attacks of their enemies and the vicissitudes of the seasons, must necessarily obtain and preserve a superiority in population; while those species which from some defect of power or organization are the least capable of counteracting the vicissitudes of food, supply, &c., must diminish in numbers, and, in extreme cases, become altogether extinct. Between these extremes the species will present various degrees of capacity for ensuring the means of preserving life; and it is thus we account for the abundance or rarity of species. Our ignorance will generally prevent us from accurately tracing the effects to their causes; but could we become perfectly acquainted with the organization and habits of the various species of animals, and could we measure the capacity of each for performing the different acts necessary to its safety and existence under all the varying circumstances by which it is surrounded, we might be able even to calculate the proportionate abundance of individuals which is the necessary result.

If now we have succeeded in establishing these two points—1st, *that the animal population of a country is generally stationary, being kept down by a periodical deficiency of food, and other checks;* and, 2nd, *that the comparative abundance or scarcity of the individuals of the several species is entirely due to their organization and resulting habits, which, rendering it more difficult to procure a regular supply of food and to provide for their personal safety in some cases than in others, can only be balanced by a difference in the population which have to exist in a given area*—we shall be in a condition to proceed to the consideration of *varieties,* to which the preceding remarks have a direct and very important application.

Most or perhaps all the variations from the typical form of a species must have some definite effect, however slight, on the habits or capacities of the individuals. Even a change of colour might, by rendering them more or less distinguishable, affect their safety; a greater or less development of hair might modify their habits. More important changes, such as an increase in the power or dimensions of the limbs or any of the external organs, would more or less affect their mode of procuring food or the range of country which they inhabit. It is also evident that most changes would affect, either favourably or adversely, the powers of prolonging existence. An antelope with shorter or weaker legs must necessarily suffer more from the attacks of the feline carnivora; the passenger pigeon with less powerful wings would sooner or later be affected in its powers of procuring a regular supply of food; and in both cases the result must necessarily be a diminution of the population of the modified species. If, on the other hand, any species should produce a variety having slightly increased powers of preserving existence, that variety must inevitably in time acquire a superiority in numbers. These results must follow as surely as old age, intemperance, or scarcity of food produce an increased mortality. In both cases there may be many individual exceptions; but on the average the rule will invariably be found to hold good. All varieties will therefore fall into two classes—those which under the same conditions would never reach the population of the parent species, and those which would in time obtain and keep a numerical superiority. Now, let some alteration of physical conditions occur in the district—a long period of drought, a destruction of vegetation by locusts, the irruption of some new carnivorous animal seeking "pastures new"—any

change in fact tending to render existence more difficult to the species in question, and tasking its utmost powers to avoid complete extermination; it is evident that, of all the individuals composing the species, those forming the least numerous and most feebly organized variety would suffer first, and, were the pressure severe, must soon become extinct. The same causes continuing in action, the parent species would next suffer, would gradually diminish in numbers, and with a recurrence of similar unfavourable conditions might also become extinct. The superior variety would then alone remain, and on a return to favourable circumstances would rapidly increase in numbers and occupy the place of the extinct species and variety.

The *variety* would now have replaced the *species,* of which it would be a more perfectly developed and more highly organized form. It would be in all respects better adapted to secure its safety, and to prolong its individual existence and that of the race. Such a variety *could not* return to the original form; for that form is an inferior one, and could never compete with it for existence. Granted, therefore, a "tendency" to reproduce the original type of the species, still the variety must ever remain preponderant in numbers, and under adverse physical conditions *again alone survive*. But this new, improved, and populous race might itself, in course of time, give rise to new varieties, exhibiting several diverging modifications of form, any of which, tending to increase the facilities for preserving existence, must, by the same general law, in their turn become predominant. Here, then, we have *progression and continued divergence* deduced from the general laws which regulate the existence of animals in a state of nature, and from the undisputed fact that varieties do frequently occur. It is not, however, contended that this result would be invariable; a change of physical conditions in the district might at times materially modify it, rendering the race which had been the most capable of supporting existence under the former conditions now the least so, and even causing the extinction of the newer and, for a time, superior race, while the old or parent species and its first inferior varieties continued to flourish. Variations in unimportant parts might also occur, having no perceptible effect on the life-preserving powers; and the varieties so furnished might run a course parallel with the parent species, either giving rise to further variations or returning to the former type. All we argue for is, that certain varieties have a tendency to maintain their existence longer than the original species, and this tendency must make itself felt; for though the doctrine of chances or averages can never be trusted to on a limited scale, yet, if applied to high numbers, the results come nearer to what theory demands, and, as we approach to an infinity of examples, become strictly accurate. Now the scale on which nature works is so vast—the numbers of individuals and periods of time with which she deals approach so near to infinity, that any cause, however slight, and however liable to be veiled and counteracted by accidental circumstances, must in the end produce its full legitimate results.

Let us now turn to domesticated animals, and inquire how varieties produced among them are affected by the principles here enunciated. The essential difference in the condition of wild and domestic animals is this,—that among the former, their well-being and very existence depend upon the full exercise and healthy condition of all their senses and physical powers, whereas, among the latter, these are only partially exercised, and in some cases are absolutely unused. A wild animal has to search, and often to labour, for every mouthful of food—to exercise sight, hearing, and smell in seeking it, and in avoiding dangers, in procuring shelter from the inclemency of the seasons, and in providing for the subsistence and safety of its offspring. There is no muscle of its body that is not called into daily and hourly activity; there is no sense or faculty that is not strengthened by continual exercise. The domestic animal, on the other hand, has food provided for it, is sheltered, and often confined, to guard it against the vicissitudes of the seasons, is carefully secured from the attacks of its natural enemies, and seldom even rears its young without human assistance. Half of its senses and faculties are quite useless; and the other half are but occasionally called into feeble exercise, while even its muscular system is only irregularly called into action.

Now when a variety of such an animal occurs, having increased power or capacity in any organ or sense, such increase is totally useless, is never called into action, and may even exist without the animal ever becoming aware of it. In the wild animal, on the contrary, all its faculties and powers being brought into full action for the necessities of existence, any increase becomes immediately available, is strengthened by exercise, and must even slightly modify the food, the habits, and the whole economy of the race. It creates as it were a new animal, one of superior powers, and which will necessarily increase in numbers and outlive those inferior to it.

Again, in the domesticated animal all variations have an equal chance of continuance; and those which would decidedly render a wild animal unable to compete with its fellows and continue its existence are no disadvantage whatever in a state of domesticity. Our quickly fattening pigs, short-legged sheep, pouter pigeons, and poodle dogs could never have come into existence in a state of nature, because the very first step towards such inferior forms would have led to the rapid extinction of the race; still less could they now exist in competition with their wild allies. The great speed but slight endurance of the race horse, the unwieldy strength of the ploughman's team, would both be useless in a state of nature. If turned wild on the pampas, such animals would probably soon become extinct, or under favourable circumstances might each lose those extreme qualities which would never be called into action, and in a few generations would revert to a common type, which must be that in which the various powers and faculties are so proportioned to each other as to be best adapted to procure food and secure safety,—that in which by the full exercise of every part of his organization the animal can alone continue to live. Domestic varieties, when turned wild, *must* return to something near the type of the original wild stock, *or become altogether extinct.*

We see, then, that no inferences as to varieties in a state of nature can be deduced from the observation of those occurring among domestic animals. The two are so much opposed to each other in every circumstance of their existence, that what applies to the one is almost sure not to apply to the other. Domestic animals are abnormal, irregular, artificial; they are subject to varieties which never occur and never can occur in a state of nature: their very existence depends altogether on human care; so far are many of them removed from that just proportion of faculties, that true balance of organization, by means of which alone an animal left to its own resources can preserve its existence and continue its race.

The hypothesis of Lamarck—that progressive changes in species have been produced by the attempts of animals to increase the development of their own organs, and thus modify their structure and habits—has been repeatedly and easily refuted by all writers on the subject of varieties and species, and it seems to have been considered that when this

was done the whole question has been finally settled; but the view here developed renders such an hypothesis quite unnecessary, by showing that similar results must be produced by the action of principles constantly at work in nature. The powerful retractile talons of the falcon- and the cat-tribes have not been produced or increased by the volition of those animals; but among the different varieties which occurred in the earlier and less highly organized forms of these groups, *those always survived longest which had the greatest facilities for seizing their prey.* Neither did the giraffe acquire its long neck by desiring to reach the foliage of the more lofty shrubs, and constantly stretching its neck for the purpose, but because any varieties which occurred among its antitypes with a longer neck than usual *at once secured a fresh range of pasture over the same ground as their shorter-necked companions, and on the first scarcity of food were thereby enabled to outlive them.* Even the peculiar colours of many animals, especially insects, so closely resembling the soil or the leaves or the trunks on which they habitually reside, are explained on the same principle; for though in the course of ages varieties of many tints may have occurred, *yet those races having colours best adapted to concealment from their enemies would inevitably survive the longest.* We have also here an acting cause to account for that balance so often observed in nature, —a deficiency in one set of organs always being compensated by an increased development of some others— powerful wings accompanying weak feet, or great velocity making up for the absence of defensive weapons; for it has been shown that all varieties in which an unbalanced deficiency occurred could not long continue their existence. The action of this principle is exactly like that of the centrifugal governor of the steam engine, which checks and corrects any irregularities almost before they become evident; and in like manner no un-balanced deficiency in the animal king-dom can ever reach any conspicuous magnitude, because it would make itself felt at the very first step, by rendering existence difficult and extinction almost sure soon to follow. An origin such as is here advocated will also agree with the peculiar character of the modifications of form and structure which obtain in organized beings—the many lines of divergence from a central type, the in-creasing efficiency and power of a par-ticular organ through a succession of allied species, and the remarkable persist-ence of unimportant parts such as colour, texture of plumage and hair, form of horns or crests, through a series of species differing considerably in more essential characters. It also furnishes us with a reason for that "more specialized structure" which Professor Owen states to be a characteristic of recent compared with extinct forms, and which would evidently be the result of the progressive modification of any organ applied to a special purpose in the animal economy.

We believe we have now shown that there is a tendency in nature to the continued progression of certain classes of *varieties* further and further from the original type—a progression to which there appears no reason to assign any definite limits—and that the same princi-ple which produces this result in a state of nature will also explain why domestic varieties have a tendency to revert to the original type. This progression, by minute steps, in various directions, but always checked and balanced by the necessary conditions, subject to which alone existence can be preserved, may, it is believed, be followed out so as to agree with all the phenomena presented by organized beings, their extinction and succession in past ages, and all the extra-ordinary modifications of form, instinct, and habits which they exhibit.

Ternate, February, 1858.

Mendelian Proportions in a Mixed Population. ⁓

by G. H. HARDY

Reprinted from *Science*, Vol. 28, pp. 49–50 (1908), by permission of the editors.

Organic evolution consists essentially of long-term changes in the frequency of genes in populations. Hence evolution could not be brought into the realm of precise study until methods were available for the study of the genetics of populations in quantitative terms. In 1908 the British mathematician Hardy and a German physician, Weinberg, independently pointed out the principle of genetic equilibrium in Men-delizing populations. Their papers laid the foundations for the mathe-matical treatment of evolutionary problems. The Hardy-Weinberg equilibrium represents a condition of dynamic stability, the rest point on the scale, so to speak, against which the departures constituting evolu-tionary change can be measured.

To THE EDITOR OF Science: I am reluctant to intrude in a discussion concerning matters of which I have no expert knowledge, and I should have expected the very simple point which I wish to make to have been familiar to biologists. However, some remarks of Mr. Udny Yule, to which Mr. R. C. Punnett has called my attention, suggest that it may still be worth making.

In the *Proceedings of the Royal Society of Medicine* (Vol. I., p. 165) Mr. Yule is reported to have suggested, as a criticism of the Mendelian position, that if brachydactyly is dominant "in the course of time one would expect, in the absence of counteracting factors, to get three brachydactylous persons to one normal."

It is not difficult to prove, however, that such an expectation would be quite groundless. Suppose that Aa is a pair of Mendelian characters, A being dominant, and that in any given generation the numbers of pure dominants (AA), heterozygotes (Aa), and pure recessives (aa) are as $p: 2q: r$. Finally, suppose that the numbers are fairly large, so that the mating may be regarded as random, that the sexes are evenly distributed among the three varieties, and that all are equally fertile. A little mathematics of the multiplication-table type is enough to show that in the next generation the numbers will be as

$$(p+q)^2 : 2(p+q)(q+r) : (q+r)^2,$$

or as $p_1 : 2q_1 : r_1$, say.

The interesting question is—in what circumstances will this distribution be the same as that in the generation before? It is easy to see that the condition for this is $q^2 = pr$. And since $q_1^2 = p_1 r_1$, whatever the values of p, q and r may be, the distribution will in any case continue unchanged after the second generation.

Suppose, to take a definite instance, that A is brachydactyly, and that we start from a population of pure brachydactylous and pure normal persons, say in the ratio of $1 : 10,000$. Then $p = 1$, $q = 0$, $r = 10,000$ and $p_1 = 1$, $q_1 = 10,000$, $r_1 = 100,000,000$. If brachydactyly is dominant, the proportion of brachydactylous persons in the second generation is $20,001 : 100,020,001$, or practically $2 : 10,000$, twice that in the first generation; and this proportion will afterwards have no tendency whatever to increase. If, on the other hand, brachydactyly were recessive, the proportion in the second generation would be $1 : 100,020,001$, or practically $1 : 100,-000,000$, and this proportion would afterwards have no tendency to decrease.

In a word, there is not the slightest foundation for the idea that a dominant character should show a tendency to spread over a whole population, or that a recessive should tend to die out.

I ought perhaps to add a few words on the effect of the small deviations from the theoretical proportions which will, of course, occur in every generation. Such a distribution as $p_1 : 2q_1 : r_1$, which satisfies the condition $q_1^2 = p_1 r_1$, we may call a *stable* distribution. In actual fact we shall obtain in the second generation not $p_1 : 2q_1 : r_1$ but a slightly different distribution $p_1' : 2q_1' : r_1'$, which is not "stable." This should, according to theory, give us in the third generation a "stable" distribution $p_2 : 2q_2 : r_2$, also differing slightly from $p_1 : 2q_1 : r_1$; and so on. The sense in which the distribution $p_1 : 2q_1 : r_1$ is "stable" is this, that if we allow for the effect of casual deviations in any subsequent generation, we should, according to theory, obtain at the next generation a new "stable" distribution differing but slightly from the original distribution.

I have, of course, considered only the very simplest hyotheses possible. Hypotheses other than that of purely random mating will give different results, and, of course, if, as appears to be the case sometimes, the character is not independent of that of sex, or has an influence on fertility, the whole question may be greatly complicated. But such complications seem to be irrelevant to the simple issue raised by Mr. Yule's remarks.

G. H. HARDY
TRINITY COLLEGE, CAMBRIDGE,
April 5, 1908

P.S. I understand from Mr. Punnett that he has submitted the substance of what I have said above to Mr. Yule, and that the latter would accept it as a satisfactory answer to the difficulty that he raised. The "stability" of the particular ratio $1:2:1$ is recognized by Professor Karl Pearson (*Phil. Trans. Roy. Soc.* (A), vol. 203, p. 60).

On the Evolution of Biochemical Syntheses. ❦

by N. H. HOROWITZ

Reprinted from the *Proceedings of the National Academy of Sciences*, Vol. 31, pp. 153–157 (1945), by permission of the author.

One of the knottiest puzzles confronting the biologist is the problem of the origin of life. To the evolutionist it seems almost axiomatic that the first forms of life must have been exceedingly simple, but the full implications of this fact have only recently become apparent. Although Darwin had already pointed out that prior to the appearance of life on earth organic molecules would have had an opportunity to accumulate, it was not until the 1930's that Haldane, Oparin, and others attempted to reconstruct in biochemical terms a possible sequence of events leading to the emergence of organisms. Their conclusions, commonly known as the "heterotroph hypothesis," were to the effect that early life, possessing relatively few enzyme systems, must have been dependent upon a rich variety of ready-made organic substances in the environment. But how did biochemical complexity of the organism arise? An incisive answer to this question is suggested by Horowitz in the following paper.

ALTHOUGH IT HAS BEEN recognized for a long time that the biochemistry of the organism is conditioned by its genetic constitution, a more precise definition of this dependence has not been possible until recently. A considerable amount of evidence now exists for the view that there is a one-to-one correspondence between genes and biochemical reactions. This concept, foreshadowed in the work of Garrod on human alcaptonuria, accounts in a satisfactory way for the inheritance of pigment formation in guinea pigs, insects and flowers, and the synthesis of essential growth factors in *Neurospora*. It appears from these studies that each synthesis is controlled by a set of non-allelic genes, each gene governing a different step in the synthesis. As to the nature of this control, it is probable that the primary action of the gene is concerned with enzyme production. That genes can direct the specificities of proteins has been shown in the case of many antigens, while several mutations demonstrably affecting the production of enzymes have been reported. Evidence on the postulated gene-enzyme relationship is in most cases, however, still circumstantial; this is partly because of technical difficulties involved in the study of synthetic, or free-energy consuming reactions *in vitro,* and partly because of the insufficiency of biochemical information on those reactions which happen to be susceptible of genetic analysis.

As a corollary of the above hypothesis, each biosynthesis depends on the direct participation of a number of genes equal to the number of different, enzymatically catalyzed steps in the reaction chain. In attempting to account for the evolutionary development of such a reaction chain one meets in a clear form the problem of explaining macroevolutionary changes in terms of microevolutionary steps. The individual reactions making up the chain are of value to the organism only when considered collectively and in view of the ultimate product. Regarded individually, intermediate substances cannot, in general, be assumed to have physiological significance, and the ability to produce them does not of itself confer a selective advantage. An example from *Neurospora* genetics will serve to illustrate this point. At the present time seven different genes are known to be concerned in the synthesis of arginine by the mold. The inactivation of any one prevents the synthesis from taking place. On the basis of the above hypothesis, at least seven different catalyzed steps must occur in the synthesis. Several of the steps have been identi-

fied and controlling genes assigned to each. Two of the intermediates in the chain have been shown to be the amino acids ornithine and citrulline. Unlike arginine, neither of these substances is a general constituent of proteins. Aside from their function as precursors, they are apparently of no further use to the organism.

While the above example probably represents the general case, there are also well-known instances in which precursors serve independent functions. Thus, arginine, glycine and methionine are precursors of creatine in the rat, but the synthesis goes through the non-functional intermediate, glycocyamine. On the other hand, acetylcholine may be synthesized from choline in one step. In cases such as these, the problem is that of accounting for the synthesis of the precursors.

Since natural selection cannot preserve' non-functional characters, the most obvious implication of the facts would seem to be that a stepwise evolution of biosyntheses, by the selection of a single gene mutation at a time, is impossible. It will be shown below that this is not a necessary conclusion, but that under special conditions the stepwise evolution of long-chain syntheses may occur. First, however, an alternative to stepwise evolution will be considered; that is, the origin of a new reaction chain through the chance combination of the necessary genes.

Although the probability of the origin of a useful character through the chance association of many genes may be small, it is never zero. Indeed, a consideration of the statistical consequences of the interaction of mutation, Mendelian inheritance, and natural selection has led Wright to the conclusion that such chance associations may be of major importance in evolution. He has analyzed the evolutionary possibilities of various types of breeding structures and has shown that under certain conditions an extensive trial and error mechanism exists, whereby the species can test numerous combinations of non-adaptive genes. The breeding structure which most favors this type of evolution is that of a large population divided into many small, partially isolated groups. Within each group the cumulative effects of the accidents of sampling among the gametes are of major significance in determining gene frequencies, but the penalty of fixation of deleterious genes, ordinarily incurred under inbreeding, is avoided by exchange of migrants with other groups. The pressures of forward and reverse mutations, which between them determine an equilibrium frequency for non-adaptive genes in large, random-breeding populations, become of minor importance. As a consequence, a random drift of gene frequencies occurs. If, by chance, one group finds a particularly favorable combination of genes, a process of intergroup selection comes into play, whereby the favorable combination is spread to the population at large.

This model provides a means for the evolution of a new gene combination in spite of unfavorable mutation rates to active alleles and in the absence of selection of individual genes. It is thus favorable for the evolution of systems of individually non-adaptive, but collectively adaptive, genes. The effectiveness of the process would seem to be strongly dependent on the size of the gene combination required, however, decreasing approximately exponentially with increasing numbers of genes, other factors remaining constant. There would result a tendency toward the evolution of short reaction chains involving the recombination of molecular units already available. There is no doubt that a conservative tendency of this sort actually exists in nature. The wide variety of biologically important compounds built up on the pyrrole nucleus, to mention but one example, is a case in point.

The application of Wright's theory to the particular problem under consideration is limited by the fact that it operates only under biparental reproduction. It is probable that a large number of basic syntheses evolved prior to sexual reproduction. The universal distribution among living forms of certain classes of compounds—viz., the amino acids, nucleotides and probably the B vitamins—identifies them as essential ingredients of living matter. The synthesis of these substances must have evolved very early in geologic time, as a necessary condition for further progress, although loss of certain syntheses may have occurred in the later differentiation of some forms. It is therefore desirable to search for another solution of the problem applicable to compounds of this type, preferably one in which a minimum burden is placed on chance and a maximum one on directed evolutionary forces. It is thought that the following suggestion, while definitely a speculation, offers a possible solution along these lines.

In essence, the proposed hypothesis states that the evolution of the basic syntheses proceeded in a stepwise manner, involving one mutation at a time, but that the order of attainment of individual steps has been in the reverse direction from that in which the synthesis proceeds—i.e., the last step in the chain was the first to be acquired in the course of evolution, the penultimate step next, and so on. This process requires for its operation a special kind of chemical environment; namely, one in which end-products and potential intermediates are available. Postponing for the moment the question of how such an environment originated, consider the operation of the proposed mechanism. The species is at the outset assumed to be heterotrophic for an essential organic molecule, A. It obtains the substance from an environment which contains, in addition to A, the substances B and C, capable of reacting in the presence of a catalyst (enzyme) to give a molecule of A. As a result of biological activity, the amount of available A is depleted to a point where it limits the further growth of the species. At this point, a marked selective advantage will be enjoyed by mutants which are able to carry out the reaction $B + C = A$. As the external supplies of A are further reduced, the mutant strain will gain a still greater selective advantage, until it eventually displaces the parent strain from the population. In the A-free environment a back mutation to the original stock will be lethal, so we have at the same time a theory of lethal genes. The majority of biochemical mutations in *Neurospora* are lethals of this type.

In time, B may become limiting for the species, necessitating its synthesis from other substances, D and E; the population will then shift to one characterized by the genotype ($D + E = B$, $B + C = A$). Given a sufficiently complex environment and a proportionately variable germ plasm, long reaction chains can be built up in this way. In the event that B and C become limiting more or less simultaneously, another possibility is opened. Under these circumstances symbiotic associations of the type ($F + G \neq C, D + E = B$) ($F + G = C, D + E \neq B$) will have adaptive value.

This model is thus seen to have potentialities for the rapid evolution of long chain syntheses in response to changes in the environment. As has been pointed out by Oparin the hypothesis of a complex chemical environment is a necessary corollary of the concept of the origin of life through chemical means. The essential point of the argument is that it is inconceivable that a self-reproducing unit of the order of complexity of a nucleoprotein could have originated by the chance combination of inorganic molecules. Rather, a period of evolution of organic substances of ever-increasing degree of complexity must have intervened before such an event became a practical, as distinguished from a mathematical, probability. Or, put in another way, any random process which can have produced a nucleoprotein must at the same time have led to the production of a profusion of simpler structures. Oparin has considered in some detail the possible modes of origin of organic compounds from inorganic material and cites a number of known reactions of this type, together with evidences of their large-scale occurrence on the earth in past geologic ages. He concludes that in the absence of living organisms to destroy them highly complex organic systems can have developed. The first self-duplicating nucleoprotein originated as a step in this process of chemical evolution. The origin of living matter by physicochemical means thus presupposes the existence of a highly complex chemical environment.

To summarize, the hypothesis presented here suggests that the first living entity was a completely heterotrophic unit, reproducing itself at the expense of prefabricated organic molecules in its environment. A depletion of the environment resulted until a point was reached where the supply of specific substrates limited further multiplication. By a process of mutation a means was eventually discovered for utilizing other available substances. With this event the evolution of biosyntheses began. The conditions necessary for the operation of the mechanism ceased to exist with the ultimate destruction of the organic environment. Further evolution was probably based on the chance combination of genes, resulting to a large extent in the development of short reaction chains utilizing substances whose synthesis had been previously acquired.

Adaptive Changes Induced by Natural Selection in Wild Populations of Drosophila. ⌇

by TH. DOBZHANSKY

Abridged from *Evolution*, Vol. 1, pp. 1–16 (1947). Reprinted by permission of the author.

It commonly used to be said, as a defense against critics of the evolution theory, that natural selection was such a slow process that it was not to be expected that evolutionary changes would be perceptible within the span of a human lifetime. Such pessimism turned out to be unjustified, however. By the choice of organisms with a sufficiently short generation time, such as Drosophila *and bacteria, it has proven possible not only to detect evolutionary change in the laboratory but to measure its rate and study the effective forces in quantitative terms. An admirable example of this type of research is the following study by Dobzhansky, an outstanding contributor to the modern synthesis of genetics and evolution. So decisively have recent genetic studies vindicated Darwinism to all but a few dissidents that there is irony in the recollection that the early geneticists believed that the facts of Mendelian inheritance cast serious doubts upon the Darwinian hypothesis.*

INTRODUCTION

THE THEORY OF the origin of adaptations through natural selection is more than a century old, if one takes as its inception the date of Darwin's first essay written in 1842. Nevertheless, no agreement as to the rôle played by natural selection in evolution has as yet been reached. Weismann called natural selection "all powerful," but, during the first quarter of the present century, the idea fell into disrepute because of a failure to comprehend the meaning of the mutation theory and Johannsen's experiments on pure lines. So wide a divergence of opinion has been possible because the theory of natural selection has rested either on deductions from very general propositions or on inference from in-

direct evidence. That adaptive evolution in nature is too slow a process to be observed within a human lifetime has been taken for granted almost universally. Furthermore, selection pressures which act upon non-pathological traits of wild species have been assumed to be small.

Recent observations have shown, however, that natural populations, even of higher organisms, sometimes undergo rapid adaptive changes. Some wild species react to seasonal alterations in their environment by cyclic modifications of their genetic structure. Knowing these facts, direct observation and experimentation on natural selection has become possible. Controlled experiments can now take the place of speculation as to what natural selection is or is not able to accomplish. Furthermore, we need no longer be satisfied with mere verification of the existence of natural selection. The mechanics of natural selection in concrete cases can be studied. Hence, the genesis of adaptation, which is possibly the central problem of biology, now lies within the reach of the experimental method.

The first discovery of cyclic changes in the genetic composition of populations of wild species was made by Timofeeff-Ressovsky (1940). European as well as North American and Asiatic populations of the beetle *Adalia bipunctata* vary greatly in the elytral color pattern. Two color types, red and black, can easily be distinguished. They are known to differ by a single Mendelian gene. Near Berlin, where the species produces two and possibly three generations per year, the black type increases in relative frequency from about 37 per cent to 59 per cent from spring until autumn. During the winter the frequency of the black type is reduced and that of the red is increased. The beetle hibernates as an adult, the mortality among hibernating individuals being high. Only 4 per cent of black individuals survive hibernation, while about 11 per cent of the reds survive. The inference can be drawn that the black type is selected during the warm season.

The coloration of the Adalia beetle is a visible character easy to work with. In the corresponding Drosophila work, a character is used which is discernible only by microscopic examination of the larval salivary glands, namely the gene arrangement in the chromosomes. Variation of this character in species of Drosophila is due almost entirely to inversion of chromosome segments. Two or more such gene arrangements frequently occur in the same population. Since the carriers of different arrangements interbreed freely, some individuals have paired chromosomes with the same gene arrangements (inversion homozygotes) and others with unlike gene arrangements (inversion heterozygotes). Be-

cause the inversion homozygotes and heterozygotes are indistinguishable in external appearance, there was no reason to suppose that inversions are other than adaptively neutral characters. Not until Dobzhansky (1943, in *D. pseudoobscura*) and Dubinin and Tiniakov (1945, 1946, in *D. funebris*) found that populations which live in different habitats often differ in the relative frequencies of their gene arrangements, and that the composition of a single population may vary appreciably from season to season, was it realized that carriers of different gene arrangements may be favored or discriminated against by different environments.

The seasonal changes in the composition of the Adalia and Drosophila populations are adaptive responses of the living species to the succession of seasonal environments. It is important to note that such seasonal changes occur not only in organisms which, like the ones named above, produce several generations per year, but also in the longer lived ones. Gershenson (1945) has found changes of this sort in the hamster, *Cricetus cricetus*. Black and agouti individuals occur in Russian populations of this mammal, and the relative frequencies of these coat colors differ significantly in different seasons and in different places. The difference between the two color forms is due to a single gene.

Observations and experiments on natural selection in *Drosophila pseudoobscura* will be reviewed in the following pages. Previously published as well as unpublished data are discussed briefly; the latter will be presented in more details elsewhere.

LOCAL RACES

Fifteen different gene arrangements are known in the third chromosome of *Drosophila pseudoobscura*. None of them occur in the entire distribution area of the species. Hence, there is no "normal" or "wild-type" gene arrangement. On the other hand, the populations of most localities contain more than one, and up to seven, gene arrangements. Because of the free interbreeding of the carriers of different arrangements, many, frequently a majority, of wild individuals are inversion heterozygotes. The population of any locality can be described in terms of relative frequencies of different gene arrangements. The frequencies may differ in populations of different localities. Sometimes the differences are more or less proportional to the distances which separate the localities. Geographic gra-

dients or "clines" are thus formed. An example of such clines is given in figure 1.

About 50 per cent of third chromosomes in populations of south Coast Ranges of California have the so-called Standard gene arrangement, represented by black columns in figure 1. But the frequency of Standard falls to between 20 and 30 per cent in the Sierra Nevada and in the Death Valley regions which lie to the east of the Coast Ranges. Further east, in Arizona, the frequency falls to less than 5 per cent, and still

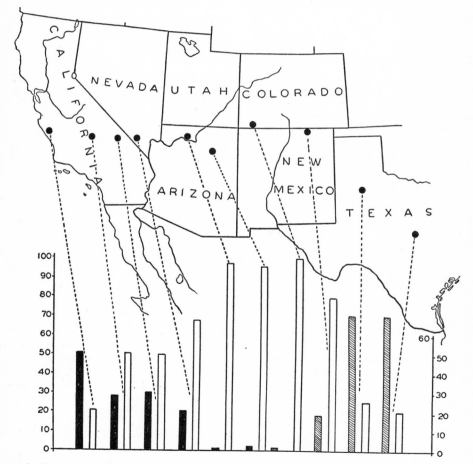

FIG. 1.—Frequencies (in per cent) of Standard (black columns), Arrowhead (white columns), and Pikes Peak (hatched columns) chromosomes in populations of *Drosophila pseudoobscura* in certain localities in the western United States.

further east Standard chromosomes occur but rarely. The Arrowhead gene arrangement (white columns in figure 2) is very common in Arizona and New Mexico, so much so that populations of some localities seem to be homozygous for it. But its frequency decreases eastward as well as westward from Arizona, reaching about 20 per cent in central Texas and in coastal California. The Pikes Peak gene arrangement (hatched columns in figure 1) is common in Texas, but rapidly decreases in frequency westward.

The transect across the southwestern United States shown in figure 1 is roughly 1200 miles long. Differences in the frequencies of gene arrangements may be observed however between populations which live in localities only a dozen or so miles apart. For example, three localities on Mount San Jacinto, California, were sampled repeatedly between 1939 and 1946. The approximate distances between these localities are 10 to 15 miles. One, Keen Camp, lies at an elevation of about 4500 feet in the ponderosa pine belt, the second, Piñon Flats, lies at 4000 feet in the much drier piñon forest, and the third, Andreas Canyon, lies at 800 feet on the desert's edge. The frequencies of gene arrangements in the populations of these localities are shown in table 1. (Chromosomes with Standard gene arrangement are henceforth denoted as ST, Arrowhead as AR, and Chiricahua as CH.)

Table 1 shows that ST chromosomes are most frequent in the lowest locality, Andreas, and least frequent in the highest locality, Keen. CH chromosomes show the opposite relationship. No significant differences appear for AR chromosomes in the three localities. How common such altitudinal gradients are is an open question. Preliminary data suggest the existence of gradients among populations that occur at different elevations in the region of the Yosemite National Park, in the Sierra Nevada in California. Here, however, the ST and AR, and not CH chromosomes, vary in frequencies from locality to locality. Thus, at Jacksonville, elevation about 800 feet, 40 to 45 per cent of third chromosomes have ST and 20 to 25 per cent have AR gene arrangement. At Lost Claim Campground, elevation about 3000 feet, the frequencies of both ST and AR are between 30 and 35 per cent. At Mather, elevation 4600 feet, ST fluctuates between 20 and 40 per cent and AR between 30 and 45 per cent. Finally, at Aspen Valley, elevation about 6800 feet, ST falls to 20 and AR rises to almost 50 per cent. The frequencies of CH chromosomes are between 15 and 20 per cent in all the localities. The horizontal distance between farthest localities, Jacksonville and Aspen Valley, is about 35 miles.

Altitudinal gradients in the frequencies of gene arrangements suggest that the differences between the inhabitants of different elevations on the same mountain range are adaptive and are produced by natural selection. This hypothesis is strengthened by the observations on seasonal changes and on

TABLE 1. *Frequencies (in per cent) of chromosomes with different gene arrangements in populations of localities on Mount San Jacinto (California)*

Locality	Gene arrangements				Numbers of chromosomes studied
	ST	AR	CH	Others	
Keen Camp	33.7	23.8	38.0	4.5	6634
Pinon Flats	40.7	25.1	29.1	5.1	4853
Andreas Canyon	57.6	24.0	15.3	3.0	3818

experimental populations discussed in the following paragraphs.

SEASONAL CYCLES

The repeated samplings of the populations in the three localities on Mount San Jacinto (see above) have disclosed a very interesting fact, namely that the composition of a population may change quite significantly from month to month. Furthermore, these changes are regular and follow the annual cycle of seasons. In two of the three localities, namely at Piñon Flats and at Andreas Canyon, the changes are qualitatively similar. Figure 2 gives a summary of the data for Piñon Flats. In this figure, the observations for all six years of collecting are grouped by months. It can be seen that in spring (March) the population contains about 50 per cent of ST chromosomes (shown in Figure 2 by circles), and slightly more than 20 per cent CH chromosomes (shown by triangles). From March to June the frequency of ST declines to less than 30 per cent and that of CH increases to just below 40 per cent. During the summer, from June to September, the reverse change takes place, namely ST increases in frequency, and CH decreases, to about the same values which these gene arrangements had during the spring. The changes of the frequencies of AR chromosomes (rectangles in figure 2) are less regular than those of ST and CH, but on the whole AR seems to follow the same path as CH. No regular changes occur

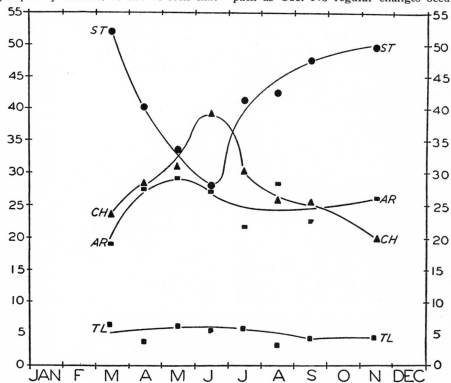

FIG. 2.—Changes in the frequencies of chromosomes with Standard (circles) Chiricahua (triangles), Arrowhead (horizontal rectangles), and Tree Line (squares) gene arrangements in the population of Piñon Flats, California. Ordinate—frequencies in per cent; abscissa—months. Combined data for six years of observation.

in the frequency of Tree Line chromosomes (squares in figure 2).

The changes at Andreas Canyon run parallel to those at Piñon Flats. From autumn till early spring the frequency of ST chromosomes keeps on a high level, and that of CH chromosomes on a low one. From March to June ST wanes and CH waxes in frequency. During the hot part of the summer very few *D. pseudoobscura* flies can be collected at Andreas Canyon. But when the population begins to build up in numbers in September, the ST chromosomes are found to have recovered their high frequency, while CH have dwindled to about the winter level. Curiously enough, no significant changes from month to month are detectable in the Keen Camp population. Because of the climate, the breeding season of the flies is clearly shorter at Keen Camp than at the other localities, but nevertheless fly samples have been collected at Keen Camp from April to September and even October. Such time intervals are amply sufficient to detect changes in the Piñon and Andreas populations, but no cyclic changes have been found at Keen Camp.

Interestingly enough, a different kind of change has taken place in the Keen Camp population during the period of observation, from 1939 to 1946. Namely, there seems to exist a non-cyclic, or at any rate non-seasonal, trend toward decreasing frequencies of AR and CH and increasing ones of ST chromosomes. In 1939, only 28 per cent of the third chromosomes found in the Keen locality had the ST gene arrangement; in 1942 the frequency rose to 36 per cent, and in 1946 to 50 per cent. The frequencies of AR and CH chromosomes in 1939 were 30 and 38 per cent respectively. In 1946 only 15 per cent of the chromosomes were AR and only about 28 per cent CH. No such directional trends of change have appeared at Piñon Flats or at Andreas Canyon, although statisti-

cally significant differences in the composition of the populations from year to year have been recorded also in these localities.

It will obviously be important to ascertain how general are the phenomena of cyclic seasonal and non-seasonal changes not only in different populations of *Drosophila pseudoobscura* but in other species as well. The fact that cyclic changes occur at Piñon Flats and at Andreas Canyon, but not at Keen Camp only some 15 miles away, makes generalizations at this time decidedly premature. Data are however available which show cyclic seasonal changes in the population of a locality in central Texas. Here the Arrowhead and Pikes Peak gene arrangements in the third chromosome of *D. pseudoobscura* are involved (Dobzhansky and Epling, 1944; cf. also figure 1). Unpublished data suggest that changes in the frequencies of ST, AR, and perhaps of CH chromosomes occur in populations of at least some of the localities in the Sierra Nevada.

NATURAL SELECTION AS A CAUSE OF THE SEASONAL CHANGES

The regular and cyclic nature of the changes observed in the populations of *D. pseudoobscura* on Mount San Jacinto can be most reasonably accounted for by natural selection as the prime causative factor. If during the spring the carriers of CH chromosomes leave more surviving progeny on the average than the carriers of ST chromosomes, then the frequency of CH will increase and that of ST will decrease. This is what happens from March to June (Figure 2). The reversal of the change during the summer months points toward the hypothesis that, in the summer environments, the carriers of ST chromosomes survive or reproduce on the average more often than do the carriers of CH chromosomes. The absence of changes during the autumn and winter at Andreas Canyon suggests that flies of different chromosomal types are equivalent in reaction to the environments prevailing during these seasons.

But the great rapidity of the observed changes constitutes an apparently serious argument against accounting for them on the ground of natural selection. Indeed, at Piñon Flats the frequency of ST chromosomes falls from about 50 per cent in March to 28 per cent in June, and increases again to about 48 per cent in September (figure 2). Even though Drosophila is a rapidly breeding insect, time intervals such as these can correspond to at most two to four generations. The selective forces that are necessary to bring about changes so swift as these must be very strong.

It should be remembered however that very little is known about the intensity of selective forces which operate in natural populations. The wide-spread opinion that these forces are generally weak, and their effects negligible except in terms of quasi-geological time is only an opinion and has no basis in factual data. To find in natural populations great selective pressures and the rapid changes produced by them may be unexpected but not inherently impossible. On the other hand, the occurrence of changes does not in itself prove that they are produced by natural selection. Such proof would be very difficult to adduce from observations of natural populations alone. The difficulty lies in the fact that, despite persistent effort, very little has been learned as yet about the food and shelter requirements of *D. pseudoobscura* in its natural habitats. Proof of selection by a method analogous to that employed by Timofeeff-Ressovsky in Adalia is still out of the question in Drosophila.

Nevertheless, the postulated high selective advantages and disadvantages of the carriers of different gene arrangements in different environments has made practicable a still more ambitious project: to demonstrate the occurrence of natural selection by means of laboratory experiments. For this purpose, a modification of the population cage devised for Drosophila by l'Héritier and Teissier is used. These cages are wooden boxes with glass or wire screen sides and a detachable glass top. The bottom has 15 circular openings closed by corks which carry glass containers with culture medium. Wire loops hold the containers in place. Several hundred flies are introduced into the cage at the beginning of the experiment. These flies are a mixture of individuals with different gene arrangements in desired proportions. Within a single generation, the population of the cage increases to the maximum compatible with the amount of food given. This is usually between two and four thousand flies. The numbers of eggs deposited in a population cage are tens to hundreds of times greater than the numbers of adult flies that hatch. The competition for survival is intense.

Once a month, or at other suitable intervals, samples of the eggs which have been deposited in the cages are taken, and the larvae which emerge from these eggs are grown in regular culture bottles. Salivary gland chromosomes of fully grown larvae are then examined.

It is known that many chromosomes in natural populations carry recessive lethals, semilethals, or viability modifiers. We are, however, interested not in the effects of individual chromosomes on the survival of the flies, but in the selective values of ST, AR, CH, and other chromosomes as classes. In other words, in our experiments it is desired to have flies which are genetically heterogeneous, regardless of whether they are inversion homozygotes or heterozygotes. Accordingly, the initial population of a cage is always made from a mixture of several strains of each of the inversion types to be studied. As a result flies homozygous for any given individual chromosome are relatively rare in such population cages.

Twenty-nine experiments have been either completed or are now under way, employing populations the chromosomes of which were derived from ancestors collected at Piñon Flats. Some cages contained mixtures of ST and CH chromosomes, others of ST and AR, or of AR and CH, or of all three gene arrangements. Some were kept in incubators or constant temperature rooms at 25° C., others at 16½° C., and still others at variable room temperatures between 20° and 26° C.; some were exposed to alternation of day and night, others were kept in the dark. Two types of results have been obtained. First, at 16½° C. no significant changes in the frequencies

of the gene arrangements have taken place. The relative frequencies present in the original population of the cage have been retained generation after generation. Second, at 25° C. or at room temperatures, the relative proportions of the gene arrangements have changed with time until certain definitive equilibrium proportions have been attained.

Figure 3 shows an example of changes in the frequency of ST chromosomes observed in the population cage No. 35 at 25° C. On March 1, 1946, a population was introduced into this cage containing 10.7 per cent ST and 89.3 per cent CH chromosomes of Piñon Flats origin. In about a month, in early April, the frequency of ST has approximately doubled (21.7 per cent), in early May nearly trebled (28.3 per cent), and in early June nearly quadrupled (37.7 per cent). By mid-November ST reached the frequency of 66.7 per cent and by the end

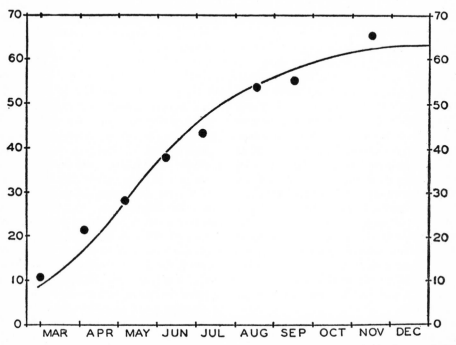

FIG. 3.—Frequency of Standard chromosomes (in per cent) in different months in the population cage No. 35.

of December 71.0 per cent. It can be seen, first, that the changes are greater when ST chromosomes are rare but relatively slight when they become frequent, and, second, that ST chromosomes never supplant entirely CH chromosomes. The final result of selection is a stable mixture of both ST and CH chromosomes.

Wright has analyzed mathematically the results of experiments like that illustrated in figure 3. He has concluded that the simplest hypothesis to account for the data is that the highest adaptive value exists in ST/CH heterozygotes, and that both homozygous classes, ST/ST and CH/CH, are inferior to the heterozygotes. Furthermore, that the adaptive value of ST/ST homozygotes is higher than that of CH/CH homozygotes. The curve shown in figure 3 is calculated on the assumption that the adaptive values of the ST/CH, ST/ST, and CH/CH classes of individuals are as 1.0:0.7:0.4, and that a fly generation had an average span of one month in population cage No. 35. The observed values fit the theoretical curve remarkably well.

Since the heterozygotes, ST/CH, are superior in adaptive values to both homozygotes, the final result of selection is not elimination of either CH or ST but establishment of a certain equilibrium at which both ST and CH gene arrangements occur in the population. Since ST/ST are superior to CH/CH homozygotes, the equilibrium frequency of ST is higher than that of CH. With the adaptive values indicated above, the population would be expected to reach equilibrium at about 67 per cent ST and 33 per cent CH. The results obtained in the experiment shown in figure 3 agree with the expectation.

All the experiments in which mixtures of ST and CH chromosomes were kept at temperatures above 20° C. have led to ST becoming more frequent than CH; whenever the experiments were continued long enough, equilibria were reached at values close to 70 per cent ST and 30 per cent CH. Under similar conditions, populations containing ST and AR have reached equilibria in which ST chromosomes are also more frequent than AR. The adaptive values of the three possible genotypes must therefore be ST/AR>ST/ST>AR/AR. Experiments with mixtures of AR and CH show that the hierarchy of adaptive values is AR/CH>AR/AR>CH/CH. Some experiments have been made in which population cages have contained mixtures of three gene arrangements, ST, AR, and CH. Equilibrium proportions are indicated at, roughly, 50–55 per cent ST, 30–35 per cent AR, and 10–15 per cent CH.

The lack of perceptible changes in the population cages kept at 16½° C. indicates that at that temperature the adaptive values of the inversion heterozygotes and homozygotes are more nearly similar than they are at higher temperatures. Such changes in the relative adaptive values of different genotypes at different temperatures have been observed experimentally.

STAGE OF THE LIFE CYCLE AT WHICH SELECTION TAKES PLACE

The experiments summarized above demonstrate that, in some environments, the adaptive values of inversion heterozygotes and homozygotes are strikingly unlike. But these experiments tell us nothing of the stage of the life cycle at which the differential survival or reproduction take place. Natural selection may operate in a variety of ways. The chromosomal types may be characterized by differential mortality, or differential longevity, or fecundity, or differences in sexual activity, or combinations of two or more of these and other variables. The adaptive value of a chromosomal type is the net effect of interaction of all the variables.

Perhaps the simplest, though by no means the only possible, hypothesis would assume a differential mortality of the different chromosomal types among the crowded larvae in the population cages. Let the frequencies of the ST and CH gene arrangements in a population cage be q and $(1 - q)$ respectively. Provided that the flies mate at random with respect to gene arrangement, the proportions of heterozygotes and homozygotes among the eggs deposited in a population cage will be:

$$q^2 \text{ ST/ST} : 2q(1 - q) \text{ ST/CH} : (1 - q)^2 \text{ CH/CH}.$$

If, however, the larvae which hatch from these eggs survive and reach the adult stage in a proportion 0.7 ST/ST : 1 ST/CH : 0.4 CH/CH, then the relative frequencies of the chromosomal types of the adult flies developed in a population cage will be:

$$0.7 \; q^2 \text{ ST/ST} : 2q(1 - q) \text{ ST/CH} : 0.4 \; (1 - p)^2 \text{ CH/CH}.$$

The frequencies of the ST/ST, ST/CH, and CH/CH types have been determined in samples of larvae hatching from the eggs deposited in population cages but grown in regular culture bottles under approximately optimal conditions. The deviations from the q^2 : $2q(1 - q) : (1 - q)^2$ proportions are found to be relatively small in such samples. A sample of adult flies hatched

in a population cage was now taken, and the chromosomal constitution of these flies was determined with the aid of a suitable method. The numbers of ST/ST, ST/CH, and CH/CH flies which would be expected to occur in this sample if there were no differential mortality between the egg and the adult stage were calculated with the aid of the Hardy-Weinberg formula $q^2 : 2q(1 - q) : (1 - q)^2$. The observed and the expected values are as follows:

	ST/ST	ST/CH	CH/CH
Observed	57	169	29
Expected	78.5	126.0	50.5
Deviation	—21.5	+43.0	—21.5

Among the adult flies, the heterozygotes, ST/CH, are considerably more frequent, and the homozygotes less frequent, than expected on the basis of the Hardy-Weinberg formula. Since, as stated above, the Hardy-Weinberg proportions are approximately realized among the eggs deposited in the population cages, a differential elimination of ST/ST and CH/CH homozygotes at some time between the egg and the adult stage may be regarded established.[1]

---

[1] The original paper should be consulted for a description of further experiments on chromosomes of different geographic origin and Dobzhansky's discussion of the biological implications of his findings.—*Editors*.

INDEX

A

Abel, 55
Absorption spectrum, 46
Accessory chromosome, 226, 255
Acetic acid, synthesis, 85
Acetylcholine, 70f
Acromegaly, 55
Adalia, 302
Adaptation, through natural selection, 301
Addison, 54
Adrenal gland, 54
Alcaptonuria, 297
Aldrich and Takamine, 55
Amoeboid movement, in tissue culture, 22
Amylase, 24
Anasa, 255
Anderson, 264
Aneurin, 82
Animal heat, 84
Antibiotics, 127
Appert, 105, 115
Areola, of pollen grain, 10
Aromatari, Joseph of, 185
Artificial fertilization, 192, 204
Ascaris, 226, 245
Askew, 73
Atmungsferment, 32, 39
Auhagen, 81
Auxins, 55, 141
Avena, 144
Avery, O. T., 134
Axolotl, 219

B

Bacon, Roger, 1
Bacteria:
  pathogenic, 120
  photosynthetic, 170
Baer, von, 186
Baeyer, A. von, 30
Balancer induction, 219
Balfour, 55
Banting, F. G., 64
Banting and Best, 56
Barnes, 153
Barry, 186

Bateson, 226, 227, 281
Bateson and Punnett, 258
Baumann, 55
Baur, 132
Bautzmann, 219
Bawden and Pirie, 132
Bayliss, W. M., 60
Bayliss and Starling, 55
Beadle, G. W., 273
Beagle, voyage, 281
Beijerinck, 124, 132
Beneden, E. van, 3, 186, 204, 225, 240, 245, 249
Beriberi, 72, 74f
  cured by cocarboxylase, 82
Bernard, Claude, 42, 54, 60, 85, 93
Berthold, A. A., 54, 57
Bertrand, 24
Berzelius, 23, 40
Biotin, 275
Black, 84
Blackman, 153
Blastomeres, isolated, 208, 210f
Blumenbach, 186
Boltwood, 282
Bonnet, 152, 185
Borel, 1
Born, 209, 216
Boussingault, 85, 153
Boveri, T., 216, 226, 249, 252
Boyle, Robert, 3, 84
Boysen-Jensen, 55, 141, 146
Brachet, J., 209
Brachystola, 249
Brefeld, 119, 121
Bridges, C. B., 227, 257
Brown, R., 2, 9
Brown-Séquard, 55
Buchner, E., 24, 27, 106
Buffon, 185, 281
Butenandt and Ruzicka, 58

C

Cagniard-Latour, 23, 105, 111
Calorimeter, 86
Calorimetry, indirect, 85
Calvin and Benson, 153
Camerarius, 225

[311]